FAILURE ATLAS FOR HERTZ CONTACT MACHINE ELEMENTS

FAILURE ATLAS FOR HERTZ CONTACT MACHINE ELEMENTS

T. E. Tallian

ASME PRESS   NEW YORK   1992

Library of Congress Cataloging-in-Publication Data

Tallian, T. E.
    Failure atlas for Hertz contact machine elements / T. E. Tallian.
        p.   cm.
    Includes bibliographical references and index.
    ISBN 0-7918-0008-3 :
    1. Machine parts—Failures—Atlases. I. Title. II. Title: Hertz
contact machine elements.
TJ243.T35 1992
621.8′2—dc20

90-21273
CIP

CONTENTS

PREFACE

This Atlas is the product of four decades of photographic failure documentation relating to Hertz machine elements, assembled by numerous workers in the United States, Europe and Japan. The documentation was contributed to the Atlas by about thirty institutions and individuals. The exacting work of assembling the images in reproducible form and providing the data required for their use, was performed selflessly by all contributors. In addition, all contributors have reviewed the Plate material prepared from their inputs. Most of the contributions are identified in the Contributors list at the end of the book. A few institutions, for business reasons, have elected not to be explicitly acknowledged. The author's sincere gratitude is extended to them as to all others.

A full review of the draft manuscript for correctness in materials science interpretation was performed by Mr. George H. Baile, an independent consultant. Without his expert advice, errors in materials science interpretation may well have been unavoidable.

The contribution of all participants notwithstanding, responsibility for the technical content of the Atlas as a whole rests, of course, with the author.

Publication of the book is made possible by ASME Press, an imprint of the American Society of Mechanical Engineers. Sincere thanks are due Ms. Caryl Dreiblatt, and the other editors of ASME Press, whose flexibility, helpfulness and patience never flagged during the rather elaborate effort of publishing a volume as complex and specialized as this Atlas.

ASME and STLE, the Society of Tribologists and Lubrication Engineers, have both supported this work by their endorsement and willingness to place announcements seeking image sources in their journals.

I owe my wife more than I can say, for the many hours of meticulous labor spent in finalizing the manuscript and its image material, into a form suitable for publication.

I GENERAL INFORMATION

1   INTRODUCTION

1.1. STRUCTURE OF THE ATLAS

This Atlas is composed of two parts. Part I, comprises the following chapters: Introduction, Failure Classification Codes, and Appearance Classification Tables. Part II consists of detailed image material showing failure morphologies and is arranged in a number of Plate chapters organized by failure modes.

More specifically, *Part I: General Information,* comprises the following:

Chapter 1. Introduction, comprises a review of background on diagnosis by failure morphology, relevant literature, general concepts of contact failure classification and distinguishing features of this Atlas.

Chapter 2. Failure Classification, describes the hierarchical classification code (*failure code, FC*) of failure modes: a decimal numbering system and text designation of each failure mode. The Atlas image material is organized around this failure classification. Numeric and alphabetic indexes of the failure code are found in this chapter.

Chapter 3. Appearance Classification, contains several pages grouping failure modes by appearance, as an aid in finding the Plate chapter appropriate to the observed failure.

Part II. Plates, is the main body of the book. It is composed of a series of chapters, each containing one or more sections consisting of image pages called Plates, which illustrate one major failure class. Each chapter is introduced by a description of the *definition, failure process, appearance, causes* and *effect* of the failure mode(s) covered.

Indexing. As stated above, the image material of the Atlas is indexed by failure code. *Cross-indexing* of failure modes is provided between Plates (as explained in Chapter 1). *Text material,* including all of Part I and the *descriptions* introducing each chapter in Part II are indexed in the usual way by key words.

1.2. BACKGROUND

1.2.1. Definitions

1. Load carrying moving contacts between machine elements exhibit peculiar *tribological* failure modes caused by time-variable stressing of the contact surfaces. Concentrated or *Hertz contacts* are characterized by their non-conforming geometry, high pressures, distinct contact materials and lubrication regimes, and exhibit a well-defined subset of these tribological failure modes.

2. A Hertz contact *component* is one featuring load-carrying Hertz contacts. A Hertz contact *machine element* is a complete subassembly of Hertz contact components and supporting (non-contact) components working together.

3. A *failure mode* is the physical condition of a component resulting from a specific physical *failure process*.

4. A (tribological) failure mode *database* for Hertz contact machine elements is an organized body of information on the failure modes of these elements and their engineering causes.

5. A failure *morphology atlas* is a failure mode data base concentrating on topographic (visual) features of the failures, using images as a main data form, supplemented by a classification of failures, and concise descriptions of failed component, failure mode, and classes of likely engineering causes of failure. Images illustrating degrees, variants and combinations of failures are used for comparison with user-observed failures.

1.2.2. Application of Morphology Atlas for Diagnosis

Tribological engineering of Hertz contact machine elements (and of their applications) is aimed at the dual objectives of: (a) achieving the function intended for the machine element; and (b) preventing, delaying or reducing any tribological failures.

Engineering for the desired *function* follows distinct principles for each of the major classes of Hertz contact machine elements such as gears, rolling bearings, traction drives, cams, etc. Engineering for *failure control,* by contrast, is based on much common ground, due to the commonality of contact failure modes, even though specific practices have evolved for each major machine element class. Owing to this commonality, it is possible to design technical aids for failure control engineering, that serve most classes of Hertz-contact machine elements.

Tribological failure control is highly empirical. It begins with the identification of operating conditions, such as geometry, load, speed, temperature, lubrication and environment. This is followed by the selection of a machine element design class with a history of successful service under the given operating conditions. Based on experience, a hierarchy of failure risks by failure mode is established which leads to specific design, manufacturing and applications choices for the control of these risks according to their severity. In many cases, prevention of tribological failure through the desired useful life of the device cannot be assured with certainty, and choices of acceptable survival probabilities are made.

After building the device, it is tested either formally or through placement in service, and any failures are observed. They are diagnosed according to failure mode and cause, and modifications in machine element design, manufacturing process and application specifications are made until reliability and longevity objectives are met.

Tribological engineering for failure control requires precise diagnosis of failure modes and the identification of their engineering causes, as guides for corrective action in design, manufacturing and application engineering.

Data concerning tribological failures can be of many types. Examples are: statistical data on service life under spalling fatigue; wear rate data; formulas relating dimensional instability of steel to retained austenite, etc. A distinct data category is: morphological data, defined as failure features that are visible by eye, by light microscope or scanning electron microscope (SEM) or, discernible by surface tracing or (micro)-geometric measurement.

Hertz contact tribology diagnosis is greatly dependent on the recognition of the morphology of a failure. Such morphological diagnosis demands very specific experience, besides proper imaging and measurement facilities. An atlas of reference images with interpretation, representing, within reason, a complete catalog of failure morphologies correlated with the design, manufacturing and application parameters of the failed machine element, is a well recognized resource for training less experienced diagnosticians and in supporting the experienced diagnostician, when confronted with a machine element or failure appearance outside his experience.

A morphology atlas differs from an illustrated textbook on failure diagnosis and supplements it. A *textbook* contains instructions on recovery of the component from the machine, cleaning, preservation, various examination techniques and record keeping methods. It may offer in-formation on corrective engineering action following failure diagnosis. Illustrations in a textbook are limited to typical failures needed to support the verbal descriptions. A morphology *atlas,* on the other hand, provides a collection of failure images illustrating degrees, variants and combinations of failures in rich detail, to facilitate matching the often untypical and complex *observed* failures. It thereby lends specificity to the diagnostic methods of the textbook. An atlas does *not* cover diagnostic methodology.

This failure atlas is, accordingly, an aid in the identification and diagnosis of failure modes and their causes which in turn forms an integral part of the methodology of failure control design and application engineering of Hertz contact machine elements.

1.2.3. Related Publications

Early publications describing tribological contact failure morphology were intended for service engineers and specialized in one of the major machine element classes (rolling bearings or gears). [1] and [2], are manuals for rolling bearing diagnosis for service engineers. They are well illustrated and comprehensive, but do not interpret failure beyond the needs of service diagnosis, and do not classify failures to the depth necessary for detailed correlation with failure causes.

Similar, but proprietary manuals have been published by many major manufacturers of Hertz contact machine elements, especially of bearings and gears.

Parallel with practical diagnostic purposes, interest in failure mode classification by morphology arose during research into machine element life prediction. As an example, classical rolling bearing life theory [3] is based on a study of spall formation from subsurface defects. Failure control research, with extensive use of morphological criteria, was later extended to the systematic classification of contact failure modes. (See [4], [5], [6].) Even more than previously listed manuals, these publications concentrate on the typical features of failures, and contain only enough illustrations to document the classifications made.

The *Rolling Bearing Damage Atlas* published in 1974 by Tallian et al. [7] was designed as a primary reference source of contact failure morphology for rolling bearings. It attempted to cover all tribological failure modes comprehensively in photographs, including macrographs, micrographs and SEM images. It contains a single-tier classification of failure modes but only terse descriptions of each failure and no specific cause correlations.

For gears, the American Gear Manufacturers Association publishes a failure nomenclature standard [8]. It is a narrative failure description with illustrations of typical failures, intended for primary failure identification. Some cause correlations are provided. A thorough practical textbook of failure diagnostics for gears is [9], by Alban. It contains extensive image material on failures with detailed tutorial diagnostic instructions, but no hierarchical classification.

The volume "Failure Analysis and Prevention" of the *ASM Metals Handbook* [10] contains wide ranging information on metallic material failures classified primarily by generic failure types and their causes. Separate chapters on rolling bearing failures and gear failures are also provided. These chapters contain narratives of failure description, with illustrations of typical failures.

A tutorial text by Wulpi [11] covers a wide range of mechanical failures, in less detail than the *Metals Handbook*. Illustrations are of typical failures.

An atlas of metal surface damage shown in SEM images, including, but not limited to Hertz contacts or to tribological failures, is [12]. This publication contains high quality image material and clear scientific descriptions, but is not systematized around Hertz contacts.

In chapters dealing with individual failure modes, references pertaining to the theory of these failure modes will be cited as required.

1.3. FEATURES OF THE ATLAS

1.3.1. New Features

This Atlas supplements other existing literature in several ways. Firstly, it permits ready comparison with observed failures through copious illustration, not only of the most typical failures, but also of commonly occurring degrees, variations and combinations of failures. It covers the major classes of Hertz contact machine elements, permitting observation of common failure characteristics. It also includes information on the failure of supporting (non-contact) components of the subassemblies, to elucidate interactions among all failure modes.

Secondly, a hierarchical failure classification is provided, for easy searching during practical diagnosis. This classification is several tiers deep. (Example: spalling in general, surface origin spalls, local surface origin spalls, and defect origin spalls.) Failure classes are formalized by numeric failure codes, so that failure modes are unambiguously classified. Some advantages of such a system are:

• The user can trace a hierarchical search path to a specific morphological match fast and with a minimum of lost motion. (For instance, he can find an image showing a spall in a surface-distressed contact with multiple debris denting.)
• Ready access is provided to families of failure appearances classified by the specific feature under study. (For example, one can find all images containing signs of galling, whether it be the principal or an incidental failure mode).
• Unambiguous cross-referencing of failure modes is available across several Plate chapters. Many Plates show composite failures. They are arranged in the Atlas by a *primary* failure mode, and also illustrate *secondary* failure modes via cross-reference tables in the appropriate chapters.

• Common causation chains operative over entire failure classes are documented.*

Failure morphology is correlated with engineering failure causes by attaching a short list of causes to each failure illustration. The user can accumulate evidence for a given cause over several diagnostic matches. As an example: If surface distress is diagnosed and also overheating of contact surfaces, both of which correlate with inadequate lubrication, then this cause assignment gains support from both correlations.

1.3.2. Format of Image Pages

This Section describes the machine element classification used in the Atlas, and the format of the image pages. Two types of image pages are used in this Atlas: Appearance Classification pages and Plate pages classified by failure mode. (The failure classification system is described in Chapter 2.)

Machine Element Classification

This Atlas covers rolling bearings, gears and cams as the primary machine elements (subassemblies) featuring moving Hertz contacts. Traction drives are treated under 'bearings', sprag clutches under 'cams', drive chains and splines under 'gears'. A group—Other machine elements—is provided to capture machine elements not falling into these categories. Table 1.1 presents the abbreviations for machine elements and their components used in the Plate texts. (The machine element symbol always precedes the component symbol.)

Appearance Classification (Chapter 3)

When the diagnostician first inspects a failed machine element, his primary guide to failure mode identification is the appearance of the failure. In tribological failures, it is not uncommon for very different failure classes to produce superficially similar failure appearances. This is one of the difficulties in tribological failure diagnosis. To facilitate the initial diagnostic orientation, the Atlas offers a chapter of images arranged by appearance class, that is, a brief collection of typical failure appearances. As far as the subject permits, appearance classes differ sharply from each other in failure appearance, while appearances apt to be confused are in one class. In this way, the user can find the right orientation page with little ambiguity, and can then use the distinctions offered by the several images on his page for differentiation between failure classes. Every effort was made to select illustrations of single failure modes (even though in diagnostic practice, multiple failure modes are common).

Each failure class identified within an Appearance Class is referenced to a chapter of Plates, devoted to that class. Images are not provided in the Appearance classification chapter, for failures which are self-classifying by their na-

_____

*A major strength of the numerical classification, viz. its appropriateness for electronic search, is better exploited in a computerized diagnostic system, and less so in a book.

Table 1.1: Machine element classification.

Symbol	Machine element	Symbol	Component
	Rolling bearings		**Rolling bearing components**
B	Rolling bearing		Contact components:
BB	Ball bearing	IR	Innerring, shaft washer
DGBB	Deep groove ball brg.	OR	Outerring, housing washer
ACBB	Angular contact ball brg.	B	Ball
MCBB	Maximum complement ball brg.	R	Roller
SABB	Self-aligning ball brg.	G	Guiding component
ABB	Axial (thrust) ball brg.	C	Closure (Seal, shield)
RB	Roller bearing	I	Integrated bearing unit
TRB	Taper roller brg.	M	Mounting part
CRB	Cylindrical roller brg.		
SRB	Spherical roller brg.		
NRB	Needle roller brg.		
TRTB	Taper roller thrust brg.		
SRTB	Spherical roller thrust brg.		
CRTB	Cylindrical roller thrust brg.		
LB	Linear bearing		
BSB	Ball screw		
RSB	Roller screw		
TDB	Traction drive		
	Gearing		**Gearing components**
G	Gear		Contact components:
SG	Spur gear	P	Pinion
HG	Helical gear	W	Wheel (bull gear)
BG	Bevel gear	O	Worm
HYG	Hypoid gear	R	Rack
WG	Worm gear	M	Mounting part
SPG	Sprocket		
RPG	Rack and pinion		
SLG	Spline		
	Cam system		**Cam system components**
			Contact components:
C	Cam and follower	CM	Cam
SC	Sprag clutch	CF	Cam follower
		CT	Tappet
		SR	Sprag ring
		S	Sprag element
		M	Mounting part
O	**Other machine element**		

ture. For example, bearing separator failures are all found in one Plate chapter, as are shaft failures. Therefore, neither is illustrated in Chapter 3. For completeness, the failure classes not illustrated in the Appearance classification are still listed there by name.

The format for Appearance Classification used in Chapter 3 is described as follows:

Class header:

An *appearance class* is printed consecutively on one or more pages. At the head of each appearance class is the *class header*, consisting of:

• *Appearance class name:* The name of the appearance class in capital letters. Example: "PLOWING MARK."
• *Appearance description:* A line of text giving the distinguishing features of appearance for the class. Example: "Depressed line defect from material removal by plowing action."

Appearance illustrations:

A series of images with descriptive text, identifying the several failure modes that show an appearance falling within the appearance class. In detail:

• *Failure code and mode:* The numeric and text designation of the illustrated failure mode according to the Failure Code classification described in Chapter 2. Example: "FC 00.02: Finishing mark (furrow, chatter, wheelhit)."
• *Appearance:* A line of text giving the distinguishing features and typical causation of the failure mode. Example: "Scratch mark by injury during assembly or mounting."
• *Images:* A line captioned 'Archive No' and one captioned 'Plate No' defined in the same way as for Plate pages (See Section 1.3.2.3). Examples: "Archive No: 080–101." "Plate No: 5.11."

An image accompanies most of the Appearance Illustration entries. When there is no illustration, an explanation is provided. Example: "Shown under 'general texture change.'"

Plate Chapters (Part II)

In this Atlas, the failure images with descriptive text, classified by failure mode, making up Part II, are designated as *Plates*. A chapter of Plates illustrates one or more *primary* failure modes, each of which occupies a Section. *Secondary* failure modes may also be present in the Plates, and if so, are identified in the text. Plates in a section differ in: the specific principal failure mode shown (within the section class), the severity of failure within a given mode, the accompanying secondary failure mode, the presentation (imaging) of the failure, or the appearance of failure as it may vary within a given mode. Each chapter and section is indexed by the Failure Code of the failure class described in it.

Chapters start with descriptive text, defining each of the failure classes illustrated in a section of that chapter, (with differentiation criteria among subordinated failure modes). The description gives *definition, nomenclature, failure process,* likely *failure causes* and principal *effects.*

Next follows a Cross-index of Secondary Failure Codes. It lists the Plate numbers in other chapters which feature secondary failure codes falling within the failure class of the chapter at hand. Such Plates can serve to augment the collection of failure illustrations in this chapter.

Finally, the body of the chapter is composed of the Plates, each of which contains a failure image, accompanied by interpretive text.

NOTE

A Plate chapter (or section) covers one failure class, but all machine elements in which it occurs. As an example, Chapter 00.12: Wear (of Hertz contact components) includes bearing ring wear, gear wear and cam wear, but not shaft wear, since a shaft is not a Hertz contact component. Shaft wear is found in Section 2.2: Shafts.

Plate Format Description

Each Plate consists of three main parts: Images, Data and Descriptions. The images are one or more related photographs illustrating the same failure mode. The data comprise quantitative information describing the illustrated failure and the imaging process, as well as four failure codes. Descriptions are given for the failure mode, the image appearance and suspected failure causes. One or more Plates may occupy a book page; if there is more than one, they are separated by a heavy line.

Page Header

Each Plate page carries a header, with the failure code of the Plate(s) shown on that page, near the outside page edge. The chapter title in the header is near the binding. The failure code(s) are copied from the *primary code* of each Plate on that page, as defined below, and serve as the principal Plate look-up coding of the Atlas. The appearance classification in Chapter 3 and the failure code in Chapter 2, both refer to this Plate coding.

Image(s)

The image(s) are printed near the top of each Plate. If there is more than one, the images are identified as 'a, b' etc.

Data

Plate No locates the Plate in the book. A Plate number has two parts, e. g. 11-25. The first part is the chapter number, the second part is the serial number of the Plate within that chapter. Plate numbers are used for cross-referencing between Plates. (See Section 1.3.4 for detail.)

Archive No is a two-part number, e. g. 066-001, and identifies the image(s) on the plate in the master image archive. These numbers serve to give source credit for image material.

Image type can be:

• View— color view of an entire component.
• Light macro or color macro— a slightly magnified or demagnified image of part of a component.

• Light microgram— black/white image at substantial magnification.
• Light metallogram— microgram of a metallographic section, etched or unetched.
• SEM— scanning electron microgram. Secondary electron images are not identified. Backscatter images are so marked.
• TEM— transmission electron microgram (of thin film or replica, as indicated).

Color images are located in a separate Appendix: 'Color Images', where they are identified by Plate number. In place of the image on the Plate, a reference appears, stating: "See image in Appendix." If there is more than one image per Plate, each is identified by 'a:, b:' etc. and each is described.

Scalebar = ... mm means that the length of the bar drawn on the image equals ... mm on the original object. These lengths are given either in millimeters (mm) or micrometers (μm). If there is more than one image, a scalebar value, identified by 'a:, b:' etc. is given for each.*

Component is the coded designation of the machine element and its parts shown on the image, with indication of material condition (if relevant) and whether the part was in service ('run'). The machine element classification code and the parts code are taken from Table 1.1.

Speed, load and lubrication are given for parts that were in service, if this information was received from the image source. This information is useful in placing the failure in perspective, but not strictly necessary to the diagnosis. It must be borne in mind that, even where the information is available, it may represent typical rather than failure-specific values. The definition of these parameters is as follows:

Speed is a linear surface speed. Speed-related failures generally correlate with peak speed in service, but that value is often unavailable.

• For rolling bearings, the simple measure used is dN [$mm.r/min$], i. e. the bore diameter of the inner ring in mm, multiplied by the shaft speed in revolutions per minute ($KdN = 10^3 \, dN$, $MdN = 10^6 \, dN$). The measure Nd_m, where the rolling element pitch circle diameter is substituted for the bore diameter, is the more modern usage, but this information is not widely enough available for the failure illustrations collected for this Atlas, to be used.
• For gears and cams, *linear rolling speed* [m/sec] at the pitchline is used.

Load for all contact components is the normal contact pressure [GPa]. No meaningful load value can be generalized for non-contact components.

---

*Image sources do not always indicate scales of views and macro images. Scales of micrographs are generally (but not always) available. Due to this uncertainty, scales given are *informational* only. An error range of ± 20% for micros, and +100%, −50% for other images is indicated on all plates as a precaution. These ranges are quite conservative, for most plates.

Lubrication is described by two elements: the lubricant type and a typical operating temperature [C^o].
• *Lubricant type* is described generically. Examples: mineral oil, synthetic polyester oil, lithium thickened mineral oil base grease etc. Often, however, only the major class is known, such as grease.
• *Temperature* is the typical bulk temperature (sustained maximum temperature) of the component. In failures where temperature rise is produced, the temperature given is that before onset of failure. Again, typical temperature is often unknown.

Failure code consists of the numerical code and text designation detailed in Chapter 2. Room is provided for four distinct failure codes, to accommodate composite failures. The four codes are ordered generally by their prominence on the image shown (not the order of their importance to the serviceability of the component or their sequence of occurrence). This ordering is somewhat loose, and great weight should not be attached to it in reading the Plates. The sequence, relative importance and mutual interaction of failure events is discussed thoroughly in the Description part of the Plate text.

'See also PLATEs' is a cross-reference to other Plates in the Atlas, which are related to, or help illuminate the contents of the present Plate.

Descriptions

The Descriptions are narrative statements explaining the failure illustrated. Uniform terminology for a given failure is attempted for bearings, gears and cams. This may make the nomenclature appear unusual to some readers. Comments regarding failure mode terminology are in the Introduction of Chapter 2, and in the Nomenclature paragraph of the General Description in each Plate chapter. There, the terminology used in the Atlas is correlated with that customary for the various machine elements.

Failure Description

This is the central statement of failure diagnosis. The failure modes are described in terms of the physical failure process. A statement is made about the serviceability of the component under further running, and its likely final failure, if expected on the basis of its observed condition.

Image Description

Diagnostic image features (those which serve to diagnose a failure) are pointed out and described.

The 'map convention' is adopted for *orientation* on the image. The upper edge of the image is Image North (N); compass points are used as on a map. 'Left' or 'right', and 'up' or 'down' are avoided in designating direction on the image plane. In describing *position* on the image, fractions of image size are used. A point one quarter of the way to the right of the left-hand edge is '1/4 E of W image edge.' These conventions may appear contrived, but they are unambiguous.

Table 1.2: List of Plate chapters

Chapter No.	Chapter code	Chapter title (failure class)	Page No.
		Contact part failures	
4	00.01	Nicks	37
5	00.02 - 05	Surface defects from manufacturing	45
6	00.06 - 09	Material and assembly defects	63
7	00.12	Mild wear	93
8	00.13 - 14	Galling, skidmarking	121
9	00.15	Fretting wear	141
10	00.16	Spalling	155
11	00.17	Surface distress	195
12	00.18	Denting	213
13	00.19	Heat imbalance failure	233
14	00.20 - 21	Corrosion, electric erosion	247
15	00.22 - 23	Bulk cracking, fracture, permanent deformation	265
16	01.1 - 2	*Guide part failures*	295
17	02	*Integral closure failures*	321
18	1	*Lubricant failures*	327
19	2	*Mounting part failures*	347

If there is more than one image on a Plate, each is referenced by '(a), (b)' etc. and each is described.

Suspected Causes

This paragraph identifies engineering causes that may lead to the diagnosed failure. Examples: service speed, load, manufacturing process. As is well known, too many possible causes exist for any given failure to present an exhaustive discussion on each Plate. The *actual* failure cause is listed on the Plate wherever the source data include it. In addition (or when actual failure causes are unknown), *most likely* causes are identified. More detailed discussion of failure causes for an entire failure class is found in the general description in each Plate chapter. If there is more than one image on a Plate, each is identified with a lowercase letter and is described.

Sorting Order of Plates

The order of Plates within each chapter is as follows:

• The primary sorting key is Failure Code 1 (FC 1). Failure codes are sorted strictly in the order listed in the Failure code list at the end of the Atlas.
• Plates with identical FC 1 are sorted by their FC 2, then FC 3 and then FC 4, if they exist.
• Plates for which all existing failure codes are identical, (of which not many occur) are sorted in arbitrary order.

• Once established, the sorting order of the plates is fixed by their sequential Plate No.

1.3.3. Failure Mode Grouping

The detailed classification of failures used in this Atlas is contained in the Failure Code presented in Chapter 2. The classes are broad, so as to encompass all of the machine element types covered in the Atlas. Of course, all failure classes do not occur on all machine element types.

An overview of the arrangement of the Atlas by failure grouping is given in the list of Plate chapter titles in Table 1.2.

1.3.4. Cross-Indexing of Failure Modes

Since each Plate carries up to four failure codes, it can serve as an illustration for more than one failure mode. Each plate is placed in the chapter corresponding to the *first (primary)* code. It can be found through each of its secondary failure codes by referring to a cross-index located after the general description in the plate chapter for the failure class sought. The cross-index lists all plates carrying a failure code within that chapter's class, giving the specific failure code on the plate which falls into the chapter's class, and the Plate number.

2 FAILURE CLASSIFICATION

This chapter presents the formal failure classification system ('failure code,' abbreviated 'FC') by which the Atlas is structured.

2.1. DEFINITION OF FAILURE AND NOMENCLATURE USAGE

In this Atlas, the word 'failure' *specifically* refers to damage occurring in service. The word 'defect' is used *specifically* for an off-specification condition or damage predating service. The Atlas covers both defects and failures. Where this distinction is irrelevant, the word 'failure' (occasionally, the word 'damage') is used in the broad sense to cover both conditions.

The failure code (both numeric and text) describing failure classes in this Atlas is applied consistently across the several Hertz contact machine element classes. Since industry designations for failures of bearings, gears and cams often differ and nomenclature variants abound even within one industry, general descriptions to each Plate chapter list the most common nomenclature alternatives for the major failure classes. Plate descriptions, however, adhere for uniformity to the designations in the formal failure classification code. The physical process causing each major failure class (failure process) is used for the brief definitions in the tables that follow in this chapter. Additional discussion of failure mechanism as well as differentiation within classes is provided in the general description in the Plate chapters and on the Plate pages showing individual failure modes.

There are occasional differences of view among tribologists regarding the failure mechanism of individual failure classes. As an example, the failure class designated '00.17: Surface distress (surface fatigue)' is considered in this Atlas to be peculiar to rolling contacts and is identified as asperity scale plastic flow brought on by high normal stresses and followed by asperity scale fatigue cracking and micro-spalling. Some authors designate it 'fatigue wear.' This designation is avoided in this Atlas, since the term 'wear' is reserved for surface material removal by tractive stresses arising in sliding. Where such differences are recognized, they will be commented upon.

2.2. FAILURE CLASSIFICATION SYSTEM

The Failure code classification system of morphological defects is an adaptation of the decimal classification principle. It is hierarchical, and coded by groups of one or two numerals, with groups separated by periods.

The classification is aimed at morphological failures, i.e. failures (defects) detectable by examination of surface topography (after suitable preparation). Other types of defects, such as dimensional errors, material structure deviations, chemical deviations or residual stresses, are covered only in their morphological manifestations.

The aim of this Atlas is completeness in classifying morphological failures of contact components, guiding-components, integral seals and lubricants, but not in classifying mounting parts. Accordingly, the detail of coverage for the former group is limited by available data only, whereas detail of coverage for mounting parts has been limited to that believed necessary in elucidating fully covered failures. Of course, many, if not most, lubricant failures, especially oil failures, are not morphological, so that the Atlas failure coding does not approach completeness in classifying lubricant failures. Also notable is the regrettable scarcity of image material on integral seal failures.

Counting code groups from the left to the right, the following coding rules apply: Group 1 designates the component function in relation to the load carrying Hertz contact. Groups 2 and higher describe progressively more detailed failure classes and failure modes applicable to the component specified in Group 1.

This chapter contains definitions of the main failure classes and lists useful as indexes for failure code lookup. Specifically:

1. Group 1 and (in most cases) group 2 cover the Main Failure Classes. They are listed in numerical order and defined in Section 2.3 of this chapter. Much additional detail is found in the general description in each Plate chapter.
2. Complete lists of the classification including all group orders are presented in Sections 2.4 through 2.6 of this chapter. Details of definition of the classification criteria for these lower-order groups can be gleaned from the failure descriptions on each Plate page, where they are readily associated with the morphology of each failure mode.

Table 2.1 enumerates the failure code lists and indexes contained in the Atlas.

Table 2.1: Failure code indexes

List title	Content
Failure class list	Listing, with interpretation, of major (1 or 2 codegroup) failure classes.
Failure code list	Listing of all failure modes in numerical code order.
Failure class index	Alphabetic index of major (1 or 2 codegroup) failure classes.
Failure mode index	Alphabetic index of all failure modes, grouped by class.

2.3. FAILURE CLASS LIST

2.3.1. Component Function

Table 2.2: Component class codes

Group No.	Digits	Classification basis
1	1 or 2	Component type

Listing of groups

Failure code	Component function	Example
00	Hertz contact component	Bearing ring, ball, gear, cam
01	Guiding-component	Bearing retainer, guidering
02	Integral closure	Integral seal, shield
1	Lubricant	Oil, grease, solid lubricant
2	Mounting part	Shaft, spacer, housing, locknut

2.3.2. Hertz Contact Component Failure

The components sustaining (rolling) Hertz contact are typically (relatively) hard, highly and cyclically stressed. Normal surface pressures dominate, with tractive stresses dependent on degree of sliding. The surfaces are typically ground (or finely cut as in some gears) and may be superfinished by polishing or honing. These components show several unique failure modes, with major classes tabulated below.

Table 2.3: Failure code group 2: Contact component manufacturing defect

Group No.	Digits	Classification basis
2	1 or 2	Major failure class

Listing of groups

Failure code	Major failure class	Definition
00.0...	Manufacturing or assembly defect	Defects from manufacturing, assembly or mounting but *prior to service*
00.00	Manufacturing or assembly defect, by location	Qualifier used in conjunction with other codes, to identify defect location
00.01	Nick	Plastic surface indentation from a sharp object pressed, impacted or moved across surface, *prior to service*
00.02	Finishing mark	Unintended surface mark caused by finish machining
00.03	Pit or unfinished area	Surface cratering *prior to service* or surface missed in a finishing operation
00.04	Forming defect	Forming (forging, pressing) defect within the material
00.05	Casting defect	Casting, molding defect within the material
00.06	Inclusion	Particle of extraneous material in the matrix
00.07	Material structure defect pre- or in heat treatment.	Deviations from specified material structure incurred prior to or during heat treatment. (e.g.: heat treat errors, off-specification structure, visible retained

Table 2.3: Failure code group 2: Contact component manufacturing defect (*continued*)

Group No.	Digits	Classification basis
2	1 or 2	Major failure class
Listing of groups		

Failure code	Major failure class	Definition
		austenite, defective ceramic binder, forging or heat treat stress origin crack).
00.08	Material structure damage, post-heat treatment	Structural change, including cracking in near-surface material due to defective hard finishing.
00.09	Geometry, assembly or mounting defect	Manufacturing error of geometry, scoring, galling, cracking in assembly.

Table 2.4: Failure code group 2: Contact component service failure

Group No.	Digits	Classification basis
2	1 or 2	Major failure class
Listing of groups		

Failure code	Major failure class	Definition
00.1... - 00.2...	Service failure, contact part	Failures arising *in service,* including machine shipment and storage.
00.12	Wear, mild	"Mild" mechanical wear. Adhesive or abrasive surface material removal through tractive forces in (sliding) contact, without macroscopic material transfer.
00.13	Galling (smearing, severe mechanical wear)	"Severe" mechanical wear. Macroscopic surface material transfer through tractive forces in (sliding) contact.
00.14	Skid marking (microscopic severe wear)	Microscopic severe wear (from high acceleration of free element).
00.15	Fretting wear	Material removal (and oxidation) through microscale vibratory motion.
00.16	Spalling (Hertzian contact fatigue)	Hertz contact fatigue failure through macroscopic surface crater formation from cracks driven by Hertz stress fields extending to macroscopic subsurface depths.
00.17	Surface distress (surface fatigue)	Fatigue failure of surface material in asperity dimensions, through microscopic surface plastic flow followed by microspall formation driven by Hertz stress fields extending to asperity dimensions.
00.18	Denting (indentation)	Local plastic depressions (points or lines) on contact surfaces *in service,* from hard edges, asperities or contaminants pressed into and/or rolled over the surface.
00.19	Heat imbalance failure	Plastic flow and/or chemical damage to component by (local) overheating.
00.20	Corrosion	Pits, stains or structural attack on surfaces, by aggressive chemical environment.
00.21	Electric erosion	Macro or micro-cratering by local melting from electric current passing through Hertz contact.
00.22	Cracking or fracture, bulk	Crack formation with or without part separation, from bulk stresses other than Hertzian. Includes bulk fatigue, residual-stress cracking, thermal cracking, cracking from chemical attack in service.
00.23	Permanent deformation, bulk	Permanent bulk change from as-manufactured dimension or shape, by plastic deformation or structure change.

2.3.3. Guiding-Component Failure
Table 2.5: Failure code groups 1 and 2: Guiding-component failure

Group No.	Digits	Classification basis
1	2	Component class
2	2	Specific component and major failure class

Listing of groups

Failure code	Major failure class	Definition
01...	Guiding-part failure	Manufacturing or service failure of (bearing) guiding-component.
01.1...	Separator failure	Separator failure from manufacture or service.
01.10	Separator manufacturing geometry defect	Separator geometry off-specification, as manufactured.
01.11	Separator bulk defect	Fracture, cracking, weld failure of metal or plastic component, melting of plastic component.
01.12	Separator plastic deformation	Permanent deformation of separator.
01.13	Separator wear	"Mild" wear of separator.
01.14	Separator galling	"Severe" wear (galling) of separator.
01.15	Separator corrosion	Chemical surface attack on separator.
01.16	Separator heat imbalance failure	Plastic flow and/or chemical change in separator from (local) overheating.
01.17	Separator contact spalling	Hertz contact fatigue failure in separator by macroscopic surface cratering.
01.2...	Guidering failure	Guidering material defect, fracture, wear, galling.

Note: See Sections 2.4 and 2.6 for listing of failure modes of guiderings.

2.3.4. Integral closure failure
Table 2.6: Failure code groups 1 and 2: Integral closure failure

Group No.	Digits	Classification basis
1	2	Component class
2	2	Specific component and major failure class

Listing of groups

Failure code	Major failure class	Definition
02...	Seal (integral), failure	Defect of integral seals
02.1...	Rubbing-seal defect	Defects of contact seals as listed below.
02.10	Material or manufacturing defect in rubbing seal	Morphological defects arising prior to service.
02.11	Rubbing seal wear	Mild wear of seal in service.
02.12	Torn rubbing seal lip	Tear of elastomer seal lip.
02.13	Rubbing seal counterface wear	Wear on (metal) surface against which seal lip slides.
02.14	Rubbing seal leak	Lubricant retention or contaminant exclusion defect.
02.15	Chemical attack on rubbing seal	Chemical attack on elastomer lips or structural parts.
02.19	Geometry or assembly defect in rubbing seal	Geometry defect from manufacture or suffered in assembly.
02.2...	Non-rubbing closure defect	Unintended contact in closure, corrosion, leakage.

2.3.5. Lubricant Failure

Table 2.7: Failure code group 1: Lubricant failure

Group No.	Digits	Classification basis
1	2	Lubricant type

Listing of groups

Failure code	Component type	Definition
1...	Lubricant failure	Failure of any lubricant
11	Oil failure	Failure of liquid organic lubricant
12	Grease failure	Failure of semi-solid lubricant with organic base oil
13	Solid, composite or gas lubricant failure	Failure of solid lubricant, liquid lubricant in porous or solid gel matrix, gas, water or cryo-fluid lubricant, etc.

Note: See Sections 2.4 and 2.6 for listing of failure modes of lubricants

2.3.6. Mounting Part Failure

Table 2.8: Failure code group 1: Mounting part failure

Group No.	Digits	Classification basis
1	2	Mounting part type

Listing of groups

Failure code	Major failure class	Definition
2...	Mounting part damage	Failure of any mounting part.
21	Housing damage	Failure of housing as mounting part (e.g. for bearing).
22	Shaft damage	Failure of shaft, integral or mounted.
23	Spacer, shoulder damage	Failure of ring shaped spacing element (not contact part) in housing or on shaft.
24	Mounting sleeve, nut, lockwasher damage	Failure of fastening element.
25	Seal (external), failure	Failure of seal (other than integral bearing seal).
26	Support bearing damage (of gear, cam)	Failure of support bearing in gear or cam assembly.

Note: See Sections 2.4 and 2.6 for listing of failure modes of mounting parts.

2.4. FAILURE CODE LIST

The Failure Code list at the end of this book enumerates all assigned Failure codes and the corresponding text designations. The list is in ascending order of numeric failure code and serves to find the text designation when the numeric code is known. Owing to the hierarchical structure of the code, this list keeps failure modes in logical relational order and thus offers a perspective of the code system structure. Plates in Part II are indexed by their primary failure code (Failure code 1).

Some failure codes are included for completeness, even though no illustration is available for the corresponding failure mode. Although the text designation for each failure mode attempts to be self-contained, reference to the hierarchically superior failure classes is helpful in placing the failure mode in context.

2.5. FAILURE CLASS INDEX

The brief list in this Section enumerates the major failure classes in ascending alphabetic order of their text designation. It is a useful overview of existing major failure classes.

Table 2.9: Failure class index

Failure designation	Failure code
Contact part failure	**00**
Casting defect	00.05
Corrosion	00.20
Cracking or fracture, bulk	00.22
Denting (indentation)	00.18
Electric erosion	00.21
Finishing mark	00.02
Forming defect	00.04
Fretting wear	00.15
Galling (smearing, severe mechanical wear)	00.13
Geometry, assembly or mounting defect	00.09
Heat imbalance failure	00.19
Inclusion	00.06
Manufacturing or assembly defect, by location	00.00
Material structure damage, post-heat treatment	00.08
Material structure defect, pre- or in heat treatment	00.07
Nick	00.01
Permanent deformation, bulk	00.23
Pit or unfinished area	

Failure designation	Failure code
Contact part failure (continued)	**00**
Skid marking (microscopic severe wear)	00.14
Spalling (Hertzian contact fatigue)	00.16
Surface distress (surface fatigue)	00.17
Wear, mild	00.12
Guiding-part failure	**01**
Lubricant failure	**1**
Grease failure	12
Oil failure	11
Solid or gas lubricant failure	13
Mounting part damage	**2**
Housing damage	21
Mounting sleeve, nut, lockwasher damage	24
Seal (external), failure	25
Shaft damage	22
Spacer, shoulder damage	23
Support bearing damage (of gear, cam)	26
Seal (integral), failure	**02**

2.6. FAILURE MODE INDEX

An alphabetic index of failure mode designations, with attached numeric failure codes is at the end of this book. The index is alphabetized in two tiers: (a) headings for the major failure classes, and (b) alphabetized entries for each failure mode in that class. This is the main index of failure mode designations. It is used to look up the image material related to a failure mode of known designation. First, one finds the numeric code assigned for the failure mode in the index, and then one looks up the Plate chapter or individual Plates using the code.

A grouped list rather than a single-level alphabetic index is provided because lookup of a failure mode by its designation proceeds logically in two steps: (1) find the failure class and (2) find the specific failure mode therein.

The alphabetized failure mode designations are identical with those in the numeric list of Failure codes cited in Section 2.4.

3 APPEARANCE CLASSIFICATION

ARRANGEMENT

This chapter classifies failure images by *appearance*. This differs from the principal classification of the Atlas, which is by failure mode. Having located the appearance class of the observed failure on a page of this chapter, the user finds, alongside the image, the failure code(s) under which similar appearances can be found in the Plate Chapters.

The principal distinguishing marks of appearance are the changes they produce in the as-manufactured surface (or the material section produced for examination).

The layout of this chapter is, briefly, as follows. (See also the detailed description of Chapter 3 page formats given in Chapter 1.)

• The chapter consists of Sections, each covering a major appearance category as listed in Table 3.1.
• Within each section are class headers, naming an appearance class and describing its appearance.
• Under each class header, individual failure modes are illustrated with images and explained in text.

In this chapter, the failed part is not specifically named if it is a contact component. However, guiding components, seals, and mounting parts are specifically named.

Table 3.1: Appearance categories.

Type of change	Explanation
Wide area failure	
General surface removal	surface uniformly ablated (wear or etching) or deformed (rolldown)
General surface texture change	discoloration, film deposit, polishing, unfinished surface
Material change	softening, decomposition, consistency change, structure defect
Point or line failure	
Material locally removed	pit, crater, gouge, electric erosion, false brinelling
Material locally deformed	nick, dent, line
Material transferred	galling, skidmarking, welding
Material separation	fracture, cracking, seam, lap
Material defect	casting defect, forming defect, finishing damage
Foreign material	inclusion, contamination
Geometry failure	
Dimension error	manufacturing tolerance error, dimension instability
Distortion	plastic deformation, residual stress, mounting error

3.1. WIDE AREA FAILURE

GENERAL SURFACE DISPLACEMENT
Original surface material displaced

FC 00.12: **Wear**
Finished topography removed, metallic
Shown under 'general texture change'.

FC 00.19: **Heat imbalance failure**
Plastic flow, surface discolored
Shown under 'general texture change'.

FC 00.15: **Fretting**
Worn surface, with rust-colored deposit
Shown under 'general texture change'.

FC 00.23: **Plastic deformation**
Cold plastic flow
Not illustrated

GENERAL TEXTURE CHANGE
Finishing marks, luster or color changed

FC 00.03: **Unfinished Area**
Surface carries the finishing marks of the next-to-last operation
Archive: 093-3.1.4
PlateNo: 5.16

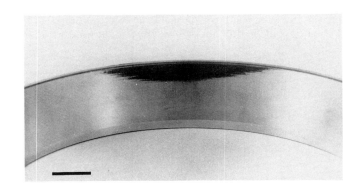

FC 00.12: **Wear**
Partially or totally replaces original finishing marks with wear-marked texture
Archive: 087-036
PlateNo: 7.8

GENERAL TEXTURE CHANGE (continued)

FC 00.15: **Fretting**

Produces a rust-colored deposit on worn steel *contact* or *fit* surface

Archive: 027-119
PlateNo: 9.3

FC 00.17: **Surface distress (glazing)**

Burnished surface on which original finishing texture is plastically smoothed

Archive: 027-234
PlateNo: 11.3

FC 00.19: **Heat imbalance failure**

Temper color, friction polymer and/or signs of plastic flow on surface

Archive: 018-617
PlateNo: 13.9(a)

GENERAL TEXTURE CHANGE (continued)

FC 00.20: Corrosion
Rust colored stains or pits on any steel surface
Archive: 027-211
PlateNo: 14.1

MATERIAL FAILURE
Composition, physical properties, structure changed

FC 00.04: Forming Defect
Metallographic. See Plate Chapter
Not illustrated

FC 00.07: Material Structure Defect
Metallographic. See Plate Chapter
Not illustrated

FC 00.08: Structural Damage, Post Heat Treatment
Metallographic. See Plate Chapter
Not illustrated

FC 00.19: Heat Imbalance Failure
Metallographic. See Plate Chapter
Not illustrated

FC 01.11: Separator Material Damage
Metallographic. See Plate Chapter
Not illustrated

FC 11: Oil Damage
See Plate Chapter
Not illustrated

FC 12: Grease Damage
Discoloration, consistency change, grittiness
Archive: 027-131
PlateNo: 18.15

MATERIAL FAILURE (continued)

FC 11 or 12: Friction Polymer from Lubricant
Brown deposit on contact surface
Archive: 027-173
PlateNo: 18.12 (a)

FC 22: Chemical Decomposition of Mounting Part
See Plate Chapter
Not illustrated

3.2. POINT OR LINE FAILURE

3.2.1. Material Locally Removed

PIT
Dark bottomed crater (not fracture surface)

FC 00.03: Surface Porosity
Crater open to surface, with metallic unmachined surface (not fracture surface)
Archive: 093-3.1.6
PlateNo: 5.15

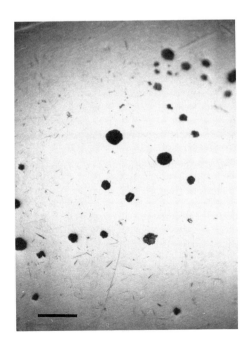

PIT (continued)

FC 00.20: Corrosion Pit
Crater open to surface, with corroded surface (not fracture surface)
Archive: 080-104
PlateNo: 14.7

FC 01.15: Corrosion Pit (Separator)
As above

SPALL
Fracture-bottomed crater

FC 00.16: Hertz Contact Fatigue
Crater left after surface material removal by fatigue cracking.
Macroscopic (depth 100 μm to several mm)
Archive: 027-133
PlateNo: 10.3

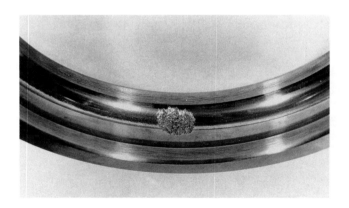

FC 00.17: Surface Distress
Black point-marks from surface material removal by fatigue cracking. Microscopic (depth $< 30\ \mu m$). See also 'surface distress (glazing)' under 'texture change'.
Archive: 074-1
PlateNo: 11.13

PLOWING MARK
Depressed line defect from material removal by plowing action

FC 00.02: Finishing Mark (Furrow, Chatter, Wheelhit)
Excessive or irregular cut-mark from chip-making finishing process
Archive: 080-101
PlateNo: 5.11

FC 00.09: Gouge (Assembly)
Scratch mark by injury during assembly or mounting
Archive: 014-54
PlateNo: 4.4

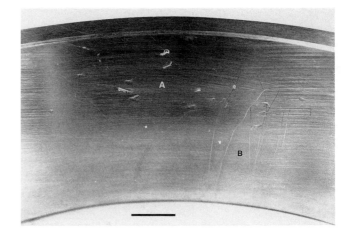

FC 00.12: Wear
Scratch mark made by sliding asperity or third body (see arrows on image)
Archive: 027-154
PlateNo: 7.18

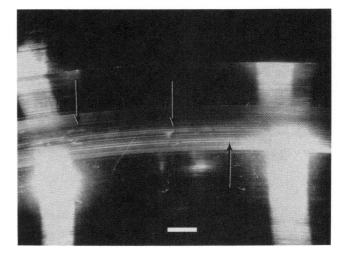

PLOWING MARK (continued)

FC 00.15: False Brinell Mark

Rounded local depression made by fretting wear in stationary
Hertz contact. See Plate chapter for discrimination from true
brinell mark (FC 00.18)
Archive: 093-15.2.1
PlateNo: 9.15

FC 00.21: Electric Current Erosion

Pit (point depression) or flute (line depression) with molten
surface, made by electric current passage through Hertz contact
Archive: 014-68
PlateNo: 14.22

FC 01.13: Separator Wear

Scratch mark made on separator by sliding asperity or third
body
Archive: 087-111
PlateNo: 16.21

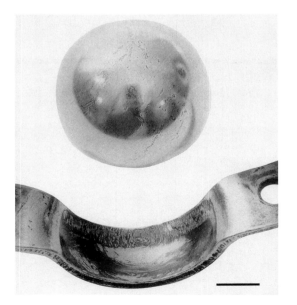

PLOWING MARK (continued)

FC 20: Mounting Part Wear
Scratch mark made on fit surface of mounting part by sliding asperity or third body. (See Plate chapter.)
Not illustrated

3.2.2. Material Locally Deformed

NICK
Material locally (point, line) depressed in manufacture.

FC 00.01: Nick
Nick is a point defect caused by plastically depressing the surface in manufacture. (Dents are caused in service. See Plate chapters for differentiation). Nick bottom is the finished surface, with finishing lines usually visible.
Archive: 003-012
PlateNo: 4.7(a)

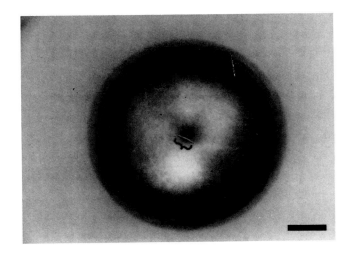

FC 00.01: Scuffmark
Line defect produced similarly to a nick. See **wear marks** and **gouges** for similar appearing defects from plowing action.
Archive: 014-50
PlateNo: 4.8

FC 01: Nick, Scuffmark (Guiding-Component)
As for contact component. (See Plate chapter.)
Not illustrated

FC 22: Nick, Scuffmark (Mounting Part)
As for contact component. (See Plate chapter.)
Not illustrated

DENT
Material locally (point, line) depressed in service

FC 00.18: Dent
Dent is a point defect caused by plastically depressing the surface in *service*. (Nicks are caused in manufacture. See Plate chapters for differentiation). Dent bottom is the finished surface, with finishing lines usually visible. Dents may be *sharp* (from metal particle), *rounded* (from soft debris) or *multi-fragment* (from brittle debris). For distinction between dent types, see Plate chapter.
Archive: 014-8
PlateNo: 12.1 (b)

FC 00.18: Rolled-in Line
Line defect in rolling direction (on ring rolling-track in image), produced as plastic depression by a contacting edge (on rollers in image). See *wear marks* and *gouges* for similar-appearing defects from plowing action.
Archive: 014-9
PlateNo: 7.14

FC 00.18: Debris Denting
Original surface covered randomly with multiple small dents from loose debris.
Archive: 014-4
PlateNo: 12.1 (a)

FC 00.18: Stippled Line
Line in rolling direction, consisting of many identically-shaped dents from an asperity or from debris imbedded in the mating contact surface. (Image is magnified about 200 x.)
Archive: 005-28
PlateNo: 12.13 (b)

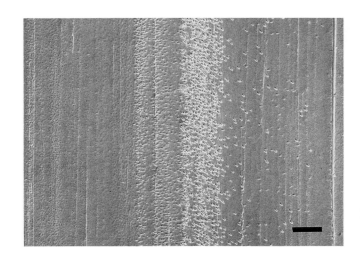

DENT (continued)

FC 00.18: Brinell Mark

Plastic impression of one contacting body into the other. See Plate chapters for distinction between *true* (FC 00.18) and *false* (FC 00.15) brinelling (fretting).
Archive: 018-109
PlateNo: 12.16

FC 01: Dent (Guiding-Component)

As for contact component. (See Plate chapter)
Not illustrated

3.2.3. Material Transferred

GALLING
Metal torn from surface and welded elsewhere on surface

FC 00.13: Galling

Lamina of original contact surface removed by tearing; material removed is welded onto contact surface elsewhere. Resulting surfaces are rolled over.
Archive: 093-027x
PlateNo: 8.7

FC 00.14: Skidmarking

Microscopic galling from temporary sliding between high-speed contact surfaces.
Archive: 027-178
PlateNo: 8.18

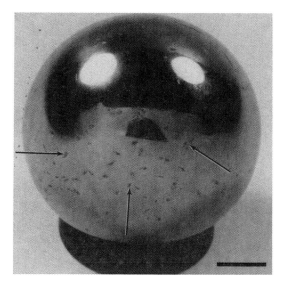

GALLING (continued)

FC 01.14: Galling (Guiding-Component)
As for contact component
Archive: 093-13.1.12
PlateNo: 16.30

FC 2: Galling (Mounting Part)
As for contact component. (See Plate chapter.)
Not illustrated

WELDING
Unintended joining of surfaces

FC 00.19: Heat Imbalance with Welding
Components unintentionally joined in seized assembly (bearing,
etc).
Archive: 093-034
PlateNo: 13.14

3.2.4. Material Separation

CRACK, FRACTURE
Separation of material

FC 00.04: **Lap, Seam**
Unintended separation interface in bulk material, usually with surface contamination, arising in a forming operation. A *lap* is material folded-over onto the surface; a *seam* is a fold normal to the surface.
Archive: 093-4.1.1
PlateNo: 5.21

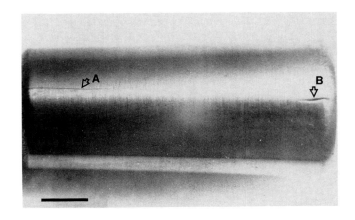

FC 00.07: **Forging or Heat Treat Crack**
See below
Not illustrated

FC 00.08: **Grinding Crack**
See below
Not illustrated

FC 00.09: **Mounting Crack**
See below
Not illustrated

FC 00.22: **Bulk Crack or Fracture in Service**
Cracks appear as dark lines on the surface or in the metallographic section. *Fractures* are part separations. For distinction among cracking causes see Plate chapters.
Archive: 018-602
PlateNo: 15.1 (a)

FC 01: **Crack or Fracture (Guiding-Component)**
See above
Not illustrated

FC 2: **Crack or Fracture (Mounting Part)**
See above
Not illustrated

3.2.5. Material Defect

FORMING OR CASTING DEFECT (LOCAL)
Local alteration of material

FC 00.04: Forming at Incorrect Temperature
Local structural alteration due to overheating in forging. May be visible in metallographic section or on etched surface (as in image).
Archive: 002-024c
PlateNo: 5.23 (a)

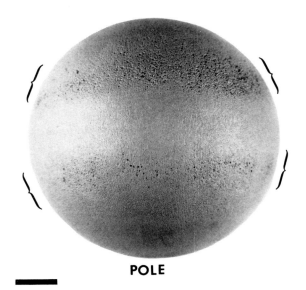

POLE

FC 00.05: Porosity, Molding Defect
Void in contact component material due to casting defect. Visible in metallogaphic section.
Not illustrated

FC 00.07: Heat Treatment Crack
Crack formed due to excessive thermal or residual stresses from heat treatment (of steel)
Archive: 087-108
PlateNo: 6.18 (b)

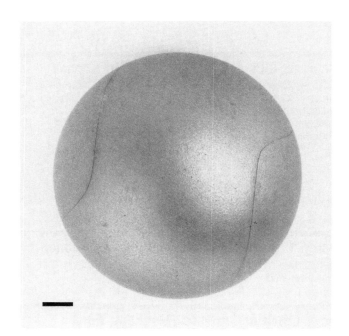

FORMING OR CASTING DEFECT (contiued)

FC 00.08: Finishing Damage (Grinding Burn)
Alteration (tempering, rehardening) of near-surface structure due to abusive finishing. May be visible on surface after diagnostic etching.
Archive: 001-36
PlateNo: 6.23

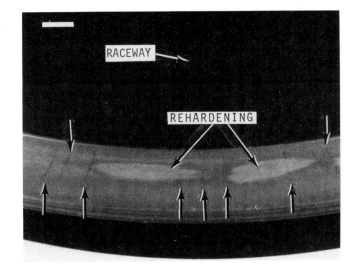

FC 01: Casting, Molding Porosity (Guiding Component)
Void in guiding component material due to casting or molding defect. (Shown in image as-repaired.)
Archive: 093-201
PlateNo: 16.14

FC 2: Mounting Part Casting, Forming Defect
Void in mounting part material due to casting or molding defect. (See Plate chapter.)
Not illustrated

3.2.6. Foreign Material

INCLUSION
Foreign body in material

FC 00.06: Inclusion
Bodies of foreign material included in the matrix material. Of
globular, elongated or fragmented shape. Occasionally visible at
surface, otherwise in metallographic section. For differentiation
among inclusion types, see Plate chapters.
Archive: 075-201
PlateNo: 6.7 (a)

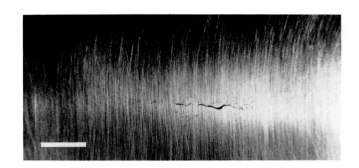

FC 01: Inclusion (Guiding-Component)
As for contact components. (See Plate chapter.)
Not illustrated

FC 1: Contamination
Solid particulates or water in oil or grease, or loose in the
chamber. (See Plate chapter.)
Not illustrated

3.3. GEOMETRY FAILURE

GEOMETRY, ASSEMBLY OR MOUNTING ERROR
Dimension or form out of tolerance

FC 00.09: Geometry, Assembly, Mounting Error
Deviation from design tolerance, incorrect assembly of machine
element or incorrect mounting in machine.
Not illustrated.

FC 01: Geometry Error (Guiding-Component)
Deviation from design tolerance, incorrect assembly of machine
element.
Not illustrated.

FC 2: Geometry Error (Mounting Part)
Deviation from design tolerance, incorrect assembly of machine
element or incorrect mounting in machine.
Not illustrated.

PERMANENT BULK DEFORMATION

Shape distorted

FC 00.23: Permanent Deformation, Bulk
Distortion of shape from as-manufactured condition, occurring during service.
Not illustrated

FC 01: Permanent Deformation (Guiding-Component)
As for contact component.
Not illustrated

FC 2: Permanent Deformation (Mounting Part)
As for contact component.
Not illustrated

Cross-index of Secondary Failure Codes

Failure code	Plate No	Failure code	Plate No
00.00.01	4.1	00.00.03	5.10
	4.2	00.01.1	10.46
	4.5	00.01.1.1	4.3
	6.29		13.12
00.00.02.1	4.3	00.01.2	4.4
	4.4		11.6
	4.6		15.6
	4.7		
	4.8		
	4.10		
	5.3		
	5.9		
	5.13		
	5.14		
	5.15		
	5.16		
	5.17		
	6.31		

NOTE: This list includes failure codes of the form 00.00 covering qualifiers for manufacturing or assembly defects by location.

Plates

DATA
Plate No: 4.1
Archive No: 087-008
Image type: light macro
Scalebar = 30 mm (micros: ±20%, others: +100%, -50%)
Component: CRB; OR & S & R, unrun
Speed:
Load:
Lubrication:
Failure code1: 00.01 Nick
Failure Code2: 00.00.01 Defect by location: in fit surface
Failure Code3: =
Failure Code4: =

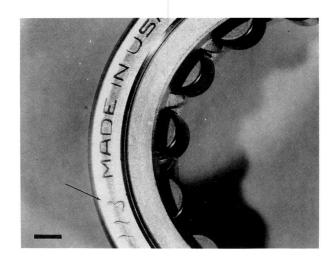

DESCRIPTIONS
FAILURE DESCRIPTION: Numerals spark-etched on sideface of CRB OR with an electric pencil form raised asperities of molten metal. In precision applications such as this aircraft turbine bearing, angular alignment is jeopardized by the out-of-square position the sideface assumes against a flange due to these asperities.

IMAGE DESCRIPTION: At arrow, dark hand-written numerals are elevated above ring sideface. This is detected by placing the ring on a flat plate with this face down and measuring squareness on the opposite face.

SUSPECTED CAUSES: The use of 'electric pencil' spark-erosion markers is common in serializing hardened parts. In some high-precision applications the resulting molten-metal asperities cause flatness tolerances to be exceeded and the use of electric pencil is prohibited.

DATA
Plate No: 4.2
Archive No: 093-005
Image type: a, b: light macro
Scalebar = 30 mm (micros: ±20%, others: +100%, -50%)
Component: CRB; OR, run
Speed:
Load:
Lubrication:
Failure Code1: 00.01.1 Local nick
Failure Code2: 00.00.01 Defect by location: in fit surface
Failure Code3: 00.16.1.1 Subsurface origin spall (high Hertz shear stress)
Failure Code4: 21.9 Geometry or assembly defect in housing

DESCRIPTIONS
FAILURE DESCRIPTION: A chip trapped between housing and OR OD, created a nick and local contact load concentration in the underlying roller path when overrolled. Fatigue spalling followed.

IMAGE DESCRIPTION: The W image half shows the OR OD with a deep nick made by a machining chip near the E–W image centerline, just W of the E ring edge. The E image half shows the roller track directly underlying the nick. An extensive spall has formed in service, starting at the E side of the track, directly underlying the nick on the OD.

SUSPECTED CAUSES: A machining chip was trapped between OR OD and housing bore, providing the primary load support in that area. During overrolling, this local support created a load concentration in the contact which then produced the spall.

DATA
Plate No: 4.3
Archive No: 087-115
Image type: light microgram
Scalebar = 100 μm (micros: ±20%, others: +100%, -50%)
Component: TRB; OR, mounted
Speed:
Load:
Lubrication:
Failure Code1: 00.01.1 Local nick
Failure Code2: 00.01.1.1 Nick with raised edges
Failure Code3: 00.00.02.1 Defect by location: in Hertz contact surface
Failure Code4: 00.09.1 Scoring from forcible assembly or mounting (no galling)
See also PLATE: 4.4

DESCRIPTIONS
FAILURE DESCRIPTION: A series of nicks (with raised edges) was created in the roller track by impact with a sharp-pointed tool.

IMAGE DESCRIPTION: Nicks similar to those in Plate 4.4. The nicks cross finishing lines. At *A*, finishing lines remain visible within nick. Also at *A*, the nearest edge of nick is raised above the surrounding surface. The very bright appearance of the south edges of each nick is due to lighting.

SUSPECTED CAUSES: These short, roughly parallel nicks are produced by repeated contact with the sharp edge of a hard tool. Scraping a tool over the surface by hand pressure may create such small nicks.

DATA
Plate No: 4.4
Archive No: 014-54
Image type: light macro
Scalebar = 100 mm (micros: ±20%, others: +100%, -50%)
Component: TRB; OR, mounted
Speed:
Load:
Lubrication:
Failure Code1: 00.01.1 Local nick
Failure Code2: 00.01.2 Scratch, toolmark, scuffmark
Failure Code3: 00.00.02.1 Defect by location: in Hertz contact surface
Failure Code4: 00.09.1 Scoring from forcible assembly or mounting (no galling)
See also PLATE: 4.3

DESCRIPTIONS
FAILURE DESCRIPTION: Several local nicks and scratches on the roller track of TRB OR.

IMAGE DESCRIPTION: This light macro shows a slightly enlarged portion of the roller track in a TRB cup (OR), with irregularly shaped depressed nicks at *A* and irregular cross-track scratches at *B*. For an enlarged view of assembly nicks see Plate 4.3.

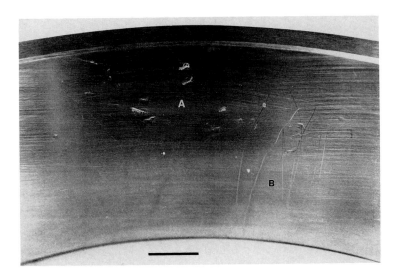

SUSPECTED CAUSES: In assembly, a punch-type tool (drift) was used on the narrow face of the cup. It slipped repeatedly into the roller track when struck with a hammer, making nicks (when impacting one point on the track) or scratches (when sliding across the track).

DATA
Plate No: 4.5
Archive No: 018-201
Image type: view
Scalebar = (micros: ±20%, others: +100%, -50%)
Component: NRB; OR & R, mounted
Speed: -
Load: -
Lubrication: -
Failure Code1: 00.01.1.1 Nick with raised edges
Failure Code2: 00.00.01 Defect by location: in fit surface
Failure Code3: 00.09.1 Scoring from forcible assembly or mounting (no galling)
Failure Code4: -

DESCRIPTIONS
FAILURE DESCRIPTION: Several deep nicks with raised edges (at OD chamfer) around the circumference of OR face, due to sharp plastic indentation. In the thin-walled deep-drawn sheet-steel cup, the indentation stoves in the sheet, creating a bulge in the inner surface facing the roller ends. Bearing may seize if run.

IMAGE DESCRIPTION: Several half-moon shaped indentations spaced circumferentially near the OD edge of the face, with raised edged at the OD. Bottom of nicks is shiny.

SUSPECTED CAUSES: Use of a hammer and punch to install the drawn needle roller bearing cup into the housing has led to plastic indentation under the impact of the punch. Bending of the thin-walled cup creates a bulge on the roller-end facing inner face of the cup and may distort the entire cup geometry.

DATA
Plate No: 4.6
Archive No: 093-1.1.2
Image type: light interference micro
Scalebar = 35 μm (micros: ±20%, others: +100%, -50%)
Component: BB; B, unrun
Speed:
Load:
Lubrication:
Failure Code1: 00.01.1.1 Nick with raised edges
Failure Code2: 00.00.02.1 Defect by location: in Hertz contact surface
Failure Code3: -
Failure Code4: -

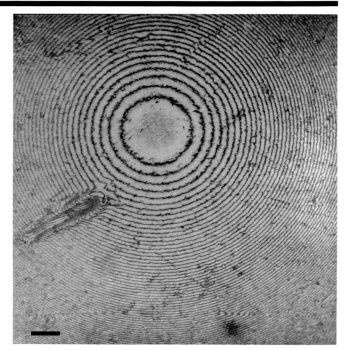

DESCRIPTIONS
FAILURE DESCRIPTION: A plastically formed nick or "gouge" in the ball surface, by indentation with a sharp-edged hard object under high normal pressure. Raised edges surround the nick. A ball with this damage runs noisily. The damaged surface may suffer surface distress (FC 00.17) and surface-origin spalling (FC.00.16) as a result of interrupted EHD film and stress concentration at the nick.

IMAGE DESCRIPTION: The image is made by multiple beam interference microscopy, which creates narrow dark contour lines spaced 1/2 light-wavelength (about 0.2 μm) apart. On an undamaged ball surface the contours are circles (with small random excursions showing lapping marks). The lines show the depressed nick bottom (about 0.4 μm deep) and a raised rim (about 0.2 μm high) surrounding it.

SUSPECTED CAUSES: In ball lapping a tool is used to extract the balls from between the lapping plates. If it is metal and develops a raised edge, it can mark the balls. The mark shown has raised edges, indicating that it must have been caused at the end of the finishing operation. Another source of nicks (less likely in view of the nick shape shown) is assembly of the bearing.

DATA

Plate No: 4.7
Archive No: 003-012 (a) & (b)
Image type: a: view, b: light microgram
Scalebar = a: 10, b: 2 mm (micros: ±20%, others: +100%, -50%)
Component: BB; B, unrun
Speed: -
Load: -
Lubrication: -
Failure Code1: 00.01.1.1 Nick with raised edges
Failure Code2: 00.00.02.1 Defect by location: in Hertz contact surface
Failure Code3: 00.09.1 Scoring from forcible assembly or mounting (no galling)
Failure Code4: -

DESCRIPTIONS

FAILURE DESCRIPTION: Straight boat-shaped plastic indentation in ball surface, made by a hard, straight-edged object pressed or impacted into the ball. A ball with this damage is noisy and is likely to spall early at surface defect. Raised edge of nick may damage ring ball-path.

IMAGE DESCRIPTION: (a): View shows appearance of nick to the unaided eye. (b): Micrograph shows 5x magnification. In both images, bracket indicates nick. The boat shape, sharp points and straight edge along nick center indicate indentation by sharp straight edge. Surface of dent is shiny, same as undented ball surface. Dark color in image is due to light reflection.

SUSPECTED CAUSES: During mounting of split-innerring ball bearing into machine, separator/ball complement may be dis-

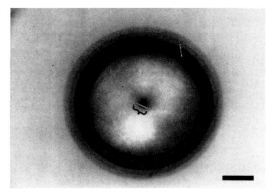

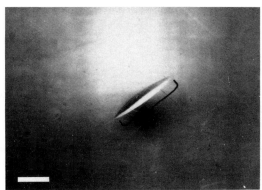

placed in OR so that IR, mounted on shaft, hits a ball during rotor insertion. As another cause: In ball manufacture or assembly into bearing, balls may drop from some height onto the sharp edge of a hard machine component. A drop of 20–40 cm suffices to cause a dent as shown.

DATA

Plate No: 4.8
Archive No: 014-50
Image type: view
Scalebar = 100 mm (micros: ±20%, others: +100%, -50%)
Component: TRB; OR (2), unrun
Speed:
Load:
Lubrication:
Failure Code1: 00.01.2 Scratch, toolmark, scuffmark
Failure Code2: 00.00.02.1 Defect by location: in Hertz contact surface
Failure Code3: 00.09.1 Scoring from forcible assembly or mounting (no galling)
Failure Code4: 00.18.3 Brinelling

DESCRIPTIONS

FAILURE DESCRIPTION: Forcible assembly of tilted rollers into OR (cup) caused: (1) series of circumferential dents aligned axially (scuffmarks), (2) axial scoremarks and (3) brinell marks. The damage causes a noisy bearing and is likely to lead to early spalling at the dents or brinell marks.

IMAGE DESCRIPTION: Dark-appearing broad fuzzy-edged axial scuffmarks on roller tracks (both OR-s). In OR at image E, also

fine flared dark brinell marks near both track edges, and axially aligned series of circumferential cuts or nicks in the N center portion of the track. The gouge marks and nicks are shiny, and may appear light or dark against the background depending on light incidence angle.

SUSPECTED CAUSES: With the OR (cup) mounted in a housing and the IR (cone) and roller assembly on the shaft, assembly of the rotor into the machine stator with inadequate alignment can force contact between roller (end) and OR roller path. Stator weight or assembly forces provide the load that can cause scuffing, nicking and brinelling.

DATA
Plate No: 4.9
Archive No: 001-12
Image type: light microgram
Scalebar = 500 μm (micros: ±20%, others: +100%, -50%)
Component: ACBB; IR, run
Speed: 1 MdN
Load: 0.7 GPa
Lubrication: synthetic polyester oil, 120° C
Failure Code1: 00.01.2 Scratch, toolmark, scuffmark
Failure Code2: 00.16.1.2.2 Shallow entry spall from surface line-defect
Failure Code3: -
Failure Code4: -

DESCRIPTIONS
FAILURE DESCRIPTION: Severe axial tool mark on land and ball groove, followed by spall in groove, extending to edge and chipping into land. Contact apparently extended to edge so that spall could form at edge. Ring has failed.

IMAGE DESCRIPTION: N 1/3 of image is land, S 2/3 is ball groove; the two separated by groove edge. Dark, teardrop-shaped gouge in land. Elongated scratch still visible in groove, just S of land edge, and near S image edge. Mushroom-shaped spall formed E of gouge (downstream in rolling direction) and broadened near land edge, from edge loading. Near land edge, spall crossed gouge and extended against rolling direction.

SUSPECTED CAUSES: Severe nick or gouge in rolling surface is cause for early spalling. Broadening of spall toward land edge suggests that contact must have overrun the edge, so that substantial edge stresses existed. This is likely to cause early spalling even without the defect.

DATA
Plate No: 4.10
Archive No: 093-1.1.5
Image type: light microgram
Scalebar = 70 μm (micros: ±20%, others: +100%, -50%)
Component: BB; B, run
Speed:
Load:
Lubrication:
Failure Code1: 00.01.3 Circular flat nick on ball
Failure Code2: 00.00.02.1 Defect by location: in Hertz contact surface
Failure Code3: 00.12.3.2.2 Scratch marks, kinematic wear marks in rolling surface
Failure Code4: -

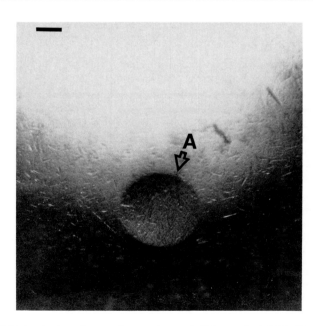

DESCRIPTIONS
FAILURE DESCRIPTION: Circular flattened nick (commonly called a "flat") on ball surface, marked by arrow A. A slight bulge of displaced metal surrounds the edge of the flat. Multiple short, small scratches and dents on ball surface both inside and outside the flat, due to wear. A flat on a ball causes noisy running but is a serious spall originator only when severe. Scratched and dented surface is likely to cause noise.

IMAGE DESCRIPTION: The ball surface is shaded by oblique lighting. The flat is outlined where the light and shadow blend, due to its differing orientation. (Unless highlighted by oblique light impinging at a grazing angle, such flats are invisible). The flat's edge is surrounded by a slight bulge. Multiple dents and scratches appear as dark streaks in the lit area and as light streaks near the edge of the unlit area.

SUSPECTED CAUSES: Flats are typical ball manufacturing defects caused by balls impacting against each other in a container or against a hard flat surface. Due to the small impact area, a ball surface is plastically deformed under a drop of as few as 20 cm onto a hardened flat. Balls packed in boxes suffer flats when the box is dropped from similar heights.

5 SURFACE DEFECTS FROM MANUFACTURING

General Description

This chapter comprises *morphological* manufacturing defects that are (or may be) visible on the finished *surface* of the component, become visible at failure, (for example, a fracture) or upon sectioning. Not covered in this chapter are *Nicks* (FC 00.01).

Many types of failure can occur in casting, forming or finishing which are not surface defects such as material defects, dimensional errors, etc. These are not covered in this chapter. Some of them, which can be diagnosed by visual means, are covered in Chapter 6. Defects such as incorrect material composition, which are inherently non-visual, are not covered in the Atlas.

5.1. FINISHING MARKS.
FAILURE CODE: 00.02

5.1.1. Definition

A finishing mark is defined as a mark of unintended shape or size, left on the finished surface by the last sequenced (intended) operation in the manufacturing process. It is distinct from a nick (FC 00.01) and a gouge (FC 00.09) caused by surface contacts occurring accidentally prior to service.

5.1.2. Nomenclature

• Abrasively finished (ground, honed, or polished) surfaces show *finishing furrows, chatter* or *wheel hits.* Some grinding methods may produce *shoe marks.*
• Turned, milled, hobbed, shaved surfaces show *gouges, tears* or *chatter.*
• Cold rolled, deep drawn and other chipless finished surfaces show marks specific to the process.

5.1.3. Failure Process

When a finish-machining operation malfunctions, the tool may leave unintended marks on the surface. Examples:

Abrasively Finished Surfaces
Any bonded abrasive used for grinding or honing may detach a grit particle which is dragged over the surface and cuts a furrow, that is deeper, or more irregular than a normal finishing mark, or runs in a different direction. It may start or end abruptly and may retain particles of grit.

Lapping compound may contain oversize or aggregated particles which make an abnormally deep furrow in the surface.
Centerless grinding methods rely on supporting machine elements to position the workpiece. Some of these (shoes) are in sliding contact with the workpiece. These supports can wear, score or polish the surface of the workpiece, producing a shoe mark.
A control error in the motion of the abrasive finishing tool may bring it into abrupt unintended contact with the workpiece, creating a surface patch with defective geometry or finish. This is a wheelhit. Similar to a wheelhit is a mark left by a hand-held grinder used to remove a local spall or dent from the surface.

Turned, Milled, Hobbed Surfaces
Tool edges may chip, with the broken-off piece caught against the workpiece and making a gouge. A tear can result from a chipped tool or a tool with a worn or improperly formed edge failing to cut cleanly.

Hard-turned surfaces are fully hardened surfaces finished by single-point carbide or ceramic tools. They show finishing marks of similar origin as do other turned surfaces, but these are on a roughness scale comparable to those on ground surfaces.

Chipless Finished Surfaces
A multitude of surface markings can result from malfunction in chipless finishing, depending on the nature of the process. Characterization requires specific information concerning the finishing process.

5.1.4. Distinctive Appearance

Finishing furrows typically are wider and deeper than the normal finishing lines. When due to a detached piece of grit, they may show one blunt end and one tailing-off end (comet-tail), as the grit is caught, dragged and expelled or shattered, or left embedded in the surface. On finely ground or honed surfaces, magnification is required to identify finishing furrows.
Chatter marks may be seen as periodic changes in the luster of the surface, as one proceeds around the circumference. Often, they become visible only after being highlighted by running. Occasionally, they are detectable only as waviness, by surface tracing.

NOTE: Chatter marking may produce grinding damage (FC 00.08), which may subsequently be obliterated by further finishing.

Wheel hits or hand grinder marks may show directions of grinding cuts that differ from other surface areas. Usually, a geometry error (depression) can be detected by surface tracing.

NOTE: Wheel hits may produce grinding damage (FC 00.08), which may subsequently be obliterated by further finishing.

Shoe marks are circumferential marks of wear, polishing or scoring, on the ground surface.

NOTE: Shoe marks may produce grinding burns (See FC 00.08: Grinding damage).

Gouges are deep or irregular tool marks. *Tears* are plastically deformed and microcracked surface irregularities. Finishing marks on chipless finished surfaces require knowledge of the finishing process for identification.

5.1.5. Causes

Causes of finishing marks require specific information on the finishing process for their identification.

5.1.6. Effects of Finishing Marks

Finishing marks may have similar effects as nicks (FC 00.01) or dents (FC 00.18). Specifically:

• Marks representing depressions without raised edges (finishing furrows and some chipless finishing marks). If present on contact surfaces they can impair the EHD film, causing surface distress (FC 00.17) in a surrounding 'halo'.

• Severe finishing furrows represent surface defects (stress concentrations) for the initiation of surface-origin spalls (FC 00.16).

• Shoe marks, if galled, are defects that will cause further galling (FC 00.13) and spalling (FC 00.16). If grinding damage exists in the marks, then rubbing cracks (FC 00.08), bulk cracks (FC 00.22) or spalls (FC 00.16) may form.

• Gouges and tears tend to have raised edges and show microcracking. They act as severe nicks and may cause wear, galling, spalling or bulk fracture.

• The effects of finishing marks from chipless finishing require evaluation using the specifics of the finishing process.

5.2. PIT OR UNFINISHED AREA. FAILURE CODE: 00.03

5.2.1. Pit. Failure Code: 00.03.1

Definition

A pit is defined as a void open to the surface, caused by a casting, or forming defect or chemical attack on the surface. All pitting, other than by chemical attack, predates service. Chemical attack (corrosion) pitting may occur at any time after final finishing throughout the life of the part. It is covered for all cases under FC 00.20.

Nomenclature

In the literature, the word 'pit' has been used to describe any sharp-edged depression in a surface, including a spall.

In this Atlas, a pit is distinguished from several other types of manufacturing defects and from spalls.

Pits are distinguished from *finishing marks, nicks, dents and unfinished areas* as follows:

• A void created on the surface by the finishing process is a finishing mark (FC 00.02).

• A void created by unintended indentation prior to service is a nick (FC 00.01). Indentation in service is a dent (FC 00.18).

• An unfinished area is a patch of surface where the second-last finishing operation has not been reworked by the last operation.

Pits are distinguished from *spalls*, which are fracture craters due to contact fatigue (FC 00.16).

Failure Process

Pits result from either manufacturing process failure, or chemical attack.

Manufacturing process failures are exemplified by the following:

• In casting, pressing, forging, rolling or other blank preparation processes, internal voids (porosity, FC 00.05) may unintentionally be created. A subsequent chip-removal process may cut into these voids, creating a pit open to the surface.

• Weak interfaces created by the forming operation may separate during finishing, leaving a pit.

• Inclusions in the material may be intersected in finishing and tear out, leaving a pit.

• Large carbides present in some steels, and ceramic grains in bonded ceramics may tear out in finishing, leaving a pit.

Chemical attack:

Any time during manufacture, mounting, storage or service of the machine element, chemical attack (corrosion, FC 00.20) may occur at a surface, causing pits.

Distinctive Appearance

Pits typically appear as sharp-edged craters. The surface in the pit does not show the finishing marks of the surrounding surface (distinguishing it from a nick). The pit surface is not a transgranular crack. This distinguishes a pit from a spall.

Differentiation of a pit from an incipient spall may require microscopic or SEM examination to detect the presence or absence of typical spall-bottom surface features (FC 00.16).

Causes

For causes of casting or forming defects, inclusions, or large grains, each of which can generate a pit if intersected in finishing, see FC 00.04 through FC 00.07. Any chip-forming finishing process can intersect one of these defects and leave a pit. More severe processes (higher cutting forces, larger depths of cut) are more prone to generating pits.

For causes of corrosion pitting see FC 00.20.

Effects of Pits

• Pits represent depressions without raised edges. If

present on contact surfaces, they impair the EHD film, causing surface distress (FC 00.17) in a 'halo' surrounding them.

- Pit surfaces are often microcracked or otherwise weak. They act as surface defects for the initiation of surface-origin spalls (FC 00.16).
- Sharp-edged pits in a contact surface are defects acting as stress concentrators for surface-origin spalls (FC 00.16).
- Corrosion pits promote further corrosion of the surface.

5.2.2. Unfinished Area.
Failure Code: 00.03.2–4

Definition

An unfinished area is left on a surface if the manufacturing operation *preceding* the last finishing, leaves insufficient stock for the last operation to perform stock removal, or if the last operation misses the area.

Nomenclature

Unfinished areas in abrasively finished (or hard-turned) surfaces are often dark due to heat treat oxidation and are then referred to as 'black areas'. Unfinished areas are also known as NCU (not cleaned-up), unground or unhoned.

Failure process

Casting, forging, cold forming and all chip removal operations may produce a surface area which is depressed relative to its nominal position. The last finishing operation may find the depression deeper than the stock allowed for finishing, so that, after completion, the surface condition created by the preceding operation effective in that area is left unchanged. Alternatively, the finishing operation may miss an area due to machine or cutting tool malfunction. The effect is as described above, except that the surface is now *raised* rather than *depressed*.

Distinctive Appearance.

Unfinished areas are identified by the difference in surface finish between that area and the surrounding surface.

In a heat treated part, an area left in the 'as heat treated' condition is usually black or grey.

Rough ground areas in a finish-ground, honed or polished surface may show grinding marks running in a different direction or deeper and sharper than the final finish. Surface tracing or microscopic examination may be needed for diagnosis.

'Lips' at edge reliefs, left when the finishing tool fails to reach the relief groove, may be visible under low magnification or detected by surface tracing.

Causes

On a cold formed part with corner radii specified to be left as formed, the forming may fail to fill out the radius at some point, leaving a depressed area running into a working surface. When the part is ground, no stock is available in the depression and it remains unfinished.

Heat treatment or chucking of a part in the machine tool can cause distortion, leaving some surfaces lower than specified. Finishing to specification may leave these areas unfinished.

Turning, prior to heat treatment and grinding, can leave gouges which are too deep for grinding to clean up.

On surfaces which are rough ground and finish ground or ground and honed, the second-to-last operation may remove excessive material (or relieve residual stresses that cause distortion) so that the finish grinding or honing fails to find stock to remove. A rough ground 'unfinished' surface is left behind.

Components with integral flanges require finishing of the roller track and the flange. If grinding is the finishing method, a *relief*, that is, a corner radius or undercut is provided between track and flange, since the grinding wheel cannot reliably produce a sharp receding edge. If the wheel fails to find a wide enough relief, it may leave an unground lip at the beginning of the relief. A similar effect may be produced if the wheel geometry is in error (the wheel edge is rounded), leaving a lip near an undercut of correct width.

Effects of Unfinished Areas

Depressed unfinished areas are (large) nicks. They do not carry their share of contact load and edge stresses may develop at the boundary of the area. *Premature spalling* may result, if the unfinished area falls within a Hertzian contact. *Galling* may result at locations where the edge of an unfinished area slides over a flange or a rolling bearing separator.

Lips are elevated above the finished surface and if contacted by a roller, cause edge stresses, local plastic deformation, and a line of fine spalls in the roller, the ring carrying the lip, or both.

High grinding stresses or grinding damage may be present at surfaces left unfinished after rough grinding.

5.3. FORMING DEFECTS.
FAILURE CODE: 00.04

5.3.1. Definition

Forming defects are *internal* defects of a formed (forged, rolled, cold formed, pressed, deep drawn, stamped) part, or of a part formed by powder compacting, that result from the forming process. They may extend to the surface of the formed part.

- A *lap* is an unintended folded-over metal lip pressed into the surface with a weak interface to the bulk material.
- A *seam* is an unwelded interface in a formed part, often bearing a laminar inclusion of foreign material.
- *Defects in formed structure* consist of weak, brittle, or otherwise off-standard volumes of material caused by a faulty forming process, such as wrong forging temperature.
- *Pipe, porosity* and *cracks* may be found in formed parts. Pipe and porosity are covered under FC 00.05; forming cracks under FC 00.07.

5.3.2. Nomenclature

Alternative nomenclature used in the forging, pressing or extruding industries is not covered. The above nomenclature is the usual one for contact machine elements.

5.3.3. Failure Process

• A *lap* forms if a volume of material is unintentionally folded over an adjacent volume during the forming operation and the fold tightly pressed together. There may be partial welding at the interface, especially if the operation is hot forming.

• A *seam* forms if scale or other foreign material is unintentionally forged or rolled into the material where it forms a laminar discontinuity. Seams are interfaces extending radially inward from the surface.

• *Defects* in a (hot)-*formed structure* arise by processes of local melting, recrystallization, segregation, etc. Details of the processes depend on the material and specific forming method used.

5.3.4. Distinctive Appearance.

Laps and seams are detected as nearly straight lines on the surface of the part. They may be obscured by plastically flowed surface material during finishing operations and reappear after running, or when a crack forms at them. A metallographic section shows oxide, voids and/or irregular structure surrounding laps and seams. In a seam, the included foreign material is typically observable. *Laps* extend at a shallow angle to the surface, and *seams* run radially into the material.

Defective formed structure is detected in metals by metallographic examination including etching. In other materials (ceramics), special microscopic techniques are required.

5.3.5. Causes

Identification of causes of forming defects requires specific knowledge of the forming method used.

5.3.6. Effects of Forming Defects

Forming defects are gross discontinuities which, under stressing, typically lead to:

• Bulk cracking or fracture (FC 00.22)
• Spalling (FC 00.16).

5.4. CASTING DEFECTS.
FAILURE CODE: 00.05

5.4.1. Definition

Morphological defects occurring in a casting or molding process include:

Porosity (macro- or micro-) i.e. voids in the cast part. (For porosity visible at the surface see FC 00.03.)

Underfill, i.e. failure of the cast material to completely fill the mold.

Pipe, i.e. a central, empty or inclusion-filled thread in a cast ingot or rolled product made from the ingot.

Cracks (FC 00.07).

Inclusions (FC 00.06).

Casting structure defects (FC 00.07).

5.4.2. Nomenclature

Alternative nomenclatures used in the casting and molding industry are not covered. The cited nomenclature is the usual one for contact machine elements.

5.4.3. Failure Process

Casting, that is, forming from the liquid state, is the initial manufacturing operation for all (except powder processed) metal parts. Plastic components are molded or extruded. (In rolled metal products, casting produces the ingot.)

The morphological defects of as-cast material appear in original form in components used without subsequent forming. They are often carried, in modified form, into the semi-finished (rolled, forged, etc.) product.

In view of the wide variety of materials and casting processes used in Hertz contact machine elements, only the following generalities can be provided on the failure process:

• *Porosity* may be due to release of dissolved gases from the solidifying melt. *NOTE: Forging porosity* may occur from local remelting of the as-cast structure under excessive forging temperature (FC 00.04).

• *Underfill* occurs when the molten material fails to reach all volumes in the mold before solidification.

• *Structure defects* may arise from a wide variety of chemical and/or physical processing errors specific to the casting process and to the material. They are covered under FC 00.07.

• *Cracks* (FC 00.07) may be due to internal stresses arising in solidification or phase transformation. *Separations* (weak interfaces) may be left where molten material reaches a cross-section in the mold from two sides and fails to bond completely.

• *Inclusions* are described under FC 00.06.

5.4.4. Distinctive Appearance

Porosity is visible as an open void:

When it produces surface pits;
When a crack failure intersects a pore;
In a metallographic section.

NOTES:
1) An inclusion may be exposed at a surface and then be torn away, leaving a pore.
2) Macro-porosity may be shown in a casting by X-ray or ultrasound imaging.

Underfill is visible as a local deviation from intended shape.

For cracks, see FC 00.07, for inclusions, FC 00.06.

5.4.5. Causes

Identification of causes of casting defects requires specific information on the casting process used.

5.4.6. Effects of casting defects

Casting defects are gross discontinuities which, under stressing, typically lead to: bulk cracking or fracture (FC 00.22), or to spalling (FC 00.16).

Cross-index of Secondary Failure Codes

Failure code	Plate No
00.02.1	5.19
	8.19
	10.60
	10.61
	11.24
	11.25
	11.26
	12.13
00.02.2	6.22
00.03	5.11
	19.10

Failure code	Plate No
00.03.4	7.12
00.04.1	8.12
00.04.2	5.23
	10.40
	15.28
00.04.3.1	6.14
00.04.3.1.1	10.33
	10.47
00.05.1	5.23
	11.10

Plates

DATA
Plate No: 5.1
Archive No: 002-001b&d
Image type: SEM
Scalebar = (a) 100 μm; (b) 20 μm
(micros: ±20%, others: +100%, -50%)
Component: ACBB; B, tool steel, lapped, run
Speed: 1.5 MdN
Load: 0.75 GPa
Lubrication: synthetic polyester oil, 176 °C
Failure Code1: 00.02.1 Grinding, honing, lapping furrow
Failure Code2: -
Failure Code3: -
Failure Code4: -

 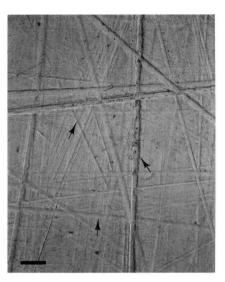

a   b

DESCRIPTIONS
FAILURE DESCRIPTION: Smooth linear scratchmarks in random direction, generally uniformly distributed but of uneven depth, from ball manufacture. The deep marks qualify as lapping furrows. Marks of this depth may initiate surface distress in critical applications and somewhat wear separator pockets. Two distinct sets of marks (one from lapping the other from service) are not present, i.e. furrows not of service origin. See FC 00.12 for wear.

IMAGE DESCRIPTION: (a): Dense pattern of randomly oriented smooth-ending scratchmarks. Some marks are deeper than others (arrows) and qualify as furrows. (b): Higher magnification shows the lack of sharp feather edges at all marks, indicating that they are likely to have undergone equal running times since scratching, i.e. that none are of service origin. Arrows mark some deeper furrows.

SUSPECTED CAUSES: The ball lapping process necessarily produces fine lapping lines. If the lapping compound is of uneven grain size, larger grains may produce the deeper furrows.

DATA
Plate No: 5.2
Archive No: 006-1
Image type: SEM
Scalebar = 10 μm (micros: ±20%, others: +100%, -50%)
Component: G, high hardness, ground, unrun
Speed: -
Load: -
Lubrication: -
Failure Code1: 00.02.1 Grinding, honing, lapping furrow
Failure Code2: -
Failure Code3: -
Failure Code4: -

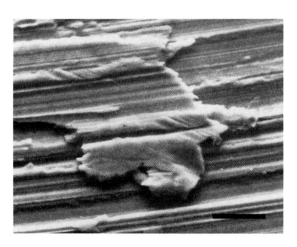

DESCRIPTIONS
FAILURE DESCRIPTION: As-ground gear tooth surface on which the grinding process has redeposited (welded) steel particles. This surface has poor resistance to wear or fatigue failure. The redeposited debris is heavily worked and heated material, welding to the surface entails high stresses and the debris increases roughness.

IMAGE DESCRIPTION: Grinding lines run E–W in the image. A particle at least 50 μm long extends from NW corner to image center where it ends in a "peninsula". Some grinding took place after welding, as evidenced by grinding lines on the particle.

SUSPECTED CAUSES: Insufficient flushing of grinding debris from the wheel/workpiece contact may cause debris to be redeposited from the grinding wheel and welded to the workpiece surface.

DATA
Plate No: 5.11
Archive No: 080-101
Image type: light macro
Scalebar = 60 mm (micros: ±20%, others: +100%, -50%)
Component: SG, high hardness, hobbed, shaved, unrun
Speed: -
Load: -
Lubrication: -
Failure code1: 00.02.4.2 Gear hobbing mark
Failure code2: 00.03 Pit or unfinished area
Failure code3: -
Failure code4: -

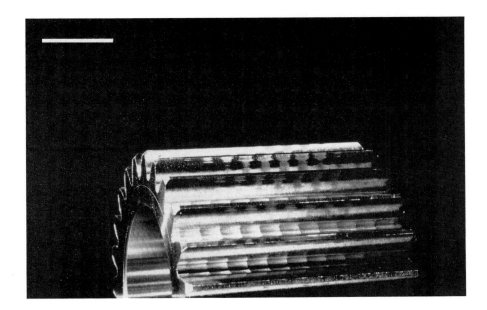

DESCRIPTIONS
FAILURE DESCRIPTION: Periodic, axial marks from gear hobbing, which subsequent shaving failed to remove. These marks are undesirable (may cause noisy running and poor EHD film condition) but rarely cause functional gear failure.

IMAGE DESCRIPTION: Axially periodic, light and dark appearing patches along tooth flank. Color depends on light incidence.

SUSPECTED CAUSES: Hobbing of gear teeth, if not followed by adequate finishing, may leave hobmarks. These are variations in surface roughness and are usually removed in finishing operations. In the case shown, the shaving operation left uncleaned hob marks.

DATA
Plate No: 5.12
Archive No: 080-103
Image type: light macro
Scalebar = 30 mm (micros: ±20%, others: +100%, -50%)
Component: SG, high hardness, shaved, unrun
Speed:
Load:
Lubrication:
Failure code1: 00.02.4.3 Gear shaving mark
Failure code2: -
Failure code3: -
Failure code4: -

DESCRIPTION
FAILURE DESCRIPTION: Plastically displaced material from gear shaving forms raised "lips" at edges between both flanks and OD of gear tooth. Unless extreme, these lips do not interfere with functioning, but they do indicate an imperfect shaving operation.

IMAGE DESCRIPTION: The surface at image NE is the gear OD. One tooth flank is visible at SW. A light-colored, raised lip appears at the edges, where each tooth flank meets the OD. The raised material at the two edges is similar in magnitude.

SUSPECTED CAUSES: The gear shaving operation may, when performed with a dull cutter, plastically deform the tooth flank material, raising an edge where the face intersects the OD. Edges at the intersection of both flanks with the OD tend to be similarly raised.

DATA
Plate No: 5.13
Archive No: 064-1001
Image type: color macro
[SEE IMAGE IN APPENDIX.]
Scalebar =: 40 mm (micros: ±20%, others: +100%, -50%)
Component: HG; P, med. hard, shaved, run
Speed:
Load:
Lubrication:
Failure code1: 00.02.4.3 Gear shaving mark
Failure code2: 00.00.02.1 Defect by location: in Hertz contact surface
Failure code3: -
Failure code4: -

[See Image in Appendix]

DESCRIPTION
FAILURE DESCRIPTION: Shaving marks on gear tooth faces. In running, the marks were selectively discolored. Shaving marks may be harmless, unless deep enough to disrupt EHD film and/or pressure distribution.

IMAGE DESCRIPTION: At about −20° angle to radial, dark brown and metallic light streaks alternate on tooth face, at about 3 mm spacing.

SUSPECTED CAUSES: The shaving operation in tooth manufacture leaves this type of mark.

DATA
Plate No: 5.14
Archive No: 093-3.1.8
Image type: SEM
Scalebar = 8 μm (micros: ±20%, others: +100%, -50%)
Component: BB; IR, tool steel, honed, unrun
Speed:
Load:
Lubrication:
Failure code1: 00.03.1 Surface porosity or pit
Failure code2: 00.00.02.1 Defect by location: in Hertz contact surface
Failure code3: 00.06.1.3 Primary carbide
Failure code4: -

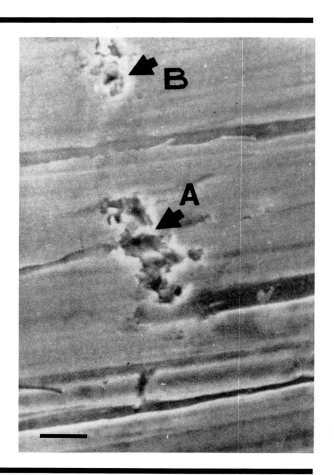

DESCRIPTION
FAILURE DESCRIPTION: Micropits formed during honing of tool steel surface. Pits of this small magnitude (about 10 μm long) are often harmless except in instrument bearings requiring extreme smooth operation. Surface distress (FC 00.17) may form at larger pits and initiate spalling failure (FC 00.16).

IMAGE DESCRIPTION: Honing lines run E–W. At *A* and *B*, irregularly shaped sharp-edged angular depressions. At S end of pit at *A*, a deeper furrow emanates, and propagates to image E.

SUSPECTED CAUSES: In tool steel (and stainless steel) bearing materials, relatively large carbides are common. During honing, such carbides may be torn from the surface and leave a pit. They may also be dragged along the surface, making a furrow.

DATA
Plate No: 5.15
Archive No: 093-3.1.6
Image type: light microgram
Scalebar = 150 μm (micros: ±20%, others: +100%, -50%)
Component: BB; B, unrun
Speed:
Load:
Lubrication:
Failure code1: 00.03.1 Surface porosity or pit
Failure code2: 00.00.02.1 Defect by location: in Hertz contact surface
Failure code3: 00.20.2 Corrosion pitting
Failure code4: -

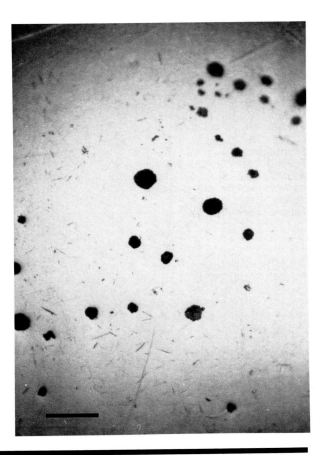

DESCRIPTION
FAILURE DESCRIPTION: Multiple pores in the surface, not removed in finishing. A ball operated with surface defects of this magnitude will fail rapidly in spalling fatigue. It may copy indentations onto the contacting part and it may run noisily.

IMAGE DESCRIPTION: Round black spots of varying size on a background of fine short scratches in the lapped surface. Near the W edge of the image where light-incidence is grazing, the rim of the spots is seen to be depressed below the spherical ball surface.

SUSPECTED CAUSES: A likely cause of the pits is corrosion of the hardened unfinished ball. The corrosion pits were too deep to be removed in the hard finishing operations.

DATA
Plate No: 5.16
Archive No: 093-3.1.4
Image type: view
Scalebar = 20 mm (micros: ±20%, others: +100%, -50%)
Component: TRB; OR, unrun
Speed:
Load:
Lubrication:
Failure Code1: 00.03.2 Unground area
Failure code2: 00.00.02.1 Defect by location: in Hertz contact surface
Failure code3: -
Failure code4: -

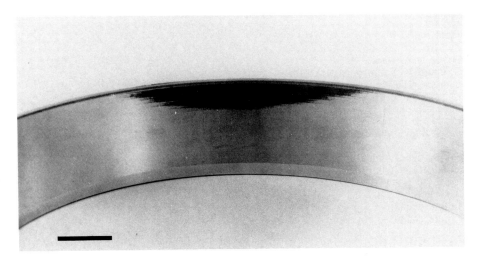

DESCRIPTIONS
FAILURE DESCRIPTION: Unfinished surface at edge of TRB cup roller track. Surface is as heat-treated. This area is depressed below the finished contact surface and does not carry its share of load, leaving the contact area, especially the edge of the unground patch, overstressed. If the unground area should make contact, its rough surface and poor integrity (scale) will cause it to fail early in spalling fatigue.

IMAGE DESCRIPTION: The shiny finished surface of the TRB cup roller path is interrupted at image N by a half-moon shaped black area with feathery border. In natural color, the black area is a dark grey (color of heat-treat scale).

SUSPECTED CAUSES: The TRB cup shown is a case hardened thin-walled ring. Such parts may distort in quenching (fixture quenching is often used in larger rings). If insufficient grinding stock is provided, the grinding operation fails to reach the entire surface and unground patches remain.

DATA
Plate No: 5.17
Archive No: 093-3.1.1
Image type: light macro
Scalebar = 1 mm (micros: ±20%, others: +100%, -50%)
Component: TRB; R, unrun
Speed:
Load:
Lubrication:
Failure Code1: 00.03.2 Unground area
Failure code2: 00.00.02.1 Defect by location: in Hertz contact surface
Failure code3: -
Failure code4: -

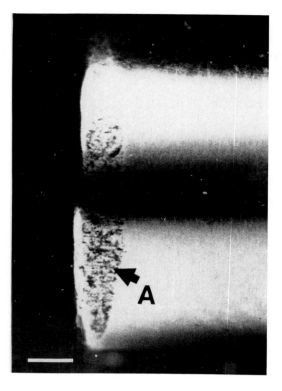

DESCRIPTIONS
FAILURE DESCRIPTION: Near roller end face, the rolling contact surface of this TRB roller shows a partially ground area at A. The grinding operation skimmed some high points but the valleys remain as heat-treated. Load carried by this partially ground area will be poorly distributed on a few high spots, leading to early spalling failure.

IMAGE DESCRIPTION: Near W image edge, at A, a mottled dark crescent is the partially ground area. In natural color, the dark area is dark grey (heat treat scale).

SUSPECTED CAUSES: TRB rollers are mostly cold headed from wire stock in automated headers. If the cutoff operation preparing the headed slug provides insufficient volume of material, an 'underfill' is produced in the die, leaving a surface near the large end of the roller depressed. The grinding operation then fails to remove sufficient material to provide a clean ground surface.

DATA
Plate No: 5.18
Archive No: 003-009
Image type: view
Scalebar = 3 mm (micros: ±20%, others: +100%, -50%)
Component: CRB; IR, run
Speed: 60 KdN
Load: 1.5 GPa
Lubrication: synthetic polyester oil, 110 °C
Failure code1: 00.03.2 Unground area
Failure code2: 00.12.3.2.1 Smooth rolling surface wear (finish marks removed)
Failure code3: -
Failure code4: -

DESCRIPTIONS
FAILURE DESCRIPTION: Improperly machined undercuts at roller track edges (trail into roller track). Trailing edges not finished. Polishing of roller track by wear (where finished), during running. Excessive undercut deprives rollers of contact near their ends. Edge spalling may result.

IMAGE DESCRIPTION: Roller track (light color) is flanked by (dark) undercuts, which, at arrows, extend into track (darker than polished track).

SUSPECTED CAUSES: Improper machining of undercuts.

6 MATERIAL AND ASSEMBLY DEFECTS

General Description

This chapter encompasses a variety of manufacturing defects, not covered in Chapter 5. The *material* defects covered are typically *not* surface defects. However, the *assembly* defects often are. The division between Chapters 5 and 6 is not dictated by a sharp distinction in subject.

6.1. INCLUSIONS. FAILURE CODE: 00.06

6.1.1. Definition

Inclusions are volumes of unintended foreign material embedded in the matrix of the component material. In *metals* produced by a casting process (including parts used as-cast, pressed, rolled, extruded or forged), inclusions are mostly *non-metallic*. In *powder metals* and *ceramics*, inclusions may be either non-metallics or foreign metals.

NOTES:

1. Hardenable steels contain carbides as structural elements. These are not inclusions, defined as defects.
2. Some metals are precipitation hardened. The precipitates are not inclusions, defined as defects.
3. Cermets and some ceramics consist of (hard) grains embedded in a binder. An inclusion (defect) is a volume of material other than the intended grains or binder.

6.1.2. Nomenclature

In metals, inclusions may be referred to as non-metallics or slag.

Macro-inclusions are large enough to be visible with the unaided eye (0.2 - 0.5 mm minimum).

- *Stringers* are strongly elongated macro-inclusions.
- *Globular* inclusions are roughly spherical macro-inclusions.

Micro-inclusions are similar to, but smaller than the above, and discernible by metallography.

6.1.3. Failure Process

An inclusion forms during melt (or powder) processing of the material, when a foreign substance agglomerates into distinct volumes and is enclosed in the matrix material.

In molten metals, indigenous non-metallics may be generated during the melt processing (including slagging) or casting. Exogenous non-metallics result from extraneous contamination of the melt (for example, from the furnace lining or ladle).

In powder-based material (powder-metal, cermets, ceramics), the powder may be externally contaminated, or contain slag from its own manufacture.

6.1.4. Distinctive Appearance

Macro-inclusions are directly visible if they extend to a surface or appear in a fracture, as spots or (if stringers) as streaks in the otherwise uniform surface. If inclusions do not extend to the surface, they appear in metallographic section, on an X-ray or ultrasound image or as eddy-current indications. Inclusions extending to a finished surface are often covered in the finishing operation by a thin layer of plastically flowed metal. During running under stress, this layer may be removed and the inclusion revealed.

Micro-inclusions are identified by examination (of sections) at high magnification.

Depending on material and its manufacturing process, a multitude of distinct inclusion classes and appearances occur. Their differentiation requires specific information on material manufacture and appropriate examination methods.

6.1.5. Causes

The material of inclusions is originally admixed to or generated in the melt (or powder) during processing of the raw material. Solidification (or sintering) forms them into distinct inclusion volumes. Subsequent forming steps may significantly change the size and shape of the inclusions.

Identification of the processing conditions conducive to each type of inclusion requires specific information on the material and its manufacturing process.

6.1.6. Effects of Inclusions

At the inclusion/matrix interface, stress concentrations arise. Both *strong* (high ultimate strength) and *weak* inclusions are detrimental due to these stress concentrations. Factors affecting the severity of the stress concentration are: inclusion size, shape, interface (such as: smooth or jagged, bonded or unbonded), elastic modulus difference from the matrix, brittleness and particulars of the macro-stress field.

Macro-inclusions are macroscopic weak volumes. Macro-inclusions may cause failure by the following processes:

• Bulk cracking and fracture (FC 00.22), if located anywhere in a stressed cross-section;
• Spalling (FC 00.16), if located in the Hertz stress volume;
• Galling (FC 00.13), if extending to a contact surface.

Micro-inclusions are microscopic weak volumes which may cause failure through:

• Subsurface-origin spalling (FC 00.16), if located in the Hertz stress volume;
• Surface distress (FC 00.17) and surface-origin fatigue (FC 00.16), if located in the contact surface layer;
• Wear (FC 00.12), if extending to the contact surface.

6.2. MATERIAL STRUCTURE DEFECTS PRIOR TO, OR IN HEAT TREATMENT. FAILURE CODE: 00.07

This Section is included for completeness, to permit material-structure related morphological failures to be traced to this source. Diagnosis of structure defects requires laboratory methods of materials analysis, specific for the material, for its condition and for the defect to be diagnosed.

In metals, the examination methods are primarily hardness testing, fracture examination, metallography including appropriate etching, and X-ray diffraction. Ultrasound, magnetic or eddy-current methods may also be used.

6.2.1. Definition

Defects of material structure are those physical deficiencies in a material which impart to it less resistance to an imposed stress (mechanical, thermal or chemical) than the specified structure possesses.

The great majority of contact components is made of steel, heat-treated to optimal properties for the specific application (high hardness surface for most bearings, high or medium hardness surface for gears and cams). This Section covers structure defects in these steels.

Other contact component materials, such as cast iron, non-steel metals, ceramics, cermets or plastics have different structure requirements and defects.

6.2.2. Nomenclature

Alternative nomenclature for structure defects is not covered.

6.2.3. High Hardness Steel Components

Definition

The common structural defects in high hardness (>50 RC) steel contact components are:

Hardness defect. Most often, the part is softer than specified.

• *Carbon loss (decarburization)* at the surface of through-hardened parts;
• *Carbon gradient defect* in carburized parts;
• *Nitrogen gradient defect* in nitrided parts.

Defects in required constituents.

• Many hardened steels are *martensitic.* The morphology of the martensite needles may deviate from specification. *Untempered martensite* may be present from rehardening.
• Other hardened steels may be (lower) *bainitic.* The specific metallographic morphology of the bainite may deviate from specification.

Impermissible structural constituents. In fully hardened steels, these are generally soft constituents. Ferrite and upper bainite are recognizable soft constituents.
Retained austenite. Excessive quantities of austenite retained in the finished product.
Grain boundary defects. Weaknesses in the (prior austenitic) grain of the material.
Carbide segregation. Carbides in the steel are too large, or segregated into bands, networks, etc.

Failure Process

Material structure defects in parts of hardened steel are the result of deficiencies in: Raw material composition; forming and/or heat treatment processes which interfere with the grain size control; recrystallization in hot forming; deviations from proper casing (carburizing or nitriding, flame or induction hardening); errors in austenitizing, quenching, tempering or other post-quench treatment.

Distinctive Appearance

Material structure defects are detected by materials laboratory methods.

Causes

Identification of the processes resulting in material structure defects in hardened steel requires detailed information on casting, hot forming and heat treatment methods for the material.

Effects of Defects in Material Structure

The material properties typically affected by defects in structure are:

- *Tensile strength or hardness:* the limit of plasticity under tensile stressing or indentation;
- *Ductility or toughness:* the ability to sustain plastic deformation without fracture.
- *Fatigue resistance.* Especially in Hertz contacts, fatigue resistance (resistance to spalling failure) does not uniquely correlate with other macroscopic strength parameters.
- *Temperature resistance.* Improperly heat treated steel may show dimensional instability or soften at operating temperatures.
- *Corrosion resistance.* In corrosion resistant steels, structure defects detract from corrosion resistance.

6.2.3. Medium Hardness Steel Components.

Structure defects and their consequences in medium hardness steels are somewhat similar to those in fully hardened steel.

The structure elements of lower-hardness steels, however, differ quantitatively, and qualitatively from fully hardened steels. Lower-hardness steels may differ in that:

- The required and the impermissible structural constituents may be different from fully hardened steels;
- Metallographically identifiable carbides may not be present;
- Retained austenite may not be present.

6.3. FINISHING DAMAGE TO MATERIAL STRUCTURE. FAILURE CODE: 00.08

6.3.1. Definition

The last or near-last finishing processes of component surfaces may damage the subsurface material structure. This damage is defined as *finishing damage to material structure.* Classes of such damage are: grinding damage, coating damage and cold forming damage.

6.3.2. Grinding damage. Failure Code: 00.08.1-3

Definition

Grinding damage is damage to the near-surface material due to aggressive grinding (or other abrasive finishing).

Nomenclature

The common designations for types of grinding damage are: grinding burns, grinding temper, and grinding cracks.

Failure Process

Grinding damage to subsurface material is the result of overheating of the surface under strong pressure and shear forces transmitted by the grinding wheel, honing or polishing tool, and typically affects hardened (martensitic) steel components. The overheating results in three types of change in these components:

1. *Grinding temper* arises when the material is locally heated above its specified tempering temperature and thus becomes softer than the bulk material. Since tempering results in volume change, some residual stresses are set up.
2. *Grinding burns* occur when the overheating exceeds the austenitizing temperature of the steel and reaustenitizes a volume. The hot volume, being surrounded by cold steel is rapidly cooled and quenched but not tempered, leading to a rehardened volume surrounded by a tempered shell which was heated but not reaustenitized. Severe residual stresses are set up since the austenite/martensite transformation upon quenching results in great volume change.

   When grinding burns of substantial severity are created by the *second-last* finishing operation, it is possible for the *last* operation to remove the surface evidence of the damage (making it undetectable by Nital etching), but leave severe residual stresses which can lead to local cracking in service.
3. *Grinding cracks* are the result of the residual stresses described above, when they exceed the strength of the material.

Distinctive Appearance

- Grinding cracks may be discernible with the unaided eye or under low magnification. Magnetic particle, eddy current or dye-penetrant inspection provide more sensitive detection.
- Grinding temper and burns are detectable by Nital etching of the surface. The *tempered* volume etches dark, the *rehardened* volume etches lighter than normal. Eddy current methods for grinding damage detection are in limited use.

  NOTES:
  1. In some steels, such as secondary-hardening tool steels, detection of grinding damage by etching is difficult.
  2. Grinding burns obscured by re-finishing are detectable only by a destructive etching method. Some success is claimed for eddy current detection.

Causes

- Excessive grinding parameters (high infeed); excessive pressure on honing or polishing tool.
- Inappropriate selection of grinding wheel or other abrasive.
- Insufficient or inadequate coolant.
- Sensitive material structure: Inadequately tempered material is easily damaged in grinding.
- High pressure, high sliding speed or unsuitable material of sliding support elements (shoes) in grinding.

Effects of Grinding Damage

- *Cracking* (either local, or bulk (FC 00.22)), as a result of residual stresses.
- *Surface distress* (FC 00.17) or *spalling* (FC 00.16). Damaged material has low Hertzian fatigue resistance.

6.3.3. Coating Damage.
Failure Code: 00.08.6

Definition

Coatings commonly used on *contact* surfaces are:

• Chemical (oxide, phosphate, molybdenum disulfide) coatings for dry lubrication and rust protection purposes;
• Electroplating with tin or cadmium as a dry lubricant (in a few aerospace applications);
• Special (spheroidal) chromium plating in highly aggressive environments;
• Burnished-on or sputtered composite solid lubricant coatings.

Coating of *fit surfaces* by hard chromium electroplating is common for the correction of dimensional errors in manufacture or the repair of wear.

Functionally, coatings may be divided into: *hard coatings* aimed at protecting the *weaker* substrate; and *soft coatings* which act sacrificially, as solid lubricants or run-in aids, and additionally may also be corrosion protectors.

Coating damage is defined as: defects in the coating, or deleterious interaction of the coating with the substrate.

Nomenclature

Alternative designations for coating damage are not covered.

Failure Process

Defects in coatings include:

• Improper coating composition for a solid lubricant or rust protector;
• Microcracking;
• Improper structure;
• Incomplete surface coverage;
• Inadequate bonding;
• Off-specification hardness;
• Chemical decomposition due to high temperature or in interaction with the environment;
• Foreign material in the coating.

Deleterious interactions of coating and substrate include:

• Hydrogen embrittlement from electroplating;
• Attack on surface microgeometry or grain boundaries of the substrate from chemically formed coatings.
• Residual stresses at the interface between coating and substrate.

Distinctive Appearance

Improper composition may be revealed functionally by wear or seizure of substrate or mating surface. It may be visible as a discoloration.
Visual inspection (with or without magnification) will reveal *microcracking*, and, by showing islands of uncovered substrate, *incomplete surface coverage*.
Improper structure or *foreign material in the coating* may be discernible by metallographic examination or by gross appearance (color, gloss, etc.) and requires specific information as to the type of coating.

Inadequate bonding or *improper hardness* may be detectable by laboratory scratch tests, but is more often diagnosed from inadequate wear performance.
Hydrogen embrittlement is diagnosed from the cracking or flaking it causes in the substrate.
Residual stresses at the coating to substrate interface are generally detectable only from their effect on fatigue.
Diagnosis of *chemical attack* requires specific information as to the type of coating. In coatings which can be chemically stripped without damage to the substrate:

• *Damage to surface microgeometry* is diagnosed by increased roughness, pit formation or waviness observed on the stripped substrate;
• *Intergranular attack* is detected metallographically as differential etching of grain boundaries or microcracks in the substrate.

Causes

Causes of coating failure require specific information on the coating process for their identification.

Effects of Coating Failure

Hard coating defects promote component failure by these processes:

• Inadequate wear resistance;
• Inadequate corrosion protection;
• Surface origin spalling, which may initiate in the coating or at the interface and propagate into the substrate;
• Detached flakes of coating cause denting of contact surfaces.

Soft coating defects manifest themselves as:

• Inadequate solid lubricating performance;
• Inadequate corrosion protection.

6.3.4. Cold Forming Damage.
Failure Code: 00.08.7

Definition

Cold forming damage is defined as damage to the subsurface structure due to a cold-forming finishing operation.

Cold forming as a finishing operation for contact components is used, in the following examples:

• *Deep drawing* is the finish-forming method for drawn needle roller bearing cups.
• *Shot peening* has been used as a second-last or last finishing operation on working surfaces, with the intent of providing work hardening of the near-surface material.
• *Roll burnishing* or ball burnishing has been used to work-harden blend radii subject to heavy bending stresses.

Nomenclature

There are no other common designations for cold forming damage.

Failure Process

• Structure damage due to *deep drawing* of needle bearing cups has not been identified. The work hardening effect of cold drawing is generally considered advantageous. (Cracks, folds, surface defects can occur. See FC 00.02 and FC 00.04).

• *Shot peening* of surfaces in Hertz contact as the last finishing operation leaves considerable roughness and waviness. If run in Hertz contact, such surfaces experience high asperity stresses.

The work hardening and compressive stress formation in the near-surface material, achieved by shot peening is beneficial to bulk fatigue. It is doubtful whether resistance to Hertz contact fatigue is improved by the work hardening and compressive residual stress, or impaired by microscopic damage to the material. The outcome may depend on processing conditions, raw material and operating conditions.

• *Roll* or *ball burnishing* of blend radii as used in highly stressed shafts and similar components is intended to strengthen the blend radius by smoothing the surface (reduce stress concentrations) and work harden and compressively prestress the near-surface material. The high Hertzian pressures needed to produce the required plastic deformation may cause cracking leading to premature bending fatigue.

Distinctive Appearance

• No visible damage to subsurface material is expected in *deep drawing*.
• The appearance of a *shot peened* surface shows the surface roughness. Subsurface material damage is typically not visually observable and is diagnosed by early contact fatigue.
• Cracks in *roll burnished* blend radii may be visible or can be diagnosed by magnetic particle or dye-penetrant inspection.

Causes

Identification of shot peening parameters (shot size, impact energy, duration of peening) conducive to subsurface damage, requires specific knowledge of material and processing conditions.

Effects of Structural Damage by Cold Forming

The effects of structural damage by cold forming are: *Contact fatigue* as a result of diminished integrity of the near-surface material; and *bulk fatigue* arising from cracks in cold finished (roll burnished) material.

6.4. GEOMETRY, ASSEMBLY OR MOUNTING FAILURE. FAILURE CODE: 00.09

6.4.1. Definition

• *Assembly* is defined as the combination of parts into a Hertz contact machine element. Example: the assembly of components into a bearing.
• *Mounting* is defined as the installation of the Hertz contact machine element into the machine in which it will operate. Example: the placement of a gear set in the gearbox.

Failures covered in this Section encompass: geometry defects; and score marks, gouges and cracks due to assembly or mounting.

6.4.2. Nomenclature

Alternative designations of these failures (other than geometry defects) are: 'assembly (mounting) error' and 'assembly (mounting) damage'.

6.4.3. Geometry Defect. Failure Code: 00.09.0

Definition

• A *geometry defect* is defined as off-specification geometry of the component or the mounting, through manufacturing error, assembly or mounting error, including use of wrong parts or omission of parts.

Nomenclature

Alternative designations of this failure are: 'geometry error' and 'dimensional error'.

Failure Process

Depending on the machine element and its assembly or mounting method, geometry errors can arise at any point in manufacture of the components, their assembly into a machine element or in mounting the element into the machine.

Specific causes of mounting geometry errors are:

• Mounting with off-specification shaft or housing;
• Excessive fastening forces;
• Misaligned mounting;
• Mounting on a debris-contaminated surface;
• Inadvertent omission of a part, misplacement of a part or use of the wrong part.

Distinctive Appearance

• Gross geometry defects are visually detectable by comparison of the machine element or mounted assembly with the product drawing.
• Moderately out-of tolerance manufacturing geometry requires metrological examination.
• In as-run components, geometry defects are often detectable by incorrect wear patterns, such as: edge contact, improper load distribution etc. (See FC 00.12.)

Causes

Causes of geometry defects require specific information on the manufacturing, assembly or mounting process for diagnosis.

Effects of Geometry Defect

The range of possible effects from defective geometry encompasses virtually every in-service failure mode. The principal mechanisms through which geometry errors produce failure are:

• Maldistribution of load among contacts or of pressure within a contact;

- Parasitic loads from lack of internal looseness;
- Excessive or insufficient fit interference to mounting parts;
- In rolling bearings, incorrect separator clearances, producing excessive separator loads or unintended contacts;
- Lubrication failure from excessive surface roughness;
- Gross malfunction from missing, improper or misassembled parts.

6.4.4. Scoring, Galling or Cracking in Assembly or Mounting.
Failure Code: 00.09.1-3

Definition

- *Scoring*, in assembly or mounting, arises from ploughing of the surface by a hard, sharp implement, by a process of *wear* (FC 00.12).
- *Galling* in assembly or mounting occurs from *material transfer* in high-pressure sliding contact of ineffectively lubricated surfaces on each other. (See FC 00.13.)
- *Cracks* and *fracture* of components, in assembly or mounting, arise from excessive stresses imposed on a component, which are the result of assembly or mounting geometry errors.

Nomenclature

Nomenclature for assembly scoring and galling is unsettled. 'Scuff marks', 'scratch marks', and 'gouges' are used for either failure. 'Smear marks' designate galling.

There is no alternative nomenclature for cracks or fracture.

Distinctive Appearance

Scoring is a ploughing mark with a lustrous bottom and sharp, often raised, edges. The position and orientation of the score mark on the component may serve to distinguish it from a finishing furrow (FC 00.02) or service wear (FC 00.12). Score marks from tool impact tend to be on free surfaces which may suffer hammer blows or scraping by a 'drift'. Axial score marks in the bore of a bearing inner-ring or gear, or on the OD of a bearing outer-ring may arise

from mounting on the mating shaft or housing with interference fit or over a sharp edge.

Light score marks may alter only the surface asperity tips, resulting in a stippled mark.

Galling marks in assembly arise under similar conditions as score marks, but galling marks show signs of metal transfer. Differentiation may require magnification. Galling in assembly is distinguished from in-service galling (FC 00.13) in the same way as for scoring.

Cracks and *fractures* are material separations. Their origin in assembly or mounting is usually diagnosed from their location (for example, chipping at a flange edge), accompanying impact marks, score or galling marks or geometric distortion.

Causes

The causes of scoring, galling and cracks differ only in severity, which increases in the order listed. The principal causes are:

- Improper use of assembly or mounting tools, leading to slippage of the tool over a component surface, scratches, galling marks, impact damage, chipping or fracture.
- Sliding of working or fit surfaces over each other during assembly or mounting, when: (a) the interference is excessive, (b) surface roughness is excessive or sharp edges exist, (c) mounting is attempted under misalignment, (d) lubrication is inadequate, (e) solid contaminant is present in the interface.

Effects of Scoring, Galling or Cracks in Assembly or Mounting

- *Scoring* or *galling* on *fit* surfaces during assembly or mounting may lead to cracking under service loading (FC 00.22).
- *Scoring* or *galling* in *contact* surfaces during assembly or mounting may lead to bulk cracking (FC 00.22), surface distress (FC 00.17), surface-origin spalling (FC 00.16), wear (FC 00.12) or in-service galling (FC 00.13).
- Cracks and fracture during assembly or mounting represent gross failure making the machine element unserviceable either immediately or after further crack propagation.

DATA

Plate No: 6.6
Archive No: 003-013a&b&014
Image type: a,b: SEM; c: light macro
Scalebar = a, b: 25 μm c: 5 mm
(micros: ±20%, others: +100%,
-50%)
Component: ACBB; (a,c: OR; b: B),
tool steel, run
Speed: 1 ? MdN
Load:
Lubrication: synthetic polyester oil,
? °C
Failure code1: 00.06.1.3 Primary
carbide
Failure code2: 00.18.2.2.2 Stippled
line(s) or band(s) from rolled-in debris
Failure code3: 00.16.02.4 Incipient
spalling, multiple spalls
Failure code4: -

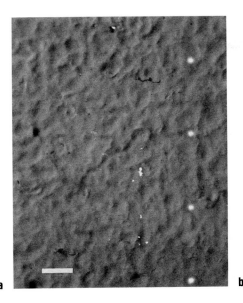

a

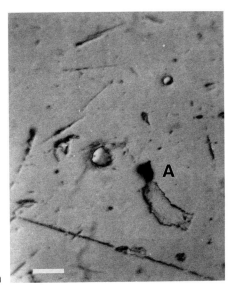

b

DESCRIPTIONS

FAILURE DESCRIPTION: Tool steel balls of this bearing contained hard Vanadium carbides (15 μm diameter), which created a profusely dented IR surface. During running, a band of this damaged surface failed in a line of spalls. The bearing has failed.

IMAGE DESCRIPTION: (a): Surface of OR in ball path, completely covered with rolled-over rounded dents from contact with spherical hard carbides in balls. (b): Ball surface. At image center and 1/2 to NE corner, spherical hard carbides. Elsewhere, dents and scratches, perhaps a microspall at *A*. (c); OR, with ball path between white circle and scalloped edge, mottled by dents. A band of dark spalls in center of ball path.

SUSPECTED CAUSES: Tool steels may contain hard primary carbides, which remain prominent during ball lapping. When rolled against ring surface, carbides create profuse dents, eventually 'peening' the surface. Plasticity is exhausted and surface forms spalls upon further running.

c

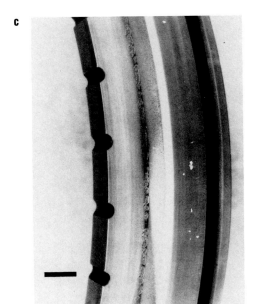

DATA
Plate No: 6.7
Archive No: 075-201&202&204
Image type: a: light macro, b: SEM,
c: SEM composite
Scalebar = a: 5 mm, b: 200,
c: 100 μm (micros: ±20%, others:
+100%, -50%)
Component: CRB; IR, unrun
Speed: -
Load: -
Lubrication: -
Failure code1: 00.06.2 Inclusion
stringer
Failure code2: -
Failure code3: -
Failure code4: -

DESCRIPTIONS
FAILURE DESCRIPTION: Inclusion stringer totaling 10 mm in
length or more, open to the rolling surface is determined by X-
ray spectrum to be a layered stringer of largely alumina inclusions. A stringer so located as to be open to the surface, and
of this great length, is an imminent source of spalling failure.

IMAGE DESCRIPTION: (a): On the as-ground surface, grinding
lines run N–S. A 10 mm long interrupted wavy black line running E–W is the inclusion. More non-metallics show as fine
black points at W end and to the N of the stringer. (b): Intentional fracture along stringer. Rolling surface is N section edge.
Parallel white E–W lines are the inclusion. (c): Layout as in
(b). 3 or more E–W layers of light-color inclusion "pebbles" in
fracture surface.

SUSPECTED CAUSES: Alumina inclusions may be exogenous
(emanating from the refractory used in steelmaking equipment),
or endogenous (from aluminum added for deoxidizing). In view
of its large size, this stringer is believed to be exogenous. It
assumes its elongated shape parallel to the direction of material
elongation during tube rolling or forging.

a
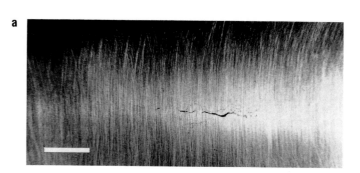

b

c

DATA

Plate No: 6.8
Archive No: 002-004d&g
Image type: a: SEM, b: light
metallogram, unetched
Scalebar = a: 200, b: 20 μm
(micros: ±20%, others: +100%, -50%)
Component: BG; G, carburized AISI
4310 steel, run
Speed: 106 m/sec
Load: 0.5 GPa
Lubrication: synthetic polyester oil, 176 °C
Failure code1: 00.06.2 Inclusion stringer
Failure code2: 00.22.01.4 Gear tooth
crack or fracture
Failure code3: 00.22.2 Bulk fatigue crack
Failure code4: -
See also PLATE: 15.19

DESCRIPTIONS

FAILURE DESCRIPTION: Alumina inclusion stringer in gear
tooth material has caused tooth bending fatigue fracture. Alumina inclusions are hard and brittle and represent severe stress
raising defects. This stringer is at least 2 mm long, giving it
direct macroscopic effect on fatigue strength. (See Plate 15.19
for the gear tooth fatigue caused by this stringer).

IMAGE DESCRIPTION: (a): The image background is the fracture surface. The three arrows bracket a long, fragmented
stringer of alumina non-metallic. (b): White S image half is
tooth cross-section. Fracture surface forms N boundary of section. (Black mottled N half is mounting). Arrows show grey
alumina inclusions at and beneath fracture surface.

SUSPECTED CAUSES: Non-metallics are steelmaking defects.
Aluminum is used in steelmaking as a deoxidizer. Large aluminum oxides (alumina) are removed by slagging, but micro inclusions of it are never wholly absent from melted steel. A
macroscopic stringer (elongated, often multiple inclusion) as
shown, is an accident of the steelmaking process.

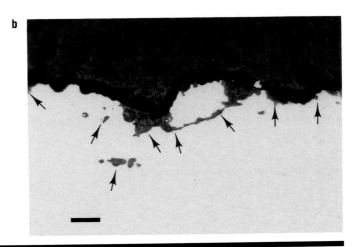

DATA

Plate No: 6.9
Archive No: 018-603
Image type: light macro
Scalebar = 4 mm (micros: ±20%,
others: +100%, -50%)
Component: BB; B, 52100 steel, run
Speed:
Load:
Lubrication:
Failure code1: 00.07.1.1 Insufficient
bulk hardness
Failure code2: 00.16.02.5 Advanced
spalling
Failure code3: 00.12.3.2.3 Step worn in rolling surface or
dimension worn off-spec
Failure code4: -

DESCRIPTIONS

FAILURE DESCRIPTION: Hardness of ball was 21 HRc throughout, compared to approx. 60 HRc specified. Generalized spalling and heavy wear resulted from inability of soft material to
carry load.

IMAGE DESCRIPTION: Light macrograph shows entire ball with
extensively spall-cratered surface. Between craters, the surface

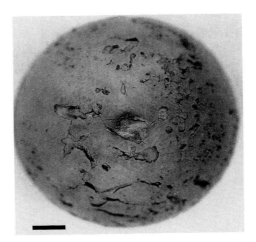

is streaked and matte, due to wear. No sign of original surface
is left. The low hardness was established by hardness testing.

SUSPECTED CAUSES: Through handling error a ball may avoid
heat treatment and be placed with heat treated balls to be finished. While ordinarily such a ball is conspicuous by a different
luster, it may be overlooked. The soft material cannot carry
normal ball loads and spalls and wears extensively under them.

DATA
Plate No: 6.10
Archive No: 093-7.1.2
Image type: light metallogram, Nital etch
Scalebar = 8 μm (micros: ±20%, others: +100%, -50%)
Component: 52100 bearing steel raw material
Speed: -
Load: -
Lubrication: -
Failure Code1: 00.07.1.2 Ferritic constituent
Failure code2: -
Failure code3: -
Failure code4: -

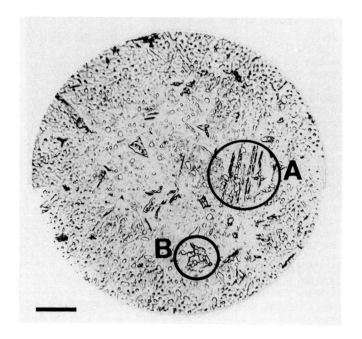

DESCRIPTIONS
FAILURE DESCRIPTION: Excessive soft ferritic constituent in hardened 52100 steel. This structure has less resistance to fatigue spalling than properly hardened structure.

IMAGE DESCRIPTION: Background is finely distributed martensitic matrix with small carbides (dark dots). Streaky constituent is soft ferrite, as in circles at *A* and *B*.

SUSPECTED CAUSES: Soft constituents in a hardened structure may arise if the austenitizing temperature is insufficient.

DATA
Plate No: 6.11
Archive No: 093-7.1.4
Image type: light metallogram, Nital etch
Scalebar = 8 μm (micros: ±20%, others: +100%, -50%)
Component: 52100 steel raw material
Speed: -
Load: -
Lubrication: -
Failure Code1: 00.07.1.3 Upper bainitic constituent
Failure code2: -
Failure code3: -
Failure code4: -

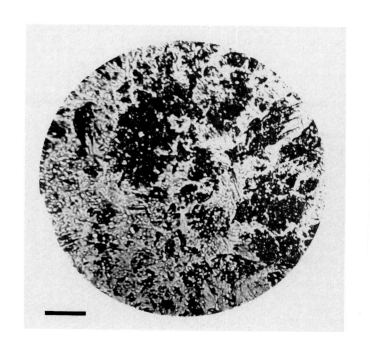

DESCRIPTIONS
FAILURE DESCRIPTION: Soft constituent formed by insufficient quenching is 'upper bainite' believed to be detrimental to fatigue resistance. It is distinct from 'lower bainite' obtained by a special high-temperature quench and used for improved toughness compared to conventional martensitic quench.

IMAGE DESCRIPTION: Grey background is martensitic structure. Dark areas are upper bainite.

SUSPECTED CAUSES: If quenching is performed too slowly or is interrupted before completion, upper bainite can form.

DATA
Plate No: 6.12
Archive No: 093-8.1.2
Image type: light metallogram, Nital etch
Scalebar = 10 μm (micros: ±20%, others: +100%, -50%)
Component: M50 tool steel specimen
Speed: -
Load: -
Lubrication: -
Failure code1: 00.07.2 Off-specification martensite platelet size
Failure code2: -
Failure code3: -
Failure code4: -

DESCRIPTIONS
FAILURE DESCRIPTION: Martensite platelets formed in hardening may develop excessive size if heat treatment conditions are improper. This condition is thought to increase brittleness and lead to cracking, especially under high hoop stress. (It is not established whether the large platelets are the cause or merely an indication of increased brittleness). Limits are often set for permissible martensite platelet size.

IMAGE DESCRIPTION: Martensite platelets appear as streaks or needles in the etched section. Their size is too large (for this steel) to be accepted. The outline at *A* surrounds an excessively long martensite needle.

SUSPECTED CAUSES: Austenitizing at excessive temperature during heat treatment causes large martensite needle size.

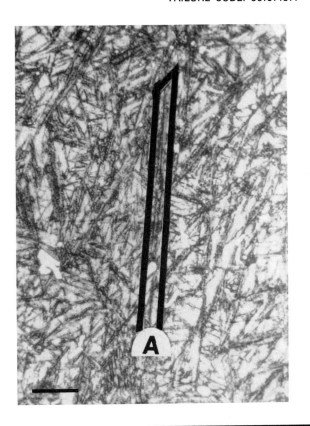

DATA
Plate No: 6.13
Archive No: 018-320&321
Image type: a: light metallogram, etched; b: SEM
Scalebar = a, b: 100 μ (micros: ±20%, others: +100%, -50%)
Component: heat treated M50 steel, 100x100 mm billet
Speed: -
Load: -
Lubrication: -
Failure code1: 00.07.3.1 Carbide segregation
Failure code2: -
Failure code3: -
Failure code4: -

DESCRIPTIONS
FAILURE DESCRIPTION: (a): Segregated primary carbides in high-alloy tool steel. (b): Sizeable primary carbides in M50 tool steel. Two types (Molybdenum-rich and Vanadium-rich), are arrayed in streaks. Large carbides may impair surface finishing. Segregation is thought to reduce resistance to cracking. Requirements exist for limits on carbide segregation in steels used in bearings.

IMAGE DESCRIPTION: (a): Dark background is heavily etched matrix. White linear design consists of segregated primary carbides. (b): Grey patterned background is etched hardened matrix. At image N is a string of Molybdenum-rich carbide, shown white in the SEM. Slightly N of image center is a keyhole shaped large Vanadium-rich carbide shown grey in the SEM.

SUSPECTED CAUSES: High alloy tool steels tend to develop carbide segregation during ingot processing. Degree of segregation depends on processing method.

a

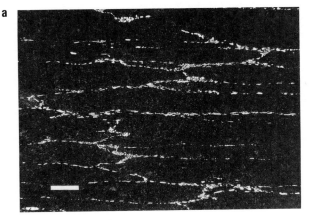

b

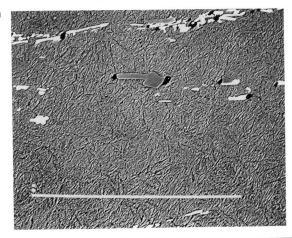

DATA

Plate No: 6.14
Archive No: 002-002i&j&f
Image type: a,b,c: light metallogram Nital/Zephiran etch
Scalebar = a: 1 mm, b,c: 100 μm (micros: ±20%, others: +100%, -50%)
Component: ACBB; B, tool steel, run
Speed: 0.8 MdN
Load: 2.2 GPa
Lubrication: synthetic polyester oil, 176 °C
Failure code1: 00.07.3.2 Lamellar carbide
Failure code2: 00.04.3.1 Forging at excessive temperature
Failure code3: 00.16 Spalling Hertzian contact fatigue
Failure code4: 00.22.01.3 Rolling element (ball, roller) crack

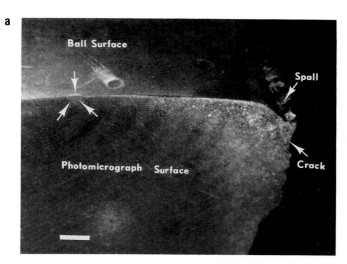

a

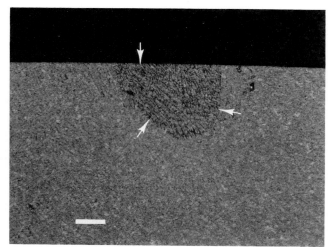

b

c

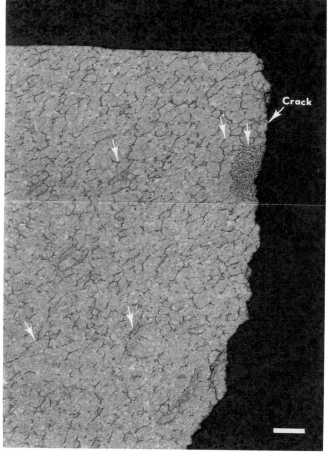

DESCRIPTIONS

FAILURE DESCRIPTION: Island of defective structure characterized by lamellar carbides due to forging at excessive temperature with recrystallization. Bulk fatigue crack, spalling. Material volumes with recrystallized structure are weak volumes, at which spalls may form prematurely. This ball also shows incipient melting. A spall has formed from one of the material defects. Bulk cracking has resulted.

IMAGE DESCRIPTION: (a): At image NW, material with lamellar carbides extending to ball surface (3 arrows). Spall and crack marked by arrows at E edge. The white, keyhole shaped mark on surface is an artifact. (b): At N center, recrystallized zone (arrows) etches dark and shows lamellar carbide striations. (c): Jagged E boundary of etched section is bulk crack (labeled). Lamellar carbides throughout section (arrows).

SUSPECTED CAUSES: This tool steel ball was forged at excessive temperature which has caused incipient melting and recrystallization producing the lamellar carbides. Spalling and subsequent cracking occurred in the weak structure. Incipient melting was also observed.

DATA
Plate No: 6.15
Archive No: 093-10.1.2
Image type: light metallogram, Nital etch
Scalebar = 6 μm (micros: ±20%, others: +100%, -50%)
Component: 8620 steel specimen
Speed: -
Load: -
Lubrication: -
Failure Code1: 00.07.4 Visible retained austenite
Failure code2: -
Failure code3: -
Failure code4: -

DESCRIPTIONS
FAILURE DESCRIPTION: Microscopically visible retained austenite in excessive amount. Depending on steel analysis and heat treatment, varying percentages of austenite are retained after tempering. Austenite retained beyond specification suited to the application causes dimensional instability due to gradual transformation in service. It may increase wear and indentation sensitivity.

IMAGE DESCRIPTION: Dark "needles" in the image are martensite. White angular patches are retained austenite. The percentage of retained *visible* austenite can be estimated from such images but is usually less than the true percentage measurable by X-ray diffraction.

SUSPECTED CAUSES: Austenite retention depends on steel analysis and numerous heat treatment variables (austenitizing time, temperature, quench conditions, tempering temperature and time, special cold treatments etc.).

DATA
Plate No: 6.16
Archive No: 099-142
Image type: light macro
Scalebar = 10 mm (micros: ±20%, others: +100%, -50%)
Component: SG; P, med. hard, unrun
Speed: -
Load: -
Lubrication: -
Failure code1: 00.07.5.02 Heat treat crack
Failure code2: -
Failure code3: -
Failure code4: -

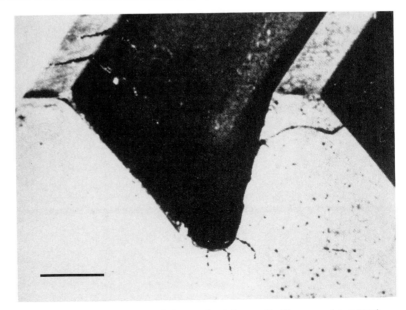

DESCRIPTIONS
FAILURE DESCRIPTION: In through hardened gears (generally about 40 HRc hardness), quenching cracks may occur as a result of mismatched material and heat treatment procedure, excessive or uneven quenching. Quenching cracks are likely to lead to early tooth bending fatigue and/or spalling.

IMAGE DESCRIPTION: At the side face of the gear, a crack crosses the tip of the tooth at image E. Three cracks extend into the root fillet. From the top land of the tooth at image W, two crosswise directed cracks extend down to the tooth flank.

SUSPECTED CAUSES: Mismatched material and heat treat practice, excessive quenching, uneven quenching or quenching in too-cold medium may precipitate quenching cracks.

DATA
Plate No: 6.17
Archive No: 002-007a&c
Image type: a: light macro,
b: fractured specimen macro
Scalebar = a: 3, b: 1 mm (micros:
±20%, others: +100%, -50%)
Component: ACBB; B, tool steel, run
Speed: 1.7 MdN
Load: 1.4 GPa
Lubrication: synthetic polyester oil,
176 °C
Failure code1: 00.07.5.1 Crack with
oxidized surface
Failure code2: 00.16.1.1.2 Spall from
subsurface defect
Failure code3: 00.16.02.2 Contact
fatigue cracking
Failure code4: 00.12.3.2.2 Scratch
marks, kinematic wear marks in rolling
surface
See also PLATE: 15.30

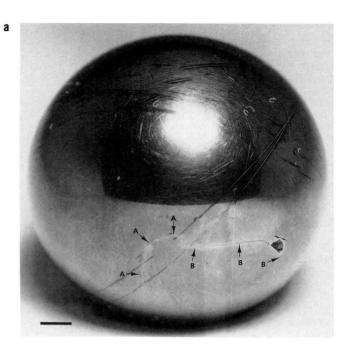

DESCRIPTIONS
FAILURE DESCRIPTION: (a): Two adjacent cracks with oxidized
surfaces formed, probably, in heat treatment of the ball. Incipient spall at one crack. Bulk fatigue crack propagation. Scratch
marks, some probably from separator contact. (b): Oxidized radial heat treat crack, extended by unoxidized bulk fatigue crack.
Heat treat cracks are severe defects that lead to fracture. See
also Plate 15.30 illustrating crack propagation by fatigue.

IMAGE DESCRIPTION: (a): Two cracks are marked with *A* and
arrows and *B* and arrows. Small spall at crack *B* (bracket).
Two major-circle scratchmarks from SW to NE. Many shallower
wearmarks in N polar region. (b): In NW, dark crescent-shaped
oxidized heat-treat crack (*A–A*). Central portion of crack extended inward by fatigue (unlettered arrows). This crack face is
unoxidized (grey). "Fresh tensile fracture" was made for examination.

SUSPECTED CAUSES: The tortuous path and oxidized surface
of the initial crack suggests a heat treat crack. Fatigue spalling
and cracking extended original failure in running. Scratchmarks
are due to service wear, perhaps aggravated by spall debris.

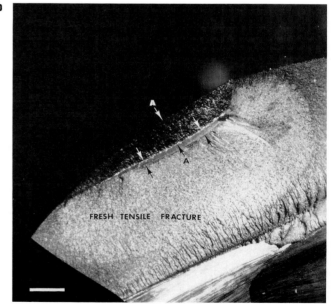

FRESH TENSILE FRACTURE

DATA
Plate No: 6.25
Archive No: 099-301
Image type: light macro of dye-penetrant tested part
Scalebar = 10 mm (micros: ±20%, others: +100%, -50%)
Component: SG; G, high hardness, unrun
Speed: -
Load: -
Lubrication: -
Failure code1: 00.08.3 Grinding crack
Failure code2: -
Failure code3: -
Failure code4: -

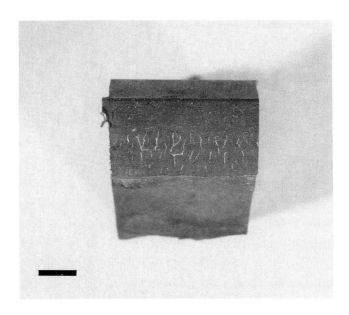

DESCRIPTIONS
FAILURE DESCRIPTION: Multiple surface cracks on the tooth contact surface. The cracks typically form from a rehardened grinding burn with high residual stresses. Grinding cracks cause surface initiated failure, such as spalling or bending fatigue. Rehardened grinding burns, containing altered structure and high stresses are early spalling sources.

IMAGE DESCRIPTION: The block is a section of a gear tooth. The narrow N surface is the tooth tip land. S of it, the wide rectangle is part of the tooth flank. The S-most surface was made in sectioning. The many forking cracks on the tooth flank are highlighted in white by a penetrant dye.

SUSPECTED CAUSES: Grinding operations using too-severe parameters of speed, feed, improper wheel or cooling cause excessive heating of the material so that it is locally re-austenitized, and immediately self-quenched by the adjacent cold metal. High residual stresses develop from the material volume change resulting from structural phase transformation and these may lead to cracking.

DATA
Plate No: 6.26
Archive No: 099-143
Image type: light macro
Scalebar = 15 mm (micros: ±20%, others: +100%, -50%)
Component: SG; G, high hardness, ground, unrun
Speed: -
Load: -
Lubrication: -
Failure code1: 00.08.3 Grinding crack
Failure code2: -
Failure code3: -
Failure code4: -

DESCRIPTIONS
FAILURE DESCRIPTION: Multiple surface cracks on the tooth flank. The cracks form typically in a rehardened grinding burn with high residual stresses. Grinding cracks cause surface initiated failure, for example, spalling or bending fatigue. Rehardened grinding burns, which contain altered structure and high stresses, are early spalling sources.

IMAGE DESCRIPTION: Flanks (dark grey) and tip lands (light grey) of several teeth in a spur gear. On the flanks, light-colored radial lines are cracks, highlighted by a penetrant dye.

SUSPECTED CAUSES: Grinding operations using too-severe parameters of speed, feed, improper wheel or cooling cause excessive heating of the material, so that it is locally re-austenitized, and immediately self-quenched by the adjacent cold metal. High residual stresses develop from the material volume change and these may lead to cracking.

DATA
Plate No: 6.27
Archive No: 087-003
Image type: view
Scalebar = 10 mm (micros: ±20%, others: +100%, -50%)
Component: DGBB; IR, 52100 steel, unrun
Speed: -
Load: -
Lubrication: -
Failure code1: 00.08.4 Hydrogen embrittlement cracking or flaking
Failure code2: -
Failure code3: -
Failure code4: -

DESCRIPTIONS
FAILURE DESCRIPTION: Hydrogen embrittlement cracking from improper electroplating of bore. Electroplating of hardened components without proper heat treatment thereafter, dissolves hydrogen in the steel which creates residual stresses sufficiently high to cause cracking after varying time periods. This is gross failure.

IMAGE DESCRIPTION: Two images of ring show extensive and erratic cracking in ball groove and on side face. The cracks have opened due to remaining residual stress. Black penmarks at various points of the surface are not defects.

SUSPECTED CAUSES: To repair oversize bores or undersize OD, electroplating (mostly with chromium) can be used. Unless properly heat treated afterwards, this method can leave dissolved hydrogen in the steel, causing very high residual stresses resulting in severe cracking.

DATA
Plate No: 6.28
Archive No: 093-20.1.5
Image type: SEM
Scalebar = 4 μm (micros: ±20%, others: +100%, -50%)
Component: ACBB; IR, black oxide coated, unrun
Speed: -
Load: -
Lubrication: -
Failure code1: 00.08.5 Chemical attack during manufacture
Failure code2: -
Failure code3: -
Failure code4: -

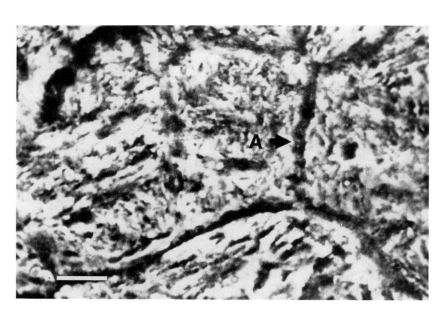

DESCRIPTIONS
FAILURE DESCRIPTION: Microscopic preferential attack by black oxide surface treatment on prior austenitic grain boundaries. This degree of preferential attack is harmless. Other surface treatments (for example, certain phosphate coatings) may produce sufficient grain boundary attack to reduce fatigue resistance of the surface.

IMAGE DESCRIPTION: In this high (4000 x) magnification SEM, three prior austenitic grains in the hardened steel are outlined by curving, dark 'canyons': (1) crossing N image edge, (2) N–S at A, (3) E–W in S image half. Black oxide coat was chemically removed, leaving striated-appearing etched surface under the coating, with prior austenitic grain boundaries preferentially attacked by the oxide coating process to form canyons.

SUSPECTED CAUSES: Black oxide treatment properly applied is an acceptable running-in aid in rolling bearings, e. g. for some aerospace uses. It also apparently mitigates the tendency of low EHD film to cause surface distress. Improper chemical surface treatments can have serious degrading effect on surface integrity and thus contact fatigue resistance, by creating more severe surface attack.

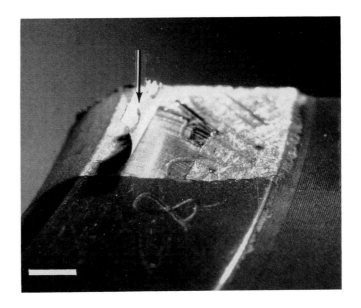

DATA
Plate No: 6.29
Archive No: 001-28
Image type: light macro
Scalebar = 2 mm (micros: ±20%, others: +100%, -50%)
Component: CRB; IR, copper plated, unrun
Speed: -
Load: -
Lubrication: -
Failure code1: 00.08.6 Coating damage
Failure code2: 00.00.01 Defect by location: in fit surface
Failure code3: -
Failure code4: -

DESCRIPTIONS
FAILURE DESCRIPTION: Copper plating on fit surface has lifted off (during adhesion test). Unless plate adheres properly, intended anti-fretting effect is not realized.

IMAGE DESCRIPTION: Cut IR segment viewed on side-face. At arrow, peeled copper plating on ground side-face of ring. Light/dark radial dividing line is an artifact.

SUSPECTED CAUSES: Processing error in copper plating.

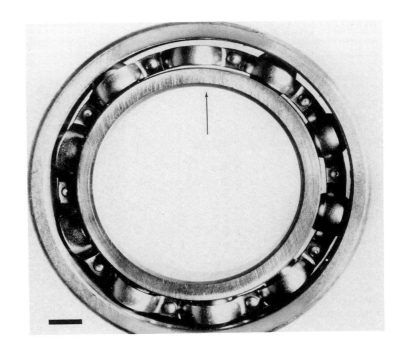

DATA
Plate No: 6.30
Archive No: 087-028
Image type: view
Scalebar = 8 mm (micros: ±20%, others: +100%, -50%)
Component: DGBB, assembled, unrun
Speed: -
Load: -
Lubrication: -
Failure code1: 00.09 Geometry, assembly or mounting defect
Failure code2: -
Failure code3: -
Failure code4: -

DESCRIPTIONS
FAILURE DESCRIPTION: One missing ball, omitted in assembly. A bearing with this defect is (a) vibratory, (b) of lesser load carrying capacity, and (c) unbalanced. Condition (a) may be objectionable in quiet running applications, (b) will spall in highly loaded applications and (c) is likely to suffer separator failure in high speed applications.

IMAGE DESCRIPTION: The ball marked by arrow is missing. While the ball regions protruding from separator are visible in the other balls, light shines past separator at arrow. Balance testing or suitable vibration testing can be used for detection in sealed or shielded bearings. Manufacturers use special magnetic sensors.

SUSPECTED CAUSES: Most ball bearings are automatically assembled. Balls are metered in, distributed and the separator is then put in place. A ball may fail to feed and the bearing is assembled with a missing ball unless a sensor for missing ball detection is present.

DATA
Plate No: 6.31
Archive No: 031-703
Image type: light macro
Scalebar = 30 mm (micros: ±20%, others: +100%, -50%)
Component: SRB; OR, run
Speed:
Load:
Lubrication:
Failure code1: 00.09.1 Scoring from forcible assembly or mounting (no galling)
Failure code2: 00.00.02.1 Defect by location: in Hertz contact surface
Failure code3: 00.09.2 Galling from forcible assembly or mounting
Failure code4: -

DESCRIPTIONS

FAILURE DESCRIPTION: Axial scuffmarks at roller spacing in the spherical roller path of a SRB OR, caused by sliding of the rollers, under pressure, across the OR surface of the stationary bearing. The marks are asperity scale plastic flow with a suspicion of incipient galling.

IMAGE DESCRIPTION: Score marks are dark, axial, fuzzy-edged lines across both roller tracks. The marks become more visible as the bearing is run. The running tracks show a different luster from the center band, because the bearing was operated. The fuzzy, faint scoring marks are probably not galled; the W-most mark in the N roller path is sufficiently sharp to suggest that it is galled. Microscopic examination is needed for differentiation.

SUSPECTED CAUSES: Spherical roller bearings are assembled with the OR placed out of the plane of the IR and the separators to permit roller insertion. Having completed roller assembly, the OR is swiveled into the bearing plane. Inattentive handling, lack of lubrication or sharp roller edges can cause excessive roller to OR contact pressure producing the scuffmarks. They may or may not contain galling streaks, depending on contact severity.

DATA
Plate No: 6.32
Archive No: 018-113
Image type: metallogram
Scalebar = 40 μm (micros: ±20%, others: +100%, -50%)
Component: metallographic section, etched
Speed: -
Load: -
Lubrication: -
Failure code1: 00.09.1 Scoring from forcible assembly or mounting (no galling)
Failure code2: 00.09.2 Galling from forcible assembly or mounting
Failure code3: 00.19.5 Local structure damage from frictional heating
Failure code4: -
See also PLATEs: 4.8 & 6.31

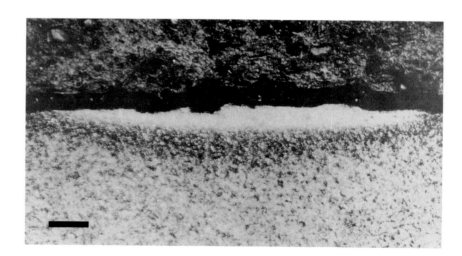

DESCRIPTIONS

FAILURE DESCRIPTION: An incipient galling event produced by scuffing. The scuffed surface is gouged (probably with material transfer). A shallow layer beneath the scuffmark was heated to austenitizing temperature and self-quenched by the surrounding cold steel. It etches light. Below is a band of less heated, tempered dark-etching material. See Plates 4.8 and 6.31 for other views of assembly scoring.

IMAGE DESCRIPTION: Metallographic section is the S half of the image (the N half is the plastic mount). The black/light-grey interface line is the rolling surface, showing depressed and elevated elements in the scuffmark due to plastic flow, wear, and possible galling. The featureless light layer (20 μm deep) is reaustenitized self-quenched martensite. The dark etching substrate blending into unaltered material below, is over-tempered martensite.

SUSPECTED CAUSES: Scuffing at sufficient pressure and speed produces localized plastic flow, wear and probably galling, with overheating of material leading to the structural changes observed. Structure change of this magnitude is rare in an assembly mark. A more common source of such damage is a grinding burn (FC 00.08).

DATA
Plate No: 6.33
Archive No: 027-262
Image type: view
Scalebar = 15 mm (micros: ±20%, others: +100%, -50%)
Component: ACBB; OR, unrun
Speed: -
Load: -
Lubrication: -
Failure code1: 00.09.1 Scoring from forcible assembly or mounting (no galling)
Failure code2: 00.12.1 Fit surface wear
Failure code3: -
Failure code4: -
See also PLATE: 6.36

DESCRIPTIONS
FAILURE DESCRIPTION: Axial scoremarks on the OD of the outerring. Marking to the extent shown here is due to mild wear and is generally harmless. More severe scoring may represent galling (FC 00.13) and may lead to subsequent cracking (FC 00.22).

IMAGE DESCRIPTION: The scoremarks are thin axial lines with luster different from that of the undisturbed OD surface . They are distributed around the circumference of the ring OD. When examined under magnification, the grinding lines are interrupted by the marks. The marks show no material transfer (as distinct from galled scoremarks which do).

SUSPECTED CAUSES: Assembly into a housing, either without adequate corner break or with excessively tight fit and/or rough surface. Assembly in the presence of solid contaminant in the fit.

DATA
Plate No: 6.34
Archive No: 002-023d
Image type: SEM
Scalebar = 1 mm (micros: ±20%, others: +100%, -50%)
Component: ACBB; B, tool steel, run
Speed: 1.7 MdN
Load: 1.4 GPa
Lubrication: synthetic polyester oil, 176 °C
Failure code1: 00.09.1 Scoring from forcible assembly or mounting (no galling)
Failure code2: 00.16.1.2.2 Shallow entry spall from surface line-defect
Failure code3: -
Failure code4: -

DESCRIPTIONS
FAILURE DESCRIPTION: Several gouges, presumably from bearing assembly, have damaged the ball surface and initiated a spall. The gouges are indentations and not wear marks, and have damaged the material to significant depth as shown by radial cracks in the spall. The ball has failed.

IMAGE DESCRIPTION: Background is ball surface with varying grey hue due to viewing angle change. At *A*, remaining ends of crossing indentations made by edges of mating parts. Irregular

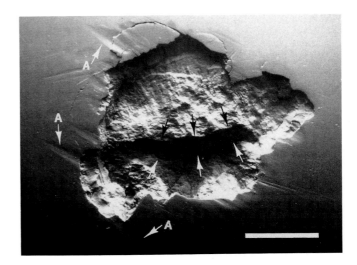

spall crater indicates multiple initiations from these nicks. Surface cracks extend the spall at N and W side. A radial crack face is between opposing arrows.

SUSPECTED CAUSES: Indentation of ball surface by forcible assembly, such as into the pocket of "snap-through" separator design, or interference with a ring edge, can cause static cracking (especially in crack-sensitive tool steel) in addition to initiating spalling.

DATA
Plate No: 6.35
Archive No: 093-015&16
Image type: a: view; b: light macro
Scalebar = a: 25, b: 3 mm (micros ±20%, others: +100%, -50%)
Component: CRB; IR, run
Speed:
Load:
Lubrication:
Failure code1: 00.09.2 Galling from forcible assembly or mounting
Failure code2: 00.09.1 Scoring from forcible assembly or mounting (no galling)
Failure code3: -
Failure code4: -

a

DESCRIPTIONS
FAILURE DESCRIPTION: Two axial score (wear) marks, and, adjacent to one, a galling streak on IR roller path, from sliding of roller over IR during assembly, without rolling, under high contact load. A rolling path with a galled score mark from assembly fails early in spalling or from additional galling during operation.

IMAGE DESCRIPTION: (a): Roller path showing circumferential running track across the contact width. One long, dark straight score (wear) mark at image center. Another, shorter mark just W of the lighting change from bright to grey. (b): Center mark enlarged. Dark uniform line is a score (wear) mark; dark-pitted oblong island with white border in image center, at E edge of dark mark, is material transferred in galling.

SUSPECTED CAUSES: Careless insertion of CRB innerring which is mounted on a shaft, into OR/roller assembly which is mounted in a housing, especially when rotor weight loads rollers. This is a common source of axial scoremarks with or without galling.

b

DATA
Plate No: 7.3
Archive No: 093-03a..i
Image type: a..i: drawing
Scalebar = -
Component: DGBB; IR & OR, run
Speed:
Load:
Lubrication:

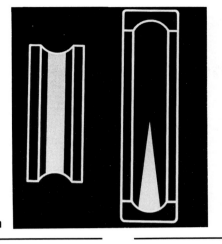
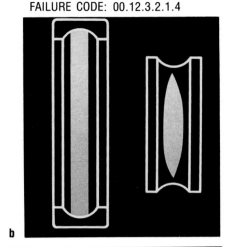

Image (a):

  Failure code1: 00.12.3.2.1.1 Wear track centered in contact
  Failure code2: 00.12.3.2.0.1 Wear track when load rotates over innerring

FAILURE DESCRIPTION: Rolling track when normal magnitude radial load rotates with respect to innerring.

IMAGE DESCRIPTION: Wear marks (polishing or scratches) in ball paths, away from both edges. The OR track is angularly confined to a load zone of less than 180° in circumference. The IR track extends through 360°.

Image (b):

  Failure code1: 00.12.3.2.1.1 Wear track centered in contact
  Failure code2: 00.12.3.2.0.2 Wear track when load rotates over outerring

FAILURE DESCRIPTION: Rolling track when normal magnitude radial load rotates with respect to outerring.

IMAGE DESCRIPTION: Wear marks (polishing or scratches) in ball paths, away from both edges. The IR track is confined to a load zone of less than 180° in circumference. The OR track extends through 360°. Both tracks centered in their grooves.

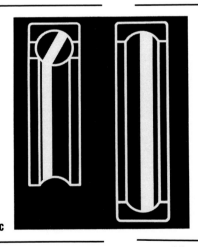
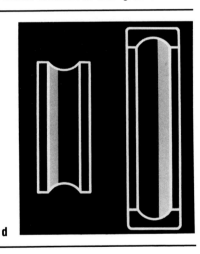

Image (c):

  Failure code1: 00.12.3.2.1.2 Wear track off-center in contact
  Failure code2: 00.12.3.2.0.5 Wear track for centered axial load

FAILURE DESCRIPTION: Illustration of rolling track when normal magnitude centered axial load is applied. Off-center, uniform width 360° load track on both rings. There may be a great circle track on the ball if the load is uninterrupted in time. Otherwise several tracks, or no discernible track on the ball.

IMAGE DESCRIPTION: Wear marks (polishing or scratches) in ball paths, shifted toward opposite edges on IR and OR, but not reaching either edge. Both tracks extend through 360° circumferentially.

Image (d):

  Failure code1: 00.12.3.2.1.4 Wear track at contact edge
  Failure code2: 00.12.3.2.0.5 Wear track for centered axial load

FAILURE DESCRIPTION: Rolling track when excessive magnitude of centered axial load is applied. Tracks extend to a groove edge in one or both rings. This condition may precipitate early spalling failure on ring or balls, from edge stresses, depending on the degree of overload.

IMAGE DESCRIPTION: Wear marks (polishing or scratches) in ball paths, shifted toward opposite edges on IR and OR, reaching atleast one groove edge. Both tracks extend through 360° circumferentially.

Plate No. 7.3, continued

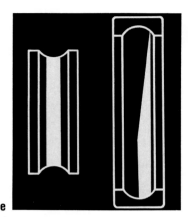

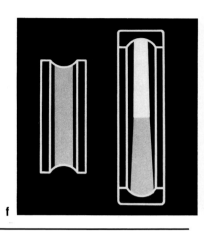

e

f

Image (e):

Failure code1: 00.12.3.2.1.2 Wear track off-center in contact
Failure code2: 00.12.3.2.0.6 Wear track for combined radial/axial load

FAILURE DESCRIPTION: Rolling track when normal magnitude axial load is combined with normal magnitude radial load rotating over the IR. In DRBB, load zones of different angle, (incl. 0) in one track, occur for combined load.

IMAGE DESCRIPTION: Wear marks (polishing or scratches) in ball paths, away from both edges. For single-row gearings, the OR track is confined to a load zone ranging from 180° to less than 360° in circumference. The IR track extends through 360°. For double-row bearings, OR track may be less than 180° in one row.

Image (f):

Failure code1: 00.12.3.2.1.1 Wear track centered in contact
Failure code2: 00.12.3.2.0.3 Wear track for radial preload

FAILURE DESCRIPTION: Rolling track for normal magnitude radial load rotating over innerring, with radial preload from negative internal looseness; wider on the radial load action side. Unintended radial preload may cause overheating and early spalling (FC 00.19 and FC 00.16).

IMAGE DESCRIPTION: Wear marks (polishing or scratches) in ball paths, away from both edges. Load zone on both rings is centered; on IR, it is uniform around 360°; on OR, it is >180°, wider on the radial load action side.

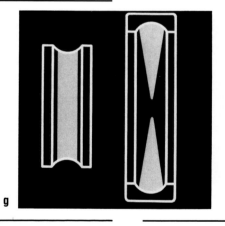

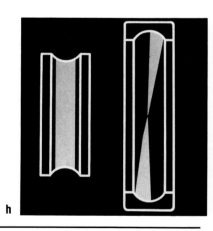

g

h

Image (g):

Failure code1: 00.12.3.2.1.1 Wear track centered in contact
Failure code2: 00.12.3.2.0.4 Wear track for out-of-round ring

FAILURE DESCRIPTION: Rolling track in an out-of-round OR.

IMAGE DESCRIPTION: Wear marks (polishing or scratches) in ball paths, away from both edges. The OR track is confined to two opposite load zones of less than 180° each in circumference. The IR track extends over 360°. If radial load rotating against the innerring is added, then one of the two load zones will be wider.

Image (h):

Failure code1: 00.12.3.2.1.3 Wear track shifts in contact
Failure code2: 00.12.3.2.0.7 Wear track for misaligned innerring

FAILURE DESCRIPTION: Rolling track in a misaligned OR.

IMAGE DESCRIPTION: Wear marks (polishing or scratches) in ball paths. The OR track is confined to two opposite load zones of less than 180° each in circumference, axially off-center in opposite directions. The edge of one or both load zones may reach the groove edge. IR load track extends uniformly through 360° and is wider than OR load zones. If radial load rotating against the innerring is added, then one of the two load zones will be wider.

Plate No. 7.3, continued

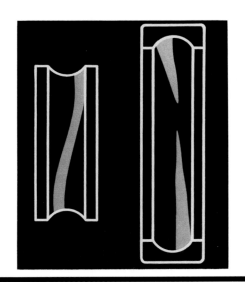

Image (i):

Failure code1: 00.12.3.2.1.3 Wear track shifts in contact
Failure code2: 00.12.3.2.0.8 Wear track for misaligned innerring

DESCRIPTIONS

FAILURE DESCRIPTION: Rolling track for a misaligned IR.

IMAGE DESCRIPTION: Wear marks (polishing or scratches) in ball paths. OR ring track is confined to two opposite load zones of less than 180° each in circumference, off-centered in opposite directions. IR track shifts from side to side of the groove and runs 360°. The edge of either load zone may reach the groove edge. If radial load is added, one of the OR load zones is wider than the other.

DATA
Plate No: 7.4
Archive No: 031-007
Image type: view
Scalebar = 30 mm (micros: ±20%, others: +100%, −50%)
Component: SRB; R, run
Speed: 25 KdN
Load: 1.4 GPa
Lubrication: mineral oil, 150 °C
Failure Code1: 00.12.3.2.1 Smooth rolling surface wear (finish marks removed)
Failure Code2: 00.12.3.3.2 Wear, centered in sliding contact
Failure Code3: 00.16.02.5 Advanced spalling
Failure Code4: 11.3.3 Abrasive contaminant in oil

DESCRIPTIONS
FAILURE DESCRIPTION: Smooth wear on all (rolling and sliding) contact surfaces of rollers. Deep spalls both within and at the extreme edges of the rolling contact. Probable failure progression: (1) abrasive wear; from contamination carried in the lubricant, (2) spalling, (3) indentations by large spall debris (not visible); (4) deep spalling at track center from dents. Edge spalls from dents or edge contact.

IMAGE DESCRIPTION: All rolling surfaces and all but the center circle of the visible roller end surfaces are worn to a matte sa-tiny finish with most finishing lines obliterated. Extremely deep spall craters centered in contact and at edges, extending onto corner radii.

SUSPECTED CAUSES: This bearing operated in a contaminated environment, causing abrasive wear. Spalling progressed extensively, creating large debris which made dents, causing extremely high local stresses leading to deep spalls. Spalling at the track edges and corner radii may be due to geometry error (too wide guidering) or skewing of rollers, resulting in edge contact.

DATA
Plate No: 7.5
Archive No: 093-12.1.3
Image type: SEM
Scalebar = 30 μm (micros: ±20%, others: +100%, −50%)
Component: DGBB; IR, honed, run
Speed: 450 KdN
Load: 3.5 GPa
Lubrication: mineral (turbine) oil, 100 °C
Failure Code1: 00.12.3.2.1 Smooth rolling surface wear (finish marks removed)
Failure Code2: 00.18.1.4 Multiple irregular denting from fine, loose hard debris
Failure Code3: 00.12.3.2.2 Scratch marks, kinematic wear marks in rolling surface
Failure Code4: -

DESCRIPTIONS
FAILURE DESCRIPTION: Uniform mild wear of rolling surface with multiple very small non-directional dents from fine solid contaminant. Few long scratchmarks from sliding. All finishing marks are obliterated, by general ablation of the surface (''sandblasted'' micro-appearance). A few surface distress microspalls (FC 00.17) may be present. Minimal wear may permit long life (with progressively impaired shaft support accuracy).

IMAGE DESCRIPTION: The image background is a featureless grey surface covered with very fine (2–10 μm dia.) smooth-

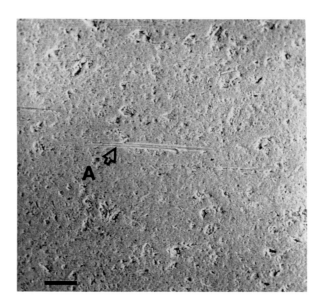

bottomed dents. Some dark-bottomed craters, probably micro-spalls from surface distress. One long E–W wear scratch at A. Others faintly visible elsewhere. No finishing lines visible.

SUSPECTED CAUSES: Operation in lubricant carrying very fine solid contaminant causes uniform slow wear. In pure rolling, debris cause multiple dents. With the small sliding component existing in DGBB, wear also occurs. Individual wear events are not discernible (except few scratches such as at A). The EHD film was thick enough to prevent generalized surface distress.

DATA
Plate No: 7.6
Archive No: 005-12
Image type: light macro
Scalebar = 5 mm (micros: ±20%, others: +100%, −50%)
Component: C; CM (carburized), run
Speed:
Load: 2.1 GPA
Lubrication: Diesel fuel, ? °C
Failure Code1: 00.12.3.2.1.1 Wear track centered in contact
Failure Code2: -
Failure Code3: -
Failure Code4: -

DESCRIPTIONS
FAILURE DESCRIPTION: Wear marks at end of the ramp part of a cam lobe, from sliding between cam and follower. If wear becomes excessive, galling or spalling failure may follow or cam geometry is lost.

IMAGE DESCRIPTION: Sectioned cam is viewed from OD. Descending ramp (between arrows) is in S image half. On ramp, circumferential, light colored wear marks. Wear marks are densest near the exit point of the (descending) ramp.

SUSPECTED CAUSES: Pressure between cam and follower varies sharply by angular position, peaking on ascending ramp and dropping to zero along descending ramp. Friction on pin retards follower. When contact pressure to lobe is insufficient to provide necessary driving force, slip occurs, which may result in wear.

DATA
Plate No: 7.7
Archive No: 093-004
Image type: view with mirror image
Scalebar = 30 mm (micros: ±20%, others: +100%, −50%)
Component: SRB; OR, run
Speed:
Load:
Lubrication:
Failure Code1: 00.12.3.2.1.1 Wear track centered in contact
Failure Code2: 00.12.3.2.0.4 Wear track for out-of-round ring
Failure Code3: 21.6 Housing deformed
Failure Code4: -

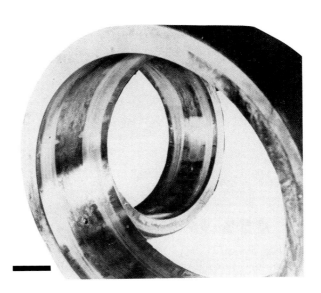

DESCRIPTIONS
FAILURE DESCRIPTION: Bearing shows two, diametrally opposite load zones in both roller tracks indicating out-of-round condition of housing. The condition causes parasitic overloading and may lead to early spalling and hot operation.

IMAGE DESCRIPTION: In this image, the W half of the roller path is seen in direct view, and its E half in a mirror placed behind the ring. In both halves, light-colored contact tracks show a load zone in both roller paths. The two sets of load zones are 180° apart indicating out of roundness.

SUSPECTED CAUSES: Out of roundness is likely in the housing (out of roundness of this magnitude in the ring proper is a rare occurrence). The housing deflects the outerring elastically, causing reduction in radial looseness along one direction, resulting in parasitic radial loading.

DATA
Plate No: 7.8
Archive No: 031-102
Image type: view
Scalebar = 20 mm (micros: ±20%, others: +100%, −50%)
Component: SRB; IR, run
Speed: 25 KdN
Load: 1.4 GPa
Lubrication: mineral oil, 120 °C
Failure Code1: 00.12.3.2.1.1 Wear track centered in contact
Failure Code2: 00.12.4 Wear of guiding-component support surface
Failure Code3: 00.18.1.2 Sharp individual dent(s) from metal debris, asperities
Failure Code4: 11.2 Water in oil

DESCRIPTIONS
FAILURE DESCRIPTION: Both roller tracks extensively worn. Solid contaminant abrasion probable. Separator support surface worn in sliding contact in the presence of contaminant. Some local denting of roller track by contaminant particles.

IMAGE DESCRIPTION: Both roller tracks show dark, matte, slightly pebbled surface from abrasive wear. Center flange supporting separator is burnished and circumferentially scratched by abrasive wear. Roller track in S image half shows a dent near its center, from a large contaminant particle. Dark discoloration of roller paths and side flanges suggests water in the oil.

SUSPECTED CAUSES: This bearing operated in a contaminated and possibly wet environment. The solid contaminant precipitated abrasive wear; water in the oil contributed to the dark discoloration of rolling surfaces and side flanges. Oil carbonization may also take place at high temperature.

DATA
Plate No: 7.9
Archive No: 087-036
Image type: view
Scalebar = 20 mm (micros: ±20%, others: +100%, −50%)
Component: DGBB; IR, run
Speed:
Load:
Lubrication:
Failure Code1: 00.12.3.2.1.3 Wear track shifts in contact
Failure Code2: 00.09.0 Geometry defect
Failure Code3: -
Failure Code4: -

DESCRIPTIONS
FAILURE DESCRIPTION: Ball track in the groove of this IR weaves laterally. Effective contact angle varies around circumference, causing cyclic ball orbital speed variation resulting in high separator stresses. Noisy operation and early separator failure are likely.

IMAGE DESCRIPTION: The black oxide coated ring shows a (bright) wavy wear band in the groove half located S of the image center.

SUSPECTED CAUSES: Distortion from relaxation of stresses or poor fixturing during manufacture may cause circumferential waviness in the ball groove. If extreme, this may lead to observable contact angle variability as in this case.

DATA
Plate No: 7.10
Archive No: 014-35
Image type: light macro
Scalebar = 20 mm (micros: ±20%, others: +100%, -50%)
Component: TRB; OR, run
Speed:
Load:
Lubrication:
Failure Code1: 00.12.3.2.1.3 Wear track shifts in contact
Failure Code2: 00.12.3.2.0.7 Wear track for misaligned outerring
Failure Code3: 00.20.1.3 Contact corrosion
Failure Code4: 00.20.2 Corrosion pitting

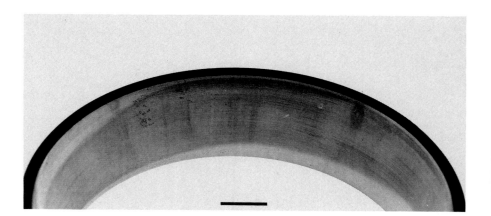

DESCRIPTIONS
FAILURE DESCRIPTION: Laterally shifting contact pattern in misaligned outerring, ranging from no contact at the large roller end to no contact at the small end. Axial streaks of contact corrosion. Misalignment produces serious edge loading at roller ends and may cause early spalling. High tractive forces act on the separator from roller orbital speed variations and may cause fracture. Incidental corrosion.

IMAGE DESCRIPTION: The contact path of the rollers on the OR appears darker grey than the un-contacted track. The contact concentrates at the small roller end (at image W) and shifts to the large roller end at image center and E. Darker axial streaks in the contact area indicate contact corrosion. 1/4 image width from W edge are two clusters of corrosion pits.

SUSPECTED CAUSES: The shifting contact path indicates a misaligned innerring due to machine geometry error or mismounting of ring in housing. Contact corrosion may arise from water in the lubricant (See FC 00.20.1.3).

CHAPTER 7: MILD WEAR

FAILURE CODE: 00.12.3.2.1.4   **105**
FAILURE CODE: 00.12.3.2.2.

DATA
Plate No: 7.11
Archive No: 087-035
Image type: view
Scalebar = 30 mm (micros: ±20%, others: +100%, -50%)
Component: DGBB; IR, run
Speed:
Load:
Lubrication:
Failure Code1: 00.12.3.2.1.4 Wear track at contact edge
Failure Code2: 00.09.0 Geometry defect
Failure Code3: -
Failure Code4: -

DESCRIPTIONS
FAILURE DESCRIPTION: Narrow wear bands near both edges of the ball path, due to mismatch of ball and groove profile radius and groove profile error. The bearing had no appreciable load carrying capacity.

IMAGE DESCRIPTION: Black oxide coated innerring shows two narrow white wear bands near, but not at, both groove edges (inboard of arrows).

SUSPECTED CAUSES: Mismatch between groove profile radius and ball diameter (conformity <50%, ball radius exceeded groove profile radius), caused two-point contact near groove edges. Since contacts are not precisely at the edges, groove profile must be non-circular (widened) at the edges.

DATA
Plate No: 7.12
Archive No: 018-302
Image type: light microgram (composite)
Scalebar = 400 μm (micros: ±20%, others: +100%, -50%)
Component: ACBB; IR, tool steel, run
Speed: 1.125 MdN
Load: 2.2 GPa
Lubrication: synthetic polyester oil, 150 °C
Failure Code1: 00.12.3.2.2 Scratch marks, kinematic wear marks in rolling surface
Failure Code2: 00.12.0.2 Abrasive mild wear
Failure Code3: 00.17.1.2 Microspalling (advanced surface distress)
Failure Code4: 00.03.4 Lapping imperfection

DESCRIPTIONS
FAILURE DESCRIPTION: Ball track marked by a dense pattern of kinematic wear marks from spinning ball with protruding carbides produces unacceptable shortening of fatigue life.

IMAGE DESCRIPTION: This composite image of IR ball path shows swirl pattern of short kinematic wear marks running NE to SW at image N, N to S in center, and NW to SE at image S. Black irregular spots may be microspalls of incipient surface distress. Rolling direction is E to W. Unworn groove areas at N and S image edges show E–W finishing marks.

SUSPECTED CAUSES: The balls were observed to have hard carbides protruding about 1 μm above surface, presumably as a result of differential stock removal in lapping the tool steel material. The carbides penetrate the (much thinner) EHD film and scratch the ring surface. A finishing process leaving protruding carbides is unacceptable.

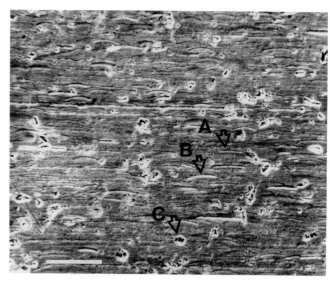

DATA
Plate No: 7.13
Archive No: 093-12.1.8
Image type: SEM
Scalebar = 35 μm (micros: ±20%, others: +100%, -50%)
Component: DGBB; IR, honed, operated
Speed: 450 KdN
Load: 3.3 GPa
Lubrication: synthetic polyester oil, 38° C
Failure Code1: 00.12.3.2.2 Scratch marks, kinematic wear marks in rolling surface
Failure Code2: 00.17.1.2 Microspalling (advanced surface distress)
Failure Code3: -
Failure Code4: -

DESCRIPTIONS
FAILURE DESCRIPTION: Mild wear events in asperity dimensions cause short scratchmarks on the contact surface which trace the relative motion of the contacting surface. In a BB with curved contact interface, ball motion has a spin component at most points, and the kinematic marks are fingernail or horseshoe shaped parabolas. Surface distress microspalling is also present. The damage promotes spalling and (if wear progresses), impairs precision.

IMAGE DESCRIPTION: Original finishing lines run straight E–W. They are covered with layers of generally E–W oriented, curved 'fingernail marks' convex from above: the kinematic wear

marks. A recent sharp mark is at *B*, a partly worn-off mark at *A*. Microspalls, i.e. small dark craters with fracture surface bottoms and a white rim ('halo') are scattered on the surface. Example at *C*.

SUSPECTED CAUSES: Kinematic wear marks occur in the presence of sliding (spin) in addition to rolling, under EHD film conditions insufficient to prevent asperity contact. *Small* amounts of fine solid contaminant, embedded in one of the contact surfaces may produce kinematic wear marks by acting as a temporary asperity. Surface distress is asperity scale contact fatigue (FC 00.17).

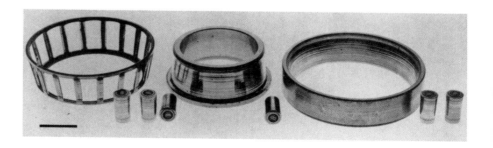

DATA
Plate No: 7.14
Archive No: 014-9
Image type: view
Scalebar = 20 mm (micros: ±20%, others: +100%, -50%)
Component: TRB; all components, run
Speed:
Load:
Lubrication:
Failure Code1: 00.12.3.2.2 Scratch marks, kinematic wear marks in rolling surface
Failure Code2: 00.18.2.2 Rolled-in line inside contact
Failure Code3: 01.13 Separator wear
Failure Code4: 12.5.1 Steel contaminant in grease

DESCRIPTIONS
FAILURE DESCRIPTION: Steel contamination in the lubricant carried by the separator caused circumferential wear marks in the rollers. Rollers transferred rolled-in lines to the ring roller tracks. Additional contaminant wore circumferential lines on the separator OD. A bearing this severely worn has lost precision, is noisy and may soon seize when the worn separator jams between rollers and ring.

IMAGE DESCRIPTION: Circumferential scratches on separator bar OD and roller OD. Rolled in lines on the roller tracks of both rings.

SUSPECTED CAUSES: Steel contaminant was found in the grease, initiating the wear process. The contaminant may arise from contaminated assembly, contaminated housing or the wear of moving parts, other than the bearing, in the same chamber.

DATA
Plate No: 7.31
Archive No: 099-119 a & b & c
Image type: light macro
Scalebar = a,b,c: 30 mm (micros:
±20%, others: +100%, -50%)
Component: HG, W; med. hard,
(a): 1 (b): 1.5 (c): 4 year run
Speed:
Load:
Lubrication:
Failure Code1: 00.12.5.2 Smooth tooth
wear
Failure Code2: 00.16.01.3 Tooth
spalling
Failure Code3: 00.12.3.2.3 Step worn
in rolling surface or dimension worn
off-spec
Failure Code4: -

DESCRIPTIONS
FAILURE DESCRIPTION: Progressive wear of medium-hard
('through hardened') gears, with initial spalls, subsequently
worn off and steps worn into tooth face. In slow speed industrial gears, this degree of wear is often acceptable. Change in
backlash and possible destructive wear may fail gear during further running.

IMAGE DESCRIPTION: (a): Smooth wear on tooth contact surfaces, interspersed with dedendum micropitting (NE quadrant)
and some spalling (near both ends of teeth at N). One tooth
chipped at E end. (b): Steps produced by wear visible near
tooth ends; copious micropitting. Loose contaminant at tooth
roots. (c): Uniform, somewhat rough wear across entire tooth;
deepest in dedendum.

SUSPECTED CAUSES: Progressive wear from operation in low
EHD film thickness regime with possible abrasive contamination
from gear wear and/or other sources. Some spalling in low
sliding areas, no large-scale craters. One tooth chipped (from
passage of a large piece of debris?).

a

b

c

DATA
Plate No: 7.32
Archive No: 099-121
Image type: light macro
Scalebar = 25 mm (micros: ±20%, others: +100%, -50%)
Component: HG; W, med. hard, run
Speed:
Load:
Lubrication:
Failure Code1: 00.12.5.3.1 Abrasive (destructive) tooth wear
Failure Code2: -
Failure Code3: -
Failure Code4: -

DESCRIPTIONS
FAILURE DESCRIPTION: Abrasive wear of gear contact surfaces by contaminated lubricant. Surface finish is destroyed and heavily grooved surface created, with grooves predominantly in the sliding direction. Gearing with wear of this severity is generally not serviceable.

IMAGE DESCRIPTION: Entire contact area on surfaces of loaded flanks is heavily grooved in radial direction. Grooves vary in depth and length, as if produced by hard particles of varying dimensions.

SUSPECTED CAUSES: This gear is known to have operated in a chamber where lubricant was severely contaminated by spalling debris from case hardened bearings. The debris are much harder than the gear material and of widely varying size. The debris operate as a coarse abrasive in the gear mesh.

DATA
Plate No: 7.33
Archive No: 099-129
Image type: light macro
Scalebar = 20 mm (micros: ±20%, others: +100%, -50%)
Component: HG; P, med. hard, run
Speed:
Load:
Lubrication:
Failure Code1: 00.12.5.3.4 Adhesive (destructive, non-galling) tooth wear
Failure Code2: 00.12.3.2.3 Step worn in rolling surface or dimension worn off-spec
Failure Code3: -
Failure Code4: -

DESCRIPTIONS
FAILURE DESCRIPTION: In contact of wider pinion with narrower wheel, in the presence of progressive wear, the pinion wear does not extend over the entire tooth length, leaving 'pads' of unworn material at the tooth ends. If during maintenance or operation, the contact pattern is shifted axially, edge contact between the 'pads' and the corner of the wheel teeth may occur, leading to fracture or other failure from edge loading.

IMAGE DESCRIPTION: Worn step in contact area of teeth, heaviest in dedendum. At both tooth ends, step leads to unworn material outside contact area (arrows).

SUSPECTED CAUSES: Progressive wear condition in the presence of pinion/wheel combination of unequal width.

DATA
Plate No: 7.34
Archive No: 099-230
Image type: view
Scalebar = 60 mm (micros: ±20%, others: +100%, -50%)
Component: HG; P, med. hard, run
Speed:
Load:
Lubrication:
Failure Code1: 00.12.5.3.2 Adhesive (destructive, non-galling) tooth wear
Failure Code2: 00.12.5.2 Smooth tooth wear
Failure Code3: 00.12.3.2.3 Step worn in rolling surface or dimension worn off-spec
Failure Code4: 00.16.02.4 Incipient spalling, multiple spalls

DESCRIPTIONS
FAILURE DESCRIPTION: Deep wear step in dedendum of gear, with spalling ("pitting"). The deep local wear suggests geometry error (misalignment?). The wear has led to a tooth fracture (not shown).

IMAGE DESCRIPTION: W-facing tooth flanks are not worn (show hob marks). E-facing flanks show generalized smooth wear, with step worn in at N edge. W of line with arrowheads is a wide wear trough with sharp demarcation lines at E and W boundaries. Line of fine spall craters just W of line with arrowheads.

SUSPECTED CAUSES: Geometry error is suspected cause of heavy wear zone. Spalling resulted from high local loading. Smooth wear (including wear step) is expected after long operation in this environment.

DATA
Plate No: 7.35
Archive No: 099-237
Image type: view
Scalebar = 50 mm (micros: ±20%, others: +100%, -50%)
Component: HG; P, med. hard, run
Speed:
Load:
Lubrication:
Failure Code1: 00.12.5.3.2 Adhesive (destructive, non-galling) tooth wear
Failure Code2: 00.13.2.1.1 Rolling surface galling, no dent or nick visible
Failure Code3: 00.16.02.2 Contact fatigue cracking
Failure Code4: 00.22.01.42 Tooth corner fracture

DESCRIPTIONS
FAILURE DESCRIPTION: Generalized wear of tooth contact surface including step at one edge. Galling (FC 00.13) and incidental spalling (FC 00.16) in addendum near other edge. The damage has led to a tooth fracture (FC 00.22). The gear has failed.

IMAGE DESCRIPTION: N-most fully visible tooth is fractured at left. Tooth flanks reached first when traveling S on the image, are named *north* flanks, the others: *south* flanks. *North* flank surfaces are as machined (see image S). *South* flanks (see image N) are worn, with step at E contact edge (wear marks run radially). W image quarter shows plastic flow and galling over much of addendum. Axial elongated spall craters in galled area.

SUSPECTED CAUSES: Overall wear from low EHD film. Heavy wear and galling from uneven loading (misalignment?). Spalls result from galling damage. Fracture is end result of galling and spalls.

DATA
Plate No: 7.36
Archive No: 099-127
Image type: light macro
Scalebar = 30 mm (micros: ±20%, others: +100%, -50%)
Component: HG; W, med. hard, run
Speed:
Load:
Lubrication:
Failure Code1: 00.12.5.3.2.1 Wavy tooth wear
Failure Code2: 00.22.01.44 Tooth tip chipping
Failure Code3: -
Failure Code4: -

DESCRIPTIONS
FAILURE DESCRIPTION: Radially progressing waviness on tooth surfaces, with wave crests parallel to contact. The waviness is believed produced by wear, probably under vibratory operating conditions. The wear does not represent immediate failure but may aggravate the vibration and ultimately lead to failure. Some tooth tips are (incidentally) chipped.

IMAGE DESCRIPTION: The luster of the contact surface shows inclined axial streaks (arrows), indicating wavy wear, with crests parallel to the contact in this helical gear. The waviness is identifiable by profile tracing. Two tooth tips near image N are chipped.

SUSPECTED CAUSES: The engineering cause of wavy wear is not firmly established. Vibratory operating conditions are suspected.

DATA
PLATE No: 7.37
Archive No: 099-303 & 302
Image type: a: view, b: light macro
Scalebar = a: 75, b: 15 mm (micros: ±20%, others: +100%, -50%)
Component: HG; W, med. hard, run
Speed:
Load:
Lubrication:
Failure Code1: 00.12.5.3.2.2 Bumpy tooth wear
Failure Code2: 00.12.5.3.1 Abrasive (destructive) tooth wear
Failure Code3: 00.16.02.3 Incipient spalling, single spall
Failure Code4: 00.22.01.4 Gear tooth crack or fracture

a

b

DESCRIPTIONS
FAILURE DESCRIPTION: Elevated 'bumps' extending in the direction of the contact line on the tooth flank, formed by material removal in the surrounding area, appearing in similar form on several consecutive teeth, on *both* contact ends. Abrasive environment likely. Spalls on 'bump.' The 'copying' of bumps on several teeth suggests a self-reinforcing vibratory activity. Mating gear believed to show corresponding depressions. (Mating gear is lost).

IMAGE DESCRIPTION: (a): 'Bumps' of similar shape at both ends of all four S-facing tooth flanks (visible best in N half of gear). N-facing flanks (visible in S half of gear) are undamaged. One tooth tip in E is fractured. (b): Tip area of a tooth flank. (section cut form a tooth). Wear pad leads to original tooth surface at W edge. Elongated 'bump' extends axially across smoothly worn tooth flank. Few small spall craters.

SUSPECTED CAUSES: Self-reinforced vibratory motions in tooth mesh are conjectured as cause of mirror-image wear on mating teeth (bumps on this gear, hollows on mating gear) which copies same wear pattern on many teeth in sequence. No metallurgical deviation (e.g. hard areas) are present. Abrasive contamination is assumed to enhance deep wear. Precise causation mechanism not known. The mating gear is unavailable for examination.

DATA

PLATE No: 7.38
Archive No: 064-101
Image type: light macro
Scalebar = 50 mm (micros: ±20%, others: +100%, -50%)
Component: HG; W, med. hard, run
Speed:
Load:
Lubrication:
Failure Code1: 00.12.5.3.2.3 Ridging tooth wear
Failure Code2: 00.16.01.3.1 Tooth pitchline or dedendum spalling
Failure Code3: 00.12.3.3.2.3 Step worn in rolling surface or dimension worn off-spec
Failure Code4: -

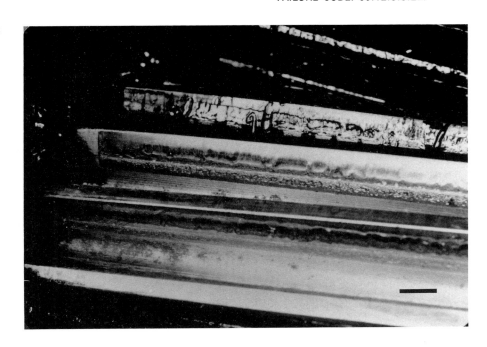

DESCRIPTIONS

FAILURE DESCRIPTION: On addendum of teeth, ridging wear consisting of destructive adhesive removal of substantial material, to uneven depth, forming radial ridges. At contact edge, wear step. In dedendum, fine spalling. Wear of this severity, and spalling, impairs tooth geometry, causing noisy running and eventual failure by deep spalls or tooth fracture.

IMAGE DESCRIPTION: Gear shown in chamber, with lubricant (thick black oil) still present. Near S image edge, gear OD, then two tooth flanks clean of oil. On both flanks: radial-running ridges worn into addendum, and step at W end of contact. Wear diminishes at pitchline, and a band of small spall craters and dents is visible in dedendum. N-most tooth of foreground gear and all of background gear carry dark tarry oil.

SUSPECTED CAUSES: High-load, slow speed operation of medium-hard gears may result in ridging wear where sliding is substantial. Concurrently, spalling near pitchline may arise in dedendum.

DATA

PLATE No: 7.39
Archive No: 099-130
Image type: light macro
Scalebar = 10 mm (micros: ±20%, others: +100%, -50%)
Component: SG; P, med. hard, hobbed, run
Speed:
Load:
Lubrication:
Failure Code1: 00.12.5.3.2.4 Furrowing tooth wear
Failure Code2: -
Failure Code3: -
Failure Code4: -

DESCRIPTIONS

FAILURE DESCRIPTION: Furrowing wear occurs in large, rough-finished gears. Fine, short radial wear marks (furrows) cross the finishing lines of hobbing. Numerous axial bands composed of furrows may arise. The origination of furrowing wear is not clearly established. For slow speed, heavy gears, furrowing is not an immediate cause of failure.

IMAGE DESCRIPTION: On the gear flank surface, N of the (artificial) fracture, axial bands of radial wear marks which decorate hobbing lines. If viewed under magnification, they are round bottomed furrows. This "furrowing" has no relation to grinding furrows (FC 00.02).

SUSPECTED CAUSES: The engineering cause of furrowing wear of gear teeth is not clearly established. It is observed as a wear phenomenon in coarse-finish large gears operating under low EHD film thickness, and may be related to rough surface finishes.

DATA
PLATE No: 7.40
Archive No: 011-001
Image type: color macro. [SEE IMAGE IN APPENDIX]
Scalebar = 1 mm (micros: ±20%, others: +100%, -50%)
Component: 0; impact printer hammer, run
Speed: impact
Load: impact
Lubrication: scant mineral oil, 50 °C
Failure Code1: 00.12.7 Impact wear
Failure Code2: -
Failure Code3: -
Failure Code4: -
See also PLATE: 7.41

[See Image in Appendix]

DESCRIPTIONS
FAILURE DESCRIPTION: Wear of impact printer hammer surface against elastomeric pushrod tip. Hammer surface burnished. Transferred elastomer and other adhering debris. This degree of wear is not a hammer failure. The elastomeric pushrod usually fails first.

IMAGE DESCRIPTION: The four grey/yellow rod-shaped elements are metal hammers from a data processing impact printer. At the broadened anvil area, an elastomer-tipped pushrod hits during operation (dark-rimmed oval with streaky green interior). Slight burnishing wear of metal, where yellow patch appears. Adhesion of elastomer debris (green) and oil (dark).

SUSPECTED CAUSES: Some data processing impact printers transmit type-carrier forces through a pushrod to a hammer. The pushrod/hammer impact, which is essentially of normal incidence with a small sliding component, transfers some elastomer to the hammer, while inflicting mild wear on its metal surface.

DATA
PLATE No: 7.41
Archive No: 011-002
Image type: light macro
Scalebar = 5 mm (micros: ±20%, others: +100%, -50%)
Component: 0; type element
Speed: impact & slide
Load: impact
Lubrication:
Failure Code1: 00.12.7 Impact wear
Failure Code2: 00.12.3.3 Sliding contact wear
Failure Code3: -
Failure Code4: -
See also PLATE: 7.41

DESCRIPTIONS
FAILURE DESCRIPTION: Impact wear with sliding on rear of impact printer type-element. One wear scar from impact between the type element and a hammer. The other is at type/backstop contact and due to vibration and impact. As wear continues, dimension is lost, resulting in printing degradation.

IMAGE DESCRIPTION: Three type-carriers are viewed from the back face. The averted face carries characters at the tip (image N). The thinned shank is elastic. Widening of sharp N–S edge at *A* is from hammer impact. Some E–W wear marks E of edges. E–W running rectangles at *B* are fretting marks, from backstop contact under vibration.

SUSPECTED CAUSES: Impact printer type carriers have characters on their tip. The back face slides past a backstop when not printing and is hit by a metal hammer to make the imprint.

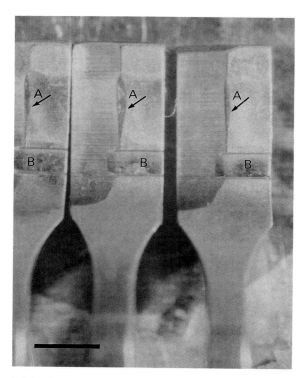

Lubrication is marginal. Misalignment may exist. Impact wear and some sliding wear occur at the hammer contact; fretting and some impact wear at the backstop contact. Eventually geometry is destroyed sufficiently to require replacement.

8 GALLING, SKIDMARKING

8.1. GALLING. FAILURE CODE: 00.13

8.1.1. Definition

Galling (of a contact component) is defined as the transfer of component surface material in macroscopic patches from a location on one contacting surface to a location on the other contacting surface, and possibly back onto the first surface, by the action, in service, of high tractive forces in multi-asperity dimensions. Galling is distinguished from:

- *mild wear* (FC 00.12), defined as removal of surface material as loose particles by the action of *tractive* forces in *asperity dimensions;*
- *surface distress* (FC 00.17) defined as surface material plastic flow and micropitting by the action of high *normal* forces in asperity dimensions;
- *fretting wear* (FC 00.15), defined as removal of surface material, often with oxidation of debris, as a result of *microscopic* surface-parallel relative movement of surfaces in nominally static contact under normal load;
- *skidmarking* (FC 00.14) defined as material transfer between surfaces in *single-asperity* dimensions.

8.1.2. Nomenclature

Galling is also designated severe wear, smearing, or scuffing. The term "scoring" may designate galling or alternatively, the formation of a scratch by plastic plowing. Occasionally the term "wear" is used loosely to designate all modes of surface material removal, including galling as well as the other modes listed above under 'definition'. In this Atlas, galling is only used to designate severe wear, which is always two-body wear.

In some gear literature [9, 10] galling is called adhesive wear, although this term is generally reserved to describe two-body mild wear (FC 00.12). In this Atlas, galling is never designated as adhesive wear.

8.1.3. Failure Process

Many common theories describing the micro-mechanism of galling hark back to the Blok *flash temperature* model [13], according to which two asperities contacting under severe conditions heat up momentarily to a temperature which (a) vaporizes the lubricant and (b) welds the asperities together. More recent theories have added the conjecture that local heating causes thermal distortion of the surface, in effect creating a "transient asperity" which becomes overloaded by being higher than the surrounding surface.

When asperities are separated at the end of the contact cycle, the separation may occur along a plane other than the original interface, so that a patch of surface material from one surface is left welded onto the opposite contact surface. It is believed that galling requires an "avalanche" process, whereby a small patch of welded surface material is moved along the surface by sliding, then welded onto a next asperity, thereby increasing in area. This process continues until it is externally interrupted. It is believed that for the macroscopic material transfer process to take place, a galling event *must bridge more than one asperity* (that is, material dragged from one welded asperity, is welded onto a second asperity, is further dragged to a third and so forth). This sequence explains the cascading nature of a galling failure, which is its most significant characteristic.

Neither the flash temperature, nor any single macro-variable of operation (speed, load, roughness, lubricant, etc.) controls the onset of galling over a broad range of contact configurations. At present, the effect of the parameters influencing galling is known only for fixed configurations. Thus, there are experimental data on threshold value for speed, load, temperature and lubricant combinations which do not precipitate galling in a *precisely defined* contact configuration including defined contact material and surface finish. However, extrapolation to untested configurations is reliable only over small incremental configuration changes.

Galling is a welding phenomenon, that is, of adhesive bonding between material volumes. Accordingly, it is primarily a failure mode of metal or thermoplastic surfaces. Surfaces which resist welding (such as ceramics) and "contaminating" layers of lubricant or coating that combat welding, all resist galling.

It is believed that asperities must deform plastically in order to initiate the welding needed for galling. Therefore the slope angle (or tip curvature) of an asperity must exceed the limit of plastic flow under the operating conditions in order to initiate galling.

The cascading nature of galling explains the tendency of galling failures to be catastrophic. A galling event, once started, tends to continue and spread the transferred metal patch in the sliding direction as long as the contact lasts. For this reason, galling does not take place in *pure* rolling, since there is no surface-parallel relative motion to spread a welded patch to multi-asperity dimensions. Galling in combined rolling-and-sliding contact increases in severity as the slide/roll velocity ratio increases. Galling in simple sliding is particularly severe as there is no surface-normal motion component to separate the contact.

Galling is a threshold event, such as cracking. If contact conditions are made progressively more severe, a regime of mild wear will *abruptly* convert to one of galling. However, since many variables influence the threshold severity, some of which vary pointwise on a surface (roughness), galling occurrences show considerable scatter in repeated experiments.

Galling is self-aggravating. The transferred metal patch is higher than the ungalled surface and acts as a large and high asperity on which load concentrates. Therefore galling tends to propagate *very rapidly* by incremental transfer of more material onto the galled patch of origin. If galling is not arrested, it can rapidly lead to gross failure by bulk fracture or seizure of parts as the transferred patch of material becomes too high to pass through the contact without destruction.

In contrast to the self-aggravating nature of galling is its ability to 'heal'. If a (temporary) external change drops the severity of the operating conditions below the galling limit, the galled patch may gradually wear down ("heal") and the galling can be arrested. Among the many possible service changes that may arrest galling, are: (a) termination of contact by surface separation in rolling; (b) arrival of a fresh local supply of cool lubricant; (c) cessation of a momentary overload or impact load; (d) a small change in the relative position of contacting parts during the next overrolling; and (e) a deliberate or coincidental reduction of speed or load, or an increase in cooling lubricant flow by the operator.

The most significant operating variable controlling galling is *sliding speed.* Galling occurs above a fixed sliding speed limit for any given set of operating conditions and configurations.

Other significant operating variables are: temperature,

contact load, surface micro-geometry, and boundary lubrication.

8.1.4. Distinctive Appearance

Galling is recognized by observation of the contact surfaces and, if necessary, the immediate subsurface material. Distinctive appearances are described below. In differential diagnosis of galling, it is important to observe that the distinctive appearance of other surface material removal failure modes (mild wear, fretting, surface distress) is *not present.* Depending on the severity of a galling occurrence, the appearance can be recognized on three levels.

Gross seizure. Advanced galling can lead to seizure of relatively moving parts (especially, confined parts such as those of a rolling bearing), producing bulk fracture, bulk plastic deformation and/or gross over-heating failure. The most destructive failures in *rolling bearings* tend to arise from galling. In these cases, detection of the initiating galling event may be difficult or impossible, having been obliterated by subsequent destruction of surfaces. If it is observed, that no other obvious initiating failure is present in a seized assembly (such as a large spall, or loose chunks of material from a major fracture), this strongly suggests that galling caused the seizure. The reverse, however, is not the case—fractures can well be secondary to galling events. In an operating machine, a gross seizure event is often accompanied by violent vibrations, loud noise, rapid temperature rise, slowdown or uneven motion of the moving part, loss of positioning accuracy, etc.

Macroscopic galling. Galling in multiple-asperity dimensions appears as a raised patch of transferred metal "smeared onto" a contact-, or fit-surface. Profile tracing over the galled patch shows raised material. The surface topography of the transferred material is often rough and scored in the sliding direction, as the opposing part surface is forced over it. There are no finishing marks on the transferred patch as it covers over the finishing marks on the underlying original surface.

Macroscopic galling in progress in a machine tends to create clicking or hammering sounds, high-pitched 'screams' or deep 'rumbles,' depending on operating conditions.

Microscopic appearance of galling. A SEM photo of the galled surface shows transferred material plastically smeared onto the original surface. The transfer patch bridges several (up to a great many) asperities. The transferred material is pressed into original surface furrows, may show plastic flow marks, lifted-off edges where welding was incomplete, or cracks, where the plasticity of a material volume was exhausted by the smearing.

Microhardness of the transferred metal is generally higher than the original surface as it is heavily worked (but subsequent tempering is possible).

A (Nital etched) metallographic section through a transferred metal patch generally shows the welded interface and may show off-specification material structure, and/or plastic flow lines.

8.1.5. Causes

General Causes of Galling

• Susceptible material class (metal, thermoplastic polymer);
• Insufficient galling resistance of material due to low hardness, ease of welding, lack of protective surface layer, etc.;
  • Severe sliding in contact (in excess of critical value);
  • Severe normal load (in excess of critical value);
  • Overheating;
  • Unfavorable surface microgeometry (local damage, general roughness);
  • Inadequate boundary lubrication;
  • Chemically aggressive environment (lubricant or atmosphere) removes protective layer.

Galling Causes Specific to Rolling Bearing Contact Components

In the rolling contact:

• Excessive angular acceleration;
• Excessive separator friction;
• Sudden heat imbalance;
• Nick or dent with raised edge.

In roller-end to flange contact:

• Edge contact due to geometry error;
• Excessive normal stress and/or sliding velocity due to axial load or roller skewing.

In Hertz contact element to separator contact:

• Edge contact due to geometry error;
• Excessive separator forces in the contact with a support-element;
• Insufficient clearance between separator and contact component.

Causes of Galling Specific to Cams

Cams and cam followers or tappets suffer the general causes of galling listed above, of which they are particularly vulnerable to the following:

• Sliding. Cam and rolling follower systems undergo high angular accelerations once every cycle as the cam and follower make contact at the start of the lift phase. Cam and tappet systems operate with continuing relative spin.
• Edge contact. Rolling cam followers are difficult to maintain in precise alignment and edge relief is difficult to provide. Tappet wear may eliminate edge clearance.
• Contamination. Cam systems are often lubricated from general circulating oil systems which carry combustion products (in internal combustion engines) and wear products.
• Rough surfaces. Camshafts often are large components; cam geometry is complex and machinery for cam finishing may not permit as good a finish as in smaller, simpler components.
• Nicks. Cam surfaces are external and camshafts are often large components difficult to handle protectively.

Galling Causes Specific to Gears

• High sliding speeds in high-velocity gears, at tip, root, nick or edge;
• Overheating.

8.1.6. Effects of Galling

Galling is often the primary cause of gross seizure of a machine element, due to severe geometric alteration, high normal and tractive contact forces and extreme overheating.

Early stages of galling create operating malfunctions, such as:

• Clicking, hammering or rumbling noise;
• Radial or angular vibrations;
• Positioning inaccuracy in cam systems.

Early stages of galling make the machine element vulnerable to deterioration from small causes:

• Excessive and time-variable forces arising in the galled contact reduce overload safety margin.
• The rough surface of transferred metal is vulnerable to further galling whenever lubrication is impaired.
• Particles worn off the (fast wearing) transferred metal contaminate the lubricant and may precipitate galling at other surface points.
• The transferred material has low resistance to spalling and surface distress. This, combined with local overloading from excess height of transferred material may cause early spalling failure.

Machine elements with controlled clearance (rolling bearings, gears) may loose all clearance over the transferred material, resulting in parasitic loads and failure from that cause.

Rolling bearing separator galling against rolling elements or ring guide surfaces cause these failure risks:

• Separator material transferred onto rolling elements is not contact-fatigue resistant, but can raise the surface causing local overloading.
• Tractive forces exerted on the separator during the galling process may cause separator failure (see FC 01).

8.2. SKIDMARKING. FAILURE CODE: 00.14

8.2.1. Definition

Skidmarking is asperity-scale surface material transfer. It is *analogous* to the macroscopic process of galling (FC 00.13), but *distinct* from galling, in which the elementary material transfer event takes place on a multi-asperity scale. Galling is a cascade process bridging several asperities by transferred material, whereas in skidmarking no cascade of transfers takes place.

8.2.2. Nomenclature

Skidmarking is a recognized failure mode of (high-speed) *rolling* bearings, where it is also called *skidding* or *frosting*. A similar (or identical) failure mode in gears is designated in *some* gear literature as "scuffing," whereas the term "scuffing" in rolling bearing technology is synonymous with galling. In this Atlas, the term skidmarking is adopted, because 'skidding' is also used in bearing technology to describe the kinematic condition of gross sliding in the contact, when, for example, a rolling element fails to maintain epicyclic speed of rotation. Frosting has been used to describe an advanced degree of surface distress (FC 00.17).

8.2.3. Failure Process

A skidmark appears as a multitude of asperity-scale spots of transferred material on the contact surface. It can arise when high sliding velocity is imposed on a Hertzian contact for a self-limited very brief period, during which the relative surface-parallel displacement of the contacting components on each other is less than typical asperity spacings, so that the cascading transfer of material characterizing galling has no opportunity to develop.

In *rolling bearings,* this circumstance can arise if a rolling body (ball, roller) orbits without maintaining epicyclic rolling velocity (such as, when contact loads are small and separator friction high) and is then suddenly accelerated to epicyclic velocity upon the onset of sharply increased contact load. The tractive forces necessary for the high acceleration may cause skidmarking. Once the rolling body is up to speed, the high tractive forces promptly disappear. If their duration is short enough, skidmarking can result, for longer durations (heavy rolling elements), outright galling may take place.

In *gears,* skidmarking (scuffing) may occur in the sliding zones of the tooth contact, for slide/roll ratios insufficient to cause galling.

Visible skidmarking builds up gradually as opposed to galling which can occur as a single catastrophic event. Individual marks are of asperity dimensions. If the precipitating condition repeats itself (typically once per separator revolution), a pattern of skidmarks develops.

Since an existing skidmark is a natural starting point for a new mark during the next cycle, skidmarks tend to line up in rows in the sliding direction. Since the elementary skidmark is small, an extension of a row of marks is easily halted by a scratch or furrow in the surface which crosses the sliding direction.

NOTE: Based on similarities in appearance, it has been proposed that skidmarking is, in part, the result of *cavitation* effects in the EHD film, under conditions of low or fast-changing load. No confirming evidence has been published.

8.2.4. Distinctive Appearance

To the unaided eye, skidmarks appear as circumscribed macroscopic areas on the contact surface, having a distinctive "frosted-glass" appearance. Under high magnification, skidmarks are asperity-size weld spots lined up in streaks running in the sliding direction. The edge of a skidmarked area may be feathered if it extends on an un-

interrupted surface, or cut off by a surface furrow (common on balls which have furrows running in random directions).

In an etched metallographic section, (prepared after overplating of the surface for the preservation of a sharp edge at the intersection of section and surface), skidmarks may appear as rehardened welded-on material overlaying a tempered surface. Aside from its small scale, this appearance is similar to that of galling (FC 00.13), *but not of surface distress* (FC 00.17) which shows no sign of welding.

8.2.5. Causes

Effect of galling sensitivity factors, (such as roughness, boundary lubrication and temperature) upon skidmarking are not well documented, but likely.

In *rolling bearings,* skidmarks are the consequence of kinematic anomalies in the motion of rolling bodies, for example:

- Slowdown of rolling body autorotation under low contact load (and significant separator friction), followed by a brief acceleration when load steps up.
- In a high speed bearing, abrupt change of epicyclic rolling body speed upon a step changed in load.

In cam and roller-follower systems, skidmarking is possible at the entrance to the lift lobe where the follower must rapidly accelerate, and also at other angular locations if rapid rolling-speed changes are forced by the cam profile. *Galling* (FC 00.13) may occur if acceleration is of longer duration.

In *gearing,* skidmarking (scuffing) has been observed in slow-speed, smooth-surface, substantially loaded gears operating below the galling limit.

8.2.6. Effects of Skidmarking

In *rolling bearings and cams:*

- Skidmarked surfaces are rougher than as-manufactured surfaces (especially on balls), accelerating failures influenced by EHD film ratio, such as surface distress, surface initiated spalling and wear. They are, for the same reason, more prone to gross galling.
- The material in a skidmark is severely plastically worked, rehardened and probably microcracked, making it much less resistant to surface-origin contact fatigue (surface distress and surface-origin spalling).
- A skidmarked high-speed bearing is more noisy and vibratory than an intact bearing.
- Friction between a skidmarked rolling body and the separator may be greater than normal. Separator wear, or overheating or both may result.

In *gearing,* skidmarking (scuffing) is not considered catastrophic failure. However, it may act as precursor to more severe wear, galling or contact fatigue failures.

Cross-index of Secondary Failure Codes

Failure code	Plate No
00.13.01	8.13
00.13.02	8.2
	8.6
	8.7
	8.14
	13.3
	13.9
	13.13
00.13.1	6.36
	10.6
	15.37

Failure code	Plate No
00.13.2.1	8.21
	13.12
	13.15
	15.34
00.13.2.1.1	7.35
	13.5
00.13.2.1.1.2	15.38
00.13.2.1.2	5.5
	10.6
00.13.2.3	8.2
00.13.3	10.17

Plates

DATA
Plate No: 8.1
Archive No: 093-019
Image type: view of sectioned ring
Scalebar = 20 mm (micros: ±20%,
others: +100%, -50%)
Component: SRB; IR, run
Speed:
Load:
Lubrication:
Failure Code1: 00.13.1.2 Galling from
rapid motion origin, fit surface
Failure Code2: -
Failure Code3: -
Failure Code4: -

DESCRIPTIONS
FAILURE DESCRIPTION: Multiple circumferential galling streaks cover an IR bore due to rapid sliding on shaft under load. Galling of this magnitude destroys bore dimension and may initiate bulk cracking. Rapid rotation in an unlubricated bore may cause overheating.

IMAGE DESCRIPTION: On grey-appearing original bore surface, a dense overlay of light-colored circumferential streaks with ragged edges. These are the galling marks. On closer inspection, patches of transferred metal would be visible.

SUSPECTED CAUSES: Insufficient interference fit between IR bore and shaft seat in a bearing operating with radial load rotating with respect to the innerring, causes epicyclic rotation of ring on shaft. The higher the load and the looser the shaft fit, the more rapid is the rotation. When the sliding velocity becomes excessive, galling sets in.

DATA
Plate No: 8.2
Archive No: 027-152
Image type: view
Scalebar = 10 mm (micros: ±20%,
others: +100%, -50%)
Component: DGBB; IR, run
Speed: 100 KdN
Load:
Lubrication: grease, 60 °C
Failure Code1: 00.13.2.1 Rolling
surface galling
Failure Code2: 00.13.02 Extensive
galling
Failure Code3: 00.18.3 Brinelling
Failure Code4: 00.13.2.3 Galling at
guiding-part contact surface

DESCRIPTIONS
FAILURE DESCRIPTION: Massive galling seizure, possibly due to lubrication failure. Groove shows extensive material transfer, rolldown, Brinell marks at ball spacings and galling on lands from separator contact. This is a gross failure.

IMAGE DESCRIPTION: At extreme S, ring was cut, presumably for dismounting. Ball groove is rolled out to irregularly larger radius. In W groove half, extensive deposited laminae of transferred metal. In groove bottom, several elliptical depressions are brinell marks from wedged balls. Land surfaces near groove show circumferential streaks of transferred material from separator rubbing after deformation.

SUSPECTED CAUSES: Loss of lubricant, galling, separator deformation and rubbing on lands, separator fracture, wedging of separator elements under balls, and brinelling of groove are the likely failure sequence.

DATA
Plate No: 8.3
Archive No: 093-13.1.8
Image type: SEM
Scalebar = 30 μm (micros: ±20%,
others: +100%, -50%)
Component: CRTB; IR, run
Speed: 150 KdN
Load: 2.0 GPa
Lubrication: mineral turbine oil, 100 °C
Failure Code1: 00.13.2.1.1 Rolling
surface galling, no dent or nick visible
Failure Code2: -
Failure Code3: -
Failure Code4: -

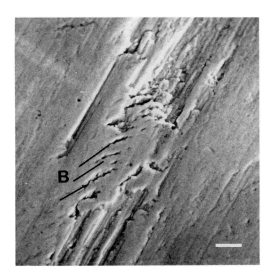

DESCRIPTIONS
FAILURE DESCRIPTION: Microscopic galling event. A gouge
created by an asperity or debris particle sliding over the surface
is filled by plastically flowed, microcracked and welded-on material. An isolated microscopic galling event may "heal" by further over-rolling. Often, however, it initiates additional material
transfer and fails the bearing by heat imbalance failure, seizure,
possibly spalling.

IMAGE DESCRIPTION: Wear marks (and finishing lines) are
straight lines running SW to NE. A wear gouge (50 μm wide)
runs diagonally SW to NE, to the E of marker lines *B*. It is
filled by almost featureless material containing microcracks (at
lines *B*) due to heavy plastic working. The deposited material

results from the galling event. Faint wear lines on galled material suggest that it was rolled over.

SUSPECTED CAUSES: Galling requires a sliding velocity component. (In a CRTB, the sliding component is large over most of
the contact width.) A high asperity or debris particle gouges a
wear mark in sliding. Subsequently, material brought from upstream in the sliding direction is rolled into the gouge and
welded on.

DATA
Plate No: 8.4
Archive No: 093-13.1.11
Image type: SEM, Nital etch
Scalebar = 20 μm (micros: ±20%,
others: +100%, -50%)
Component: CRB, IR, tool steel, run
Speed: 180 KdN
Load:
Lubrication: synthetic polyester oil, 38 °C
Failure Code1: 00.13.2.1.1 Rolling
surface galling, no dent or nick visible
Failure Code2: -
Failure Code3: -
Failure Code4: -

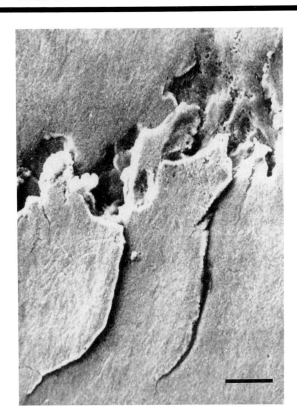

DESCRIPTIONS
FAILURE DESCRIPTION: Laminae of material transferred onto a
surface by galling contain high residual stress from cold working. Upon Nital etch, some residual stresses were relieved by
microcracking, The underlying surface is visible and heavily
worked. Microscopic galling, as shown, may heal. More often,
it initiates large-scale galling, heat imbalance failure, seizure or
spalling.

IMAGE DESCRIPTION: Matte, pebbly grey surface is the etched
surface of the transferred material. At image N, a valley of presumably original surface. In SW quadrant, two curved surface
cracks lift off laminae of transferred metal.

SUSPECTED CAUSES: Galling requires a sliding velocity component. Material brought from upstream in the sliding direction is
rolled onto the surface and welded on. The cold working is severe, leaving high residual stresses making the material vulnerable to cracking. The material is often raised above the sur-

rounding surface, causing stress concentration and initiating
further galling.

DATA
Plate No: 8.5
Archive No: 018-111
Image type: view
Scalebar = 20 mm (micros: ±20%, others: +100%, -50%)
Component: SRB; R, transported
Speed: 0
Load:
Lubrication:
Failure Code1: 00.13.2.1.1 Rolling surface galling, no dent or nick visible
Failure Code2: 00.09.2 Galling from forcible assembly or mounting
Failure Code3: -
Failure Code4: -

DESCRIPTIONS
FAILURE DESCRIPTION: Galling streaks on roller OD-s, from *axial* motion of rollers against rings under load without rotation. Such motion may occur in transporting a bearing mounted in a machine. If there is no axial motion, false brinelling might result; with dominant axial sliding, galling streaks are generated. The bearing is noisy when run and likely to fail in galling or spalling.

IMAGE DESCRIPTION: Near maximum diameter of rollers, short sharp axial lines are galling ('scoring') marks. Metallographic examination would show transferred material.

SUSPECTED CAUSES: Transportation of machinery with bearings mounted, may expose the bearings to relative motion without rotation. The most common resulting failure mode is false brinelling (FC 00.15). However, in the present case, the axial motion was of large enough amplitude to cause galling (scoring) marks by material transfer between the contacting surfaces.

DATA
Plate No: 8.6
Archive No: 093-13.1.1
Image type: light macro
Scalebar = 3 mm (micros: ±20%, others: +100%, -50%)
Component: TBB; IR, run
Speed:
Load:
Lubrication:
Failure Code1: 00.13.2.1.1 Rolling surface galling, no dent or nick visible
Failure Code2: 00.13.02 Extensive galling
Failure Code3: -
Failure Code4: -

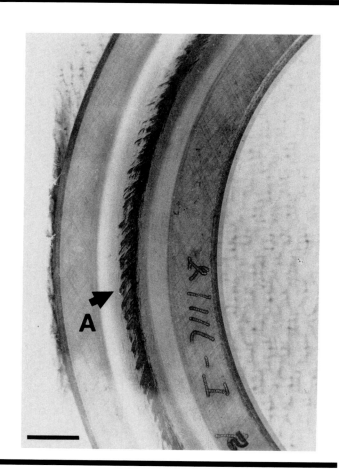

DESCRIPTIONS
FAILURE DESCRIPTION: Ball groove circled by galling streaks running in spin direction, probably from excessive speed for the applied load. The bearing is noisy and may seize, suffer heat imbalance failure or spall.

IMAGE DESCRIPTION: The ball groove is the central arc on the thrust bearing ring ('washer'). Dark-appearing streaks of transferred material (A) run from groove centerline towards groove OD, in the direction of ball spin velocity (image SW to NE). The galled material is shiny, the dark appearance in the image is due to light reflection away from the camera.

SUSPECTED CAUSES: Thrust ball bearings run with high spin to roll velocity ratio. When rotational speed is excessive and load relatively low, centrifugal forces aggravate spin. Galling is a common failure mode, especially under marginal lubrication.

DATA
Plate No: 8.7
Archive No: 093-027x
Image type: view
Scalebar = 40 mm (micros: ±20%, others: +100%, -50%)
Component: CRB; R, run
Speed:
Load:
Lubrication:
Failure Code1: 00.13.2.1.1 Rolling surface galling, no dent or nick visible
Failure Code2: 00.13.02 Extensive galling
Failure Code3: 00.12.3.2.1 Smooth rolling surface wear (finish marks removed)
Failure Code4: -

DESCRIPTIONS
FAILURE DESCRIPTION: Extensive circumferential galling streaks on rolling surface, concentrated on 2/3 of roller path width on both rollers. The rollers are extensively worn on the rolling track. Bearing is noisy and may run hot. With continued galling, seizure is likely.

IMAGE DESCRIPTION: Both rollers (from the same bearing) show wear across rolling path. Many intermittent circumferential galling marks appear matte and light colored.

SUSPECTED CAUSES: The wear and galling appears to have arisen from solid contaminant. Contamination, nicks, skidding of rollers jammed in the separator and bearing misalignment are suspected as galling causes.

DATA
Plate No: 8.8
Archive No: 074-11&12
Image type: a: light microgram, b: metallogram, etched
Scalebar =: a: 100, b: 20 μm (micros: ±20%, others: +100%, -50%)
Component: DGBB; IR, run
Speed:
Load:
Lubrication:
Failure Code1: 00.13.2.1.1 Rolling surface galling, no dent or nick visible
Failure Code2: 00.17.1.2 Microspalling (advanced surface distress)
Failure Code3: 00.19.5 Local structure damage from frictional heating
Failure Code4: -

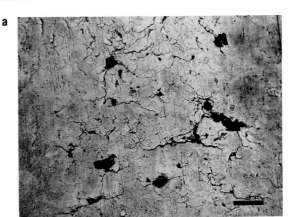

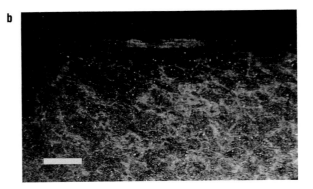

DESCRIPTIONS
FAILURE DESCRIPTION: (a): Material transferred onto surface by galling; subsequently overrolled and fatigued; surface distress microcracking and microspalling. The transferred material is expected to initiate a spall. (b): Material underlying the galled surface suffered structure damage (overtempering). The transfer particle is rehardened or heavily cold worked.

IMAGE DESCRIPTION: (a): Largely featureless grey background is material transferred in galling. Thin N–S lines are wear marks subsequent to galling. Branching irregular lines are microcracks of surface distress in the transferred material. Black spots are surface distress microspalls. (b): S 2/3 of image is cross section, etching darker from overtempering near surface. Transfer particle near image N etches light (worked or rehardened).

SUSPECTED CAUSES: Excessive sliding under high load may initiate galling. Deposited material is heavily cold worked, with high residual stress, leading to early microcracking upon overrolling. This creates surface distress microcracks and microspalls. Sliding events sufficient to cause severe galling may overheat and retemper subsurface material. Transfer particles undergo severe heating and plastic working.

DATA
Plate No: 8.9
Archive No: 093-030
Image type: light macro
Scalebar = 40 mm (micros: ±20%, others: +100%, -50%)
Component: SRB; OR, run
Speed:
Load:
Lubrication:
Failure Code1: 00.13.2.1.1.1 Ring galling at load zone entry
Failure Code2: 00.12.3.2.1.1 Wear track centered in contact
Failure Code3: -
Failure Code4: -

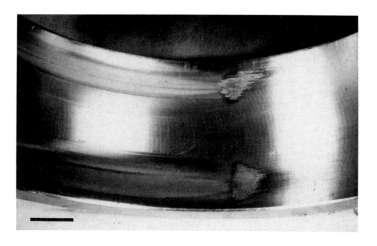

DESCRIPTIONS
FAILURE DESCRIPTION: Both rolling paths in the SRB OR show wear tracks in the load zone. At the load zone entry point, a patch of galling precedes each wear track. The rollers in this large bearing slowed autorotation in the unloaded zone (separator braking) and accelerated rapidly at load zone entry, causing galling. In the load zone, wear tracks, from contaminant or galled roller. Galling may cause seizure, heat imbalance, or spalling.

IMAGE DESCRIPTION: Two matte grey E–W wear tracks, bordered by dark-appearing shiny bands, extend over 3/4 image width, from image W. Over most of their length, the tracks are constant width, but narrow near E end. Just to the E of each track is a light-colored irregular patch of galling outlined in a dark-appearing shiny halo. The tracks mark the load zone in this OR, the galling is at its entrance.

SUSPECTED CAUSES: Rollers in the unloaded zone of a large horizontal-shaft bearing may lose epicyclic autorotation speed due to separator friction. The high accelerating moment needed to restore speed at load zone entry may exceed contact traction and lead to slip, with galling. The wear band may be due to contaminant or ring marking by the galled roller.

DATA
Plate No: 8.10
Archive No: 074-8&9
Image type: a: light macro, b: SEM
Scalebar = a,b: 50 μm (micros: ±20%, others: +100%, -50%)
Component: CRB; IR, run
Speed:
Load:
Lubrication:
Failure Code1: 00.13.2.1.1.2 Contact galling from high acceleration
Failure Code2: 00.12.3.2.2 Scratch marks, kinematic wear marks in rolling surface
Failure Code3: -
Failure Code4: -

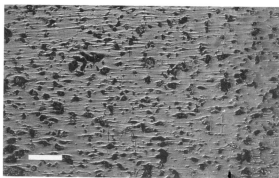

DESCRIPTIONS
FAILURE DESCRIPTION: Patch of thin discontinuous lamina of transferred material on otherwise sound rolling path. Transferred material has been worn by subsequent running. Such galling occurs when sudden acceleration is imposed on roller with insufficient friction, so that momentary high sliding results. If acceleration is not repeated, galling may heal (be worn smooth), which has already started. Further sliding tends to add gross galling at same area.

IMAGE DESCRIPTION: (a): Part of IR roller path. Dark-appearing irregular patch at arrow is galled. Other surfaces show normal wear. (b): Discontinuous layer of transferred metal (shiny) interrupted by many roughly circular patches of original surface, indicating that material transfer occurred in many small increments. Transferred material is higher than surrounding surface and wears preferentially (E–W wear scratches from sliding).

SUSPECTED CAUSES: In some high-speed CRB applications (as in gas turbine engines), load is low and variable (maneuvering loads). Roller autorotation and orbiting speed may slow down when unloaded and is rapidly accelerated when load returns. Under light load, friction does not suffice to prevent high-speed sliding, causing the galling. During continued operation the transferred material wears.

DATA
Plate No: 8.11
Archive No: 107-001a&b&c
Image type: SEM
Scalebar = a: 100, b: 100, c: 10 μm
(micros: ±20%, others: +100%, -50%)
Component: ACBB; B, run
Speed:
Load:
Lubrication: grease, 50 °C
Failure Code1: 00.13.2.1.1.2 Contact galling from high acceleration
Failure Code2: 00.12.3.2.2 Scratch marks, kinematic wear marks in rolling surface
Failure Code3: 00.12.0.1 Adhesive mild wear
Failure Code4: -

DESCRIPTIONS
FAILURE DESCRIPTION: Confined sliding mark on ball surface. The ball spun, and became worn by adhesive wear and, at points of most severe contact, galled. Such damage occurs in high-speed applications when kinematic anomalies precipitate sudden high sliding rates (for example, rapid ball acceleration). As the ball approaches epicyclic speed, sliding rate diminishes and galling occurrences fade out. Galled surfaces tend to gall again, spall or seize.

IMAGE DESCRIPTION: (a): On grey matte background, circular sector of wear marks (dark background, scratchmarks). At W sector edge, several deep tears, extending along arcs, are galling. Galling fades to the E. (b): Galling initiation area, already smoothed by rolling over. (c): Detail of galling, with plastically flown material moved and welded on surface. Small random background scratches are kinematic wear marks.

SUSPECTED CAUSES: If in a high speed bearing, unloading of a ball and/or high separator friction causes drop in ball autorotation speed, and load suddenly returns, the angular acceleration becomes very high. Friction may not suffice to prevent gross sliding, local overheating, asperity welding, tearing and redeposition of material elsewhere on the surface. See also FC 00.14: Skidmarking.

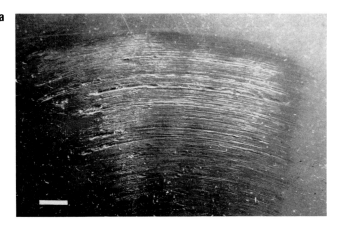

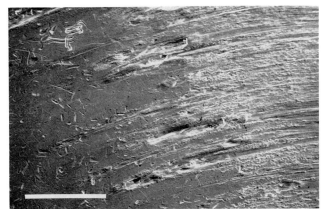

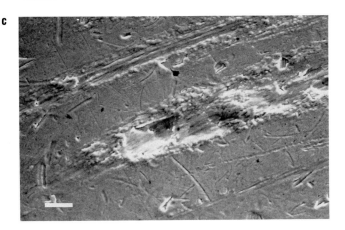

DATA
Plate No: 8.12
Archive No: 002-016c&g
Image type: a: light macro,
b: metallogram, etched
Scalebar = a: 5 mm, b: 400 μm
(micros: ±20%, others: +100%,
-50%)
Component: CRB; OR, 52100 steel, run
Speed: 0.9 MdN
Load: 0.8 GPa
Lubrication: synthetic polyester oil,
149 °C
Failure Code1: 00.13.2.1.2 Rolling
surface galling, dent or nick visible
Failure Code2: 00.18.1.2 Sharp
individual dent(s) from metal debris,
asperities
Failure Code3: 00.04.1 Forming lap
Failure Code4: -

DESCRIPTIONS

FAILURE DESCRIPTION: Foreign steel chip rolled into contact surface; welded in; galling of the chip surface extended laps over original rolling surface. This unusual damage sequence creates high stress concentration and was observed to have caused bulk cracking.

IMAGE DESCRIPTION: (a): In ball groove (S of 'rear land'), round-ended E–W streak of lighter-color material surrounded by dark area, runs E from A–A. It is a rolled-in foreign steel chip. Thin laminae of transferred metal at black arrows.
(b): Metallographic section, Nital+Zephiran etch. Heavily plastically worked chip (swirl flow-lines) in NW image quadrant. Dark weld line to base metal from SW corner to arrow A. Lap at A.

SUSPECTED CAUSES: A steel chip was entrapped on the OR roller path when operation was initiated. It was rolled into the original surface, welded in and laminae were transferred along the edges. Incorporation of such a large chip into a rolling surface during operation is extremely rare.

a

b

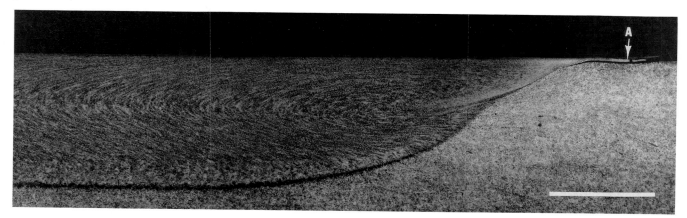

DATA
Plate No: 8.13
Archive No: 093-026
Image type: view
Scalebar = 5 mm (micros: ±20%, others: +100%, -50%)
Component: SRB; R, run
Speed:
Load:
Lubrication:
Failure Code1: 00.13.2.2 Galling of sliding contact surface
Failure Code2: 00.13.01 Incipient galling
Failure Code3: -
Failure Code4: -

DESCRIPTIONS
FAILURE DESCRIPTION: Epicycloidal galling marks on roller thrust face, extending from the roller corner radius to flange height. The marks trace the path of a locally overloaded flange point over the roller thrust face, as it transfers material to that thrust face. In this image, no sign of sharp edge contact is visible, indicating that the geometry is correct. Galling is self-aggravating, may cause seizure, heat imbalance or separator failure.

IMAGE DESCRIPTION: On grey background of roller thrust face, dark-appearing cycloid streaks end radially near the corner and curve to tangential direction at the flange height. The streak material is shiny; dark image is due to light reflection. If magnified, transferred material would be discernible. In the image, an entire half-cycloid is visible since flange and roller face con-form. Otherwise, marks appear only near corner radius or at flange edge level.

SUSPECTED CAUSES: Excessive thrust load, inadequate lubrication, skewed rollers, contamination, rough surfaces. Galling near edge indicates a sharp edge at the flange.

DATA
Plate No: 8.14
Archive No: 018-128
Image type: light macro
Scalebar = 20 mm (micros: ±20%, others: +100%, -50%)
Component: SRB; IR & R, run
Speed:
Load:
Lubrication:
Failure Code1: 00.13.2.2 Galling of sliding contact surface
Failure Code2: 00.13.02 Extensive galling
Failure Code3: 00.12.3.3.1 Wear at edge of sliding contact
Failure Code4: -

DESCRIPTIONS
FAILURE DESCRIPTION: Short epicycloidal galling marks on roller thrust faces, and IR thrust flange face, centered in thrust contact band. Step worn into roller thrust faces, to flange height, as galled workhardened material slides over mating part. The step worn into the roller end suggests excessive contact with IR flange edge. Damage destroys geometry, causes roller skewing and debris that may lead to spalling. Heat imbalance failure is likely.

IMAGE DESCRIPTION: Short angled galling streaks of light color on visible face of IR thrust flange, near both E and W image edges. Depressed annulus worn on roller thrust faces, with angled galling streaks near center of annulus. Streaks may appear light or dark colored depending on lighting.

SUSPECTED CAUSES: Contamination, rough contact surfaces or inadequate lubrication of thrust surfaces, probably acting in combination, produce the galling. Roller skewing shifts contact toward flange edge.

DATA
Plate No: 8.15
Archive No: 099-125a
Image type: light macro
Scalebar = 40 mm (micros: ±20%, others: +100%, -50%)
Component: SG; W, med. hard, run
Speed:
Load:
Lubrication:
Failure Code1: 00.13.3 Tooth contact galling
Failure Code2: -
Failure Code3: -
Failure Code4: -
See also PLATE: 8.17

DESCRIPTIONS
FAILURE DESCRIPTION: Major galling of tooth addendum surface, also designated as scoring. Welding of asperities between pinion and wheel, with immediate tearing as teeth separate. Leaves transferred material on one tooth and a matching pit on the mating tooth. High load, high sliding velocity and insufficient lubrication produce galling on teeth with unsuitable finish and/or hardness. This is a destructive failure.

IMAGE DESCRIPTION: From W edge of gear through 2/3 of image width, multiple radial galling streaks in addendum, appear light colored on grey background. Dark halo around galling is shiny, polished (worn) surface. It appears dark due to lighting. Minimal galling in dedendum.

SUSPECTED CAUSES: Geometrical inaccuracy or misalignment (overload near one sideface), rough surface, insufficient hardness, overload, high speed and inadequate lubrication all may contribute to galling. See also Plate 8.17 showing material transferred by galling between mating locations on pinion and wheel.

DATA
Plate No: 8.16
Archive No: 064-404
Image type: light macro
Scalebar = 30 mm (micros: ±20%, others: +100%, -50%)
Component: HG; W, surface hardened, run
Speed:
Load:
Lubrication:
Failure Code1: 00.13.3 Tooth contact galling
Failure Code2: 00.16.02.4 Incipient spalling, multiple spalls
Failure Code3: 00.12.5.3.1 Abrasive (destructive) tooth wear
Failure Code4: 00.18.1.2 Sharp individual dent(s) from metal debris, asperities

DESCRIPTIONS
FAILURE DESCRIPTION: Advanced tooth surface damage comprising galling, destructive mild wear (probably abrasive), denting and spalling. The galling is concentrated in the addendum, dents and abrasive wear in the dedendum, with spalls in both areas, more toward one side of the gear. The gear may still run, but would be noisy, with increased backlash. It may eventually fracture.

IMAGE DESCRIPTION: Across tooth flanks (especially well shown on tooth starting in SE corner), four distinct contact bands are visible. At the tip, a narrow band with radial wear marks, followed by a band of many axial galling streaks (light) and some black spall craters. After a sharp demarcation at the pitchline, a band of severe debris denting with some radial wear bands and many spall craters (in W), followed by the apparently unworn root.

SUSPECTED CAUSES: Contaminated operation with heavy wear over long period, at speed sufficient to promote galling (at roughened spots?) and eventual spalling.

DATA
Plate No: 8.17
Archive No: 099-126a&b
Image type: a,b: light macro
Scalebar = a,b: 30 mm (micros: ±20%, others: +100%, -50%)
Component: HG; W&P, run
Speed:
Load:
Lubrication:
Failure Code1: 00.13.3 Tooth contact galling
Failure Code2: 00.16.1.2 Surface origin spall
Failure Code3: 00.12.5.3.2 Adhesive (destructive, non-galling) tooth wear
Failure Code4: -

a

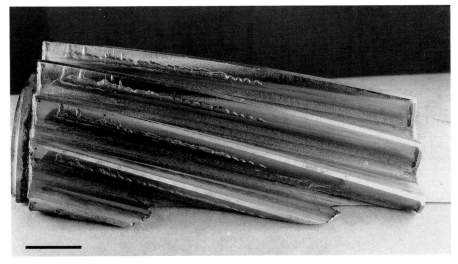

b

DESCRIPTIONS
FAILURE DESCRIPTION: In a mating gear set, asperity origin cracks form in dedendum of gear (wheel) (a). The weakened material is welded to the opposing pinion surface. Transferred metal on pinion (b) forms protrusions, mating with craters left on the wheel. Wear, denting of wheel tooth tips. Gear set is prone to early failure from overstressing of damaged flanks.

IMAGE DESCRIPTION: On wheel (a): cratering (dark pits) on dedendum. On pinion (b): transferred metal streaks on the ad-dendum are generally light colored on the addendum and mate with dedendum spall craters. Tooth tips on (a) are worn and dented.

SUSPECTED CAUSES: High-load, low-speed gear sets, of medium hardness, with poor lubrication, may develop this combined condition of spalling and galling, whereas at high speed, galling, if present, generally occurs before spalls can form, and tends to lead to gross failure.

DATA
Plate No: 8.18
Archive No: 027-178
Image type: view
Scalebar = 4 mm (micros: ±20%, others: +100%, -50%)
Component: ACBB; B, run
Speed: 270 KdN
Load: 1.8 GPa
Lubrication: grease, 60 °C
Failure Code1: 00.14 Skid marking (microscopic severe wear)
Failure Code2: -
Failure Code3: -
Failure Code4: -

DESCRIPTIONS
FAILURE DESCRIPTION: Multiple short skidmarks in random directions on entire ball surface, from many short acceleration events under insufficient load. Skidmarking causes noisy operation in quiet running bearings and may eventually lead to spalling.

IMAGE DESCRIPTION: The mirror-finished ball surface is illuminated by two spotlights (white circle reflections). The light stand and camera reflect as black shapes, covering most of N hemisphere. Elsewhere, the ball surface is grey. Multiple black brush marks in random directions are skidmarks. Three are identified by arrows.

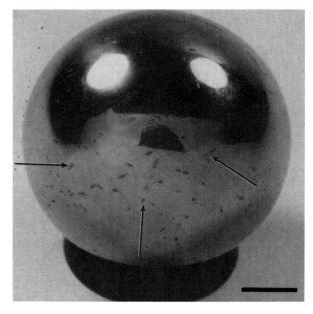

SUSPECTED CAUSES: This angular contact ball bearing must operate under preload. In the present case, preload was insufficient and at each startup of the machine, skidding occurred, making a skidmark. The ball repeatedly changed orientation.

DATA
Plate No: 8.19
Archive No: 007-109
Image type: light metallogram, unetched surface
Scalebar = 400 μm (micros: ±20%, others: +100%, -50%)
Component: ACBB; B, run
Speed:
Load:
Lubrication:
Failure Code1: 00.14 Skid marking (microscopic severe wear)
Failure Code2: 00.02.1 Grinding, honing, lapping furrow
Failure Code3: -
Failure Code4: -

DESCRIPTIONS
FAILURE DESCRIPTION: Repeated skidmarking of a lapped ball surface. Ball assumed three orientations. Skidmarking results from momentary high sliding speed in the contact, arising from insufficient traction to transmit required acceleration. In high-speed bearings, skidmarking may lead to spalling.

IMAGE DESCRIPTION: In this view of the ball surface through a metallograph, light incidence is normal and collimated. Any surface reflecting specularly away from normal appears dark. Unaffected ball surface is grey background. Lapping marks are thin, dark random straight lines. Long skidmark (interrupted parallel black streaks) runs NW to S; another crosses it W–E near center; one each in SE and NE corners, running SW to NE.

SUSPECTED CAUSES: Excessive radial looseness, sudden loss of load or excessive friction in separator contact may reduce

ball autorotation speed, requiring high acceleration when load returns, which leads to skidmarks.

DATA
Plate No: 8.20
Archive No: 027-153
Image type: light macro
Scalebar = 5 mm (micros: ±20%,
others: +100%, -50%)
Component: DGBB; OR, run
Speed: 270 KdN
Load:
Lubrication: grease, 60°C
Failure Code1: 00.14 Skid marking
(microscopic severe wear)
Failure Code2: 00.12.3.2.0.6 (Wear
track for combined radial/axial load)
Failure Code3: -
Failure Code4: -

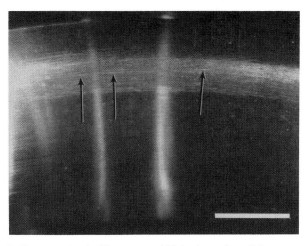

DESCRIPTIONS
FAILURE DESCRIPTION: In the wear track of this OR are numerous short streaks of skidmarking resulting from momentary sliding between ball and ring, due to: insufficient axial preload, or rapid starts, or inadequate lubrication for given operating conditions. The local heating during a sliding event causes EHD film thinning and asperity-scale galling. Skidmarks produce noisy running in quiet bearing applications and may lead to spalling.

IMAGE DESCRIPTION: Except for streaks of reflected illuminating light running N–S, the unworn rolling path surface appears dark. A grey arced band running E–W about 1/4 from N image edge is the wear track. The many whitish circumferential streaks (as at arrows) are the skidmarks. The overall appearance of a skidmarked surface is 'frosted', when seen under no or low magnification.

SUSPECTED CAUSES: This application must operate under axial preload in order to forestall sliding during rapid starts and at moments when the load drops. When preload is below specification, then insufficient traction is available to accelerate the balls for starts and when the intermittent external load returns, resulting in momentary sliding, EHD film overheating and breakdown and asperity-scale galling.

DATA
Plate No: 8.21
Archive No: 018-616
Image type: light macro
Scalebar = 5 mm (micros: ±20%,
others: +100%, -50%)
Component: ACBB; B, run
Speed: >1 MdN
Load:
Lubrication: synthetic polyester oil,
? °C
Failure Code1: 00.14 Skid marking
(microscopic severe wear)
Failure Code2: 00.13.2.1 Rolling
surface galling
Failure Code3: 00.18.1.2 Sharp
individual dent(s) from metal debris,
asperities
Failure Code4: 00.16.1.2.1 Shallow
entry spall from surface point-defect

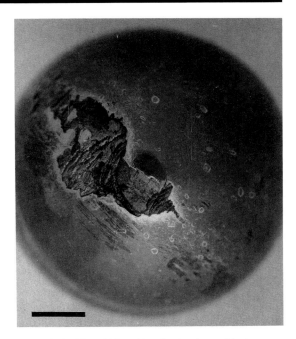

DESCRIPTIONS
FAILURE DESCRIPTION: Failure was initiated as a streak of skidmarks, followed by macro-scale galling, and initial spalling. Spall debris caused multiple dents, decorated by surface distress halos.

IMAGE DESCRIPTION: NW–SE running streaks of darker grey on uniform grey ball surface are skidmarks which, in the vicinity of the large spall appear to progress to macro-scale galling (darker irregular areas) within the light grey 'halo' of surface distress bordering the large, dark, NW–SE running spall crater. Fracture ridges show spall progression. In the E hemisphere, irregular small dents with light-grey surface-distress halo.

SUSPECTED CAUSES: The skidmarking is due to rapid changes in bearing speed and temporary unloading of this turbine engine bearing (as in aircraft maneuvers), during which insufficient tractive forces exist to maintain epicyclic ball autorotation speed. Sliding results. Macro-galling initiates from skidmarks and eventually leads to spalls. Spall debris causes dents. Depressions (dents, craters) deplete the EHD film causing surface distress halos.

DATA
Plate No: 8.22
Archive No: 093-14.1.3&5&8
Image type: a: light microgram,
b: SEM, c: metallog., etched
Scalebar = a: 850, b: 70, c: 12 μm
(micros: ±20%, others: +100%,
-50%)
Component: a,c: ACBB; IR, b: CRB;
OR, run
Speed:
Load:
Lubrication:
Failure code1: 00.14 Skid marking
(microscopic severe wear)
Failure code2: 00.19.5 Local structure
damage from frictional heating
Failure code3: -
Failure code4: -

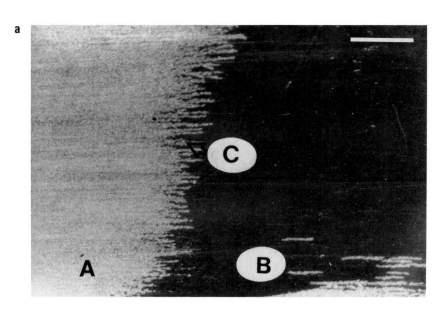

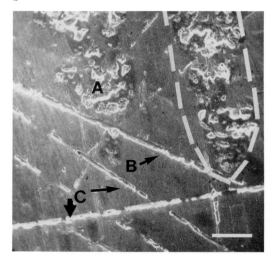

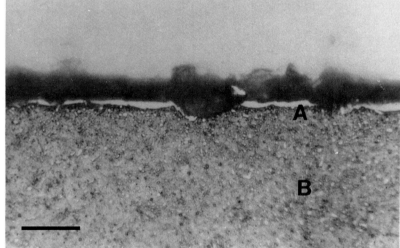

DESCRIPTIONS
FAILURE DESCRIPTION: Skidmarking represents multiple asperity-scale galling events, that do *not* individually grow into macro-galling. This occurs if tractive forces momentarily required to overcome rolling body/ring surface speed differences are excessive so that skidding occurs. Skidmarking may cause structure damage by local overheating. In high-speed applications skidmarking may lead to spalling.

IMAGE DESCRIPTION: (a): Grey, unmarked surface in NE quadrant. White E–W lines in area *A* are skidmarks. At *C*, the skidmark area feathers out. Isolated marks at *B*. (b): Two skidmark streaks (white patches) run S from N image edge (*A* and within dashed oval). Skidmarking stops at honing line *B*. Other honing lines at *C*. (c): Section through rolling surface (area *B*). White, rehardened skidmark deposits on dark tempered matrix at *A*.

SUSPECTED CAUSES: Excessive radial looseness in bearing, or unexpected loss of load or excess friction in separator to rolling body contact may slow down autorotation of rolling body outside the load zone. When load returns, rolling body must accelerate rapidly. Tractive contact force may be insufficient and skidding (gross sliding) occurs momentarily, causing skidmarking. Once rolling speed is reached, sliding stops, so no macroscopic galling occurs.

DATA
Plate No: 8.23
Archive No: 007-111&107&108
Image type: a: view, b, c: SEM
Scalebar = a: 25 mm, b: 200,
c: 40 μm (micros: $\pm$20%, others:
+100%, -50%)
Component: DGBB; IR, run
Speed: varying
Load: 3.5 GPa
Lubrication: grease, temp.: varying
Failure code1: 00.14 Skid marking
(microscopic severe wear)
Failure code2: : 00.20.01.1 Generalized
corrosion
Failure code3: -
Failure code4: -

DESCRIPTIONS
FAILURE DESCRIPTION: (a): Massive skidmarking (microscopic severe wear) of IR ballpath as a result of numerous brief high-acceleration events under high load. Incidental generalized corrosion. (b), (c): Details of skidmarking: asperity scale material transfer with subsequent microspalling, in burnished surface. The cratering will eventually destroy the ring by seizure or fracture. As now seen, ring is still serviceable. (Separator may not be).

IMAGE DESCRIPTION: (a): Varying width streak of mottled (frosted) surface down center of ball path, probably darkened by preferential corrosion after dismounting. Corrosion spotting elsewhere. (b): On featureless burnished surface, angular craters with N–S orientation. (c): Featureless transferred metal laminae in S image half, which overlap at edges (jagged black lines). In N 1/3, microscopic craters and cracks at exfoliated laminae.

SUSPECTED CAUSES: This bearing is used in a naval aircraft arresting gear which operates by absorbing landing aircraft kinetic energy via an arresting cable unwinding from this gear. Bearings undergo high acceleration under high load during each arresting cycle. Skidmarking arises from inability of ball complement to accelerate to epicyclic velocity.

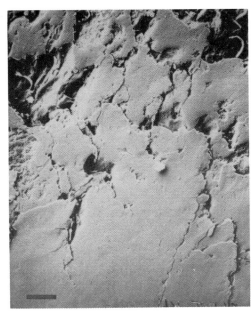

9 FRETTING WEAR

9.1. Definition

Fretting wear is adhesive wear taking place in a nominally static contact under normal load and *microscopic* surface-parallel relative motion. The two types of fretting wear are *(common) fretting* and *false brinelling*. Both are further defined below.

9.2. Nomenclature

In this Atlas, the term 'fretting wear' is adopted to cover both (common) fretting and false brinelling.

9.3. Failure Process

Fretting wear is an adhesive wear process with special features resulting from the confined geometry of the (macroscopically static) contact. Fretting wear requires normal load on the contact, and microscopically small surface-parallel motion, which can be *vibratory* (in common fretting or false brinelling) or *creeping* (in common fretting).

9.4. FRETTING. FAILURE CODE: 00.15.1

9.4.1. Definition

Fretting (common fretting) is defined as fretting wear in a conforming contact (typically a fit interface).

9.4.2. Nomenclature

Fretting wear in a conforming contact is designated (common) fretting. (The word 'wear' is not used for this case.) A commonly used alternative designation is *fretting corrosion.* This latter designation is not used in the Atlas, to avoid possible confusion with chemical attack (corrosion) unrelated to fretting.

9.4.3. Failure Process

Fretting (common fretting) occurs usually in fit interfaces that transmit radial (or combined radial and axial) load moving with respect to the fitted pair, as between bearing ring, gear or cam and fitted shaft, or bearing ring and housing. The fit must be tight enough so that rapid "spinning" of the fitted part is prevented but not so tight as to prevent entirely a slow creep (or reversing motion) in the fit interface. This creeping motion creates loose wear particles which, for common steels, oxidize in the (oxygen-starved) fit interface to become a blackish red, tightly adhering layer covering portions or all of the fit interface. This color justifies the name 'fretting corrosion', although the fretted oxide has been found to be chemically different from the brown stain of common corrosion formed on free surfaces in the presence of moisture.

9.4.4. Distinctive Appearance

A fretted (fit) surface is a patchwork of three types of appearance:

• Oxidized patches varying in color from dark reddish to virtual black;
• Burnished areas of metallic color in which the original finishing marks are effaced; these areas may show wear marks in the sliding direction;
• Areas with original finishing marks.

There may be galled areas (FC 00.13) interspersed with the others, if the interface underwent rapid sliding.

Under the (scanning electron) microscope, fretted areas (after light etching to remove the adhering oxide) show micropits, where fretted particles have been worn off, and/or clusters of short scratches, made by the wear particles during further motion.

9.4.5. Causes

The controlling *operating* parameters in (common) fretting are: normal contact pressure and the specifics of the microscopic surface-parallel motion (total displacement or number of reversing cycles, amplitude).

The controlling *contact* parameters in fretting are not

completely identified. Fit interference, which controls contact pressure and influences surface-parallel motion, is the dominant parameter. Surface material and micro-geometry also exert influence, as follows:

Hard materials appear to fret less than lower hardness materials of the same composition. Thus, hardened steel parts (bearing rings) fret less than soft steel shafts or housings.

Material composition appears to have an effect on fretting:

• Cast iron housings fret less than soft steel housings.
• Hard-chromium plated shafts or housings fitted to hardened bearing rings are more fret-resistant than soft steel shafts and housings. It is not clear whether the chromium material, or its hardness are the principal factor.

Two smooth surfaces in contact appear to fret less than rougher surfaces.

Certain plastic coatings on a fit surface retard fretting.

Suitable chemical coatings, like phosphate coatings, retard fretting.

Certain compounded lubricants are believed to alleviate fretting.

Little information has been published regarding fretting of ceramic rings in (metal) housings. Fretting is believed to occur.

NOTE: Most experience with fretting is related to corrodible steel and cast iron fit surfaces. "Stainless" steel and non-ferrous metals also fret, but the oxidation to visible reddish oxide is not observed.

Rolling Bearings

Fretting in the radial fit surfaces between rolling bearing rings and shafts or housings is a widespread phenomenon not necessarily regarded as a (disabling) failure.

Fitting practice of rolling bearing rings distinguishes three conditions:

1. *Load of stationary direction* with respect to the fit interface. In order to permit axial alignment of the bearing, such a fit is often made with *positive looseness*. The stationary load direction tends to hold ring and mounting part in a fixed relationship and fretting can be avoided. If the load *substantially* changes direction with some frequency and the fit is loose, rapid spinning in the fit surface is likely, producing polishing and galling, but not fretting. Bearing technology generally holds that this spinning is not effectively countered by end clamping; it may, at the risk of cracks, be prevented by keying. *Small* changes in load direction, that occur with some frequency, may precipitate fretting.

2. *Load of moving direction* with respect to the fit interface. Due to the traveling deflection under the moving load, the ring tends to creep circumferentially with respect to the mounting part and fretting is probable. To limit fretting, a fit for moving load is almost always made with *interference* (negative looseness). In tight fitted moving-load interfaces, fretting decreases with increased fit interference. However, excessive tensile hoop stresses in relatively thin walled rings, and mounting difficulties, limit the permissible fit interference so that fretting may not be totally avoidable.

3. A special case is where *both* rings in a bearing see loads moving with respect to the fit interface (as in shaker-screens). Interference fits for both rings may be impractical due to the resulting inability to accommodate differential thermal expansion of machine components. In these cases, surface coatings may be helpful in counteracting excessive fretting.

Gears and Cams

Gears or cams are generally not fitted into housings (with the possible exception of an internal gear), but often are mounted on shafts. The load direction in the fit interface of a gear or cam on a shaft is virtually never stationary.

Gears transmit torque so that they are often keyed to shafts. Even so, fretting is occasionally observed, from causes identical to those listed for bearings.

Cams undergo torque whenever the normal contact force on the cam lobe fails to intersect the shaft axis, that is, along all ramps, requiring fitting practices similar to gears.

9.4.6. Effects of (Common) Fretting

Fretting in a load carrying fit interface may have the following effects:

• Fretting may prevent smooth disassembly by greatly increasing friction against axial removal of a bearing ring or gear from shaft or housing. The obstruction may be severe enough to cause fractures or require cutting of rings or gears.
• Fretting roughens the surface and damages the fit geometry causing increased rate of fretting, or spinning with wear or galling. The geometric distortion may suffice to weaken load support and lead to ring or gear cross section cracking.
• A severely fretted surface may contain microcracks. If the component is subject to cyclic bending stresses (for example, a bearing ring, gear or shaft), bulk fatigue cracking may initiate from these microcracks. This is a common failure progression sequence.

9.5. FALSE BRINELLING. FAILURE CODE: 00.15.2

9.5.1. Definition

False brinelling is defined as fretting wear in a Hertzian contact.

9.5.2. Nomenclature

There is no common alternative designation for false brinelling.

9.5.3. Failure Process

False brinelling describes the creation of a surface depression in a loaded, macroscopically static Hertzian contact, by the fretting wear produced between the contacting ele-

DATA
Plate No: 9.9
Archive No: 027-282
Image type: color view [SEE IMAGE IN APPENDIX.]
Scalebar = 20 mm (micros: ±20%, others: +100%, -50%)
Component: ACBB; IR, run
Speed: 160 KdN
Load:
Lubrication: grease, 60 °C
Failure code1: 00.15.1.3 Fit sideface fretting
Failure code2: -
Failure code3: -
Failure code4: -

[*See Image in Appendix*]

DESCRIPTIONS
FAILURE DESCRIPTION: Thrust sideface of ACBB IR shows an intermittent circumferential streak of fretting corrosion due to movement under axial load against shaft thrust shoulder. Serves as indication of axial load. Not a failure.

IMAGE DESCRIPTION: On thrust face of IR, a streak of reddish-brown fretting corrosion forms a dashed circumferential line. Minor fretting elsewhere. Dark band next to bore is (unground) corner radius.

SUSPECTED CAUSES: IR moving slightly in interference fit against shaft is pressed against thrust shoulder under combined load with significant thrust component. Fretting may result.

DATA
Plate No: 9.10
Archive No: 014-61
Image type: view
Scalebar = 20 mm (micros: ±20%, others: +100%, -50%)
Component: TRB; IR, transported
Speed: 0 dN
Load:
Lubrication:
Failure code1: 00.15.2 False brinelling on contact surface
Failure code2: -
Failure code3: -
Failure code4: -

DESCRIPTIONS
FAILURE DESCRIPTION: Incipient false brinelling marks at roller spacing, on the rolling path of a TRB IR (cone). Marks as mild as these may cause no noisy running or failure.

IMAGE DESCRIPTION: Diffuse axial streaks on roller path, at roller spacing. Marks become visible by changing the luster of the surface as original finishing lines are obliterated. Profile tracing may show little depth. Microscopy would indicate change in, or removal of, some finishing lines.

SUSPECTED CAUSES: Transportation of a machine (such as a road vehicle) with the bearing mounted and weight-loaded (as in a wheel bearing) imposes small oscillatory motions on stationary bearing.

DATA
Plate No: 9.11
Archive No: 014-131
Image type: light microgram
Scalebar = 1 mm (micros: ±20%, others: +100%, -50%)
Component: TRB; OR, transported
Speed: 0 dN
Load:
Lubrication:
Failure code1: 00.15.2 False brinelling on contact surface
Failure code2: -
Failure code3: -
Failure code4: -

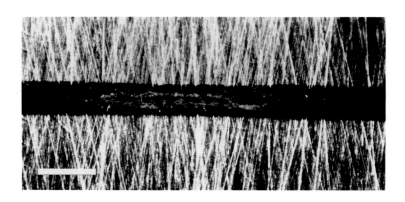

DESCRIPTIONS
FAILURE DESCRIPTION: False brinell mark from roller line contact on OR. Cross-hatch finishing marks obliterated by fretting. False brinelling may cause noisy running bearing and if severe, may lead to spalling.

IMAGE DESCRIPTION: Background shows cross-hatch honing pattern of OR roller path. N–S band running along image center is false-brinell mark. No cross-hatch marks in it. Dark and light areas in mark may be due to light reflection or possibly fretting corrosion.

SUSPECTED CAUSES: False brinelling occurs in stationary Hertzian contacts under load, subject to vibration which causes motions on the asperity scale. Transport of automobiles on carrier vehicles may cause false brinelling in wheel bearings.

DATA
Plate No: 9.12
Archive No: 093-045
Image type: light microgram
Scalebar = 300 μm (micros: ±20%, others: +100%, -50%)
Component: DGBB; IR, transported
Speed: 0 dN
Load:
Lubrication:
Failure code1: 00.15.2 False brinelling on contact surface
Failure code2: -
Failure code3: -
Failure code4: -

DESCRIPTIONS
FAILURE DESCRIPTION: False brinelling has removed finishing marks over a patch in the contact area, leaving irregular transverse markings. False brinelling arises from vibratory load, mostly in the absence of bearing rotation, as a fretting wear process. It creates noisy running bearings and may lead to spalling.

IMAGE DESCRIPTION: Finishing lines run E–W. Two deep, black scratchmarks (in NE and SE image corners) are artifacts. In image center, finishing lines are missing due to fretting over oblong area extending E–W (the contact major axis is N–S). Irregular N–S markings in the false-brinelled area were produced in the fretting process.

SUSPECTED CAUSES: False brinelling occurs in (nearly) stationary Hertzian contacts subject to vibration under load, causing motions on the asperity scale. The circumferential elongation of the false-brinelled area suggests that the ball positions shifted during the fretting process.

DATA
Plate No: 9.13
Archive No: 107-003a&b&c
Image type: SEM
Scalebar = a: 1000, b: 200,
c: 40 μm (micros: ±20%, others:
+100%, -50%)
Component: ACBB; IR, vibratory test
Speed: 0 dN
Load:
Lubrication: grease, 30 °C
Failure code1: 00.15.2 False brinelling
on contact surface
Failure code2: -
Failure code3: -
Failure code4: -
See also PLATEs: 9.11 & 9.12 & 9.16

DESCRIPTIONS
FAILURE DESCRIPTION: False-brinelling along outline of Hertzian contact subjected to strictly normal vibratory load, no rotation. Fretting starts at contour, predominantly near contact endpoints, where sliding is greatest. False brinelling begins with smoothing of finishing lines and progresses to cratering. Appearance of craters differs from surface distress: no steep crater walls. (Compare Plate 9.16.)

IMAGE DESCRIPTION: (a): View of entire contact ellipse, major axis running NW–SE and outlined as a light-colored elliptical line on darker background of finishing lines running SW–NE. (b): Ellipse end expands and contracts with load. Smoothing of finishing lines (NE of craters). Craters outlining minimum and maximum position and dotting the area between. (c): Smoothed finishing lines and craters at extreme of ellipse tip.

SUSPECTED CAUSES: Contact subjected to stationary vibratory loading in normal direction. Size of contact ellipse changes with load, with sliding due to toroidal geometry of contact area. Sliding is most pronounced at contact endpoints. This microscopic sliding produces the fretting phenomenon. Overview of false brinell mark in Plates 9.11 and 9.12.

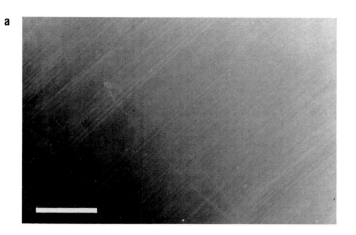

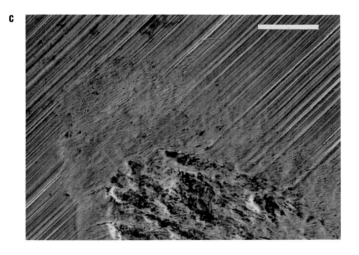

DATA
Plate No: 9.14
Archive No: 007-103
Image type: SEM
Scalebar = 20 μm (micros: ±20%, others: +100%, -50%)
Component: ACBB; OR, martensitic stainless, run
Speed:
Load:
Lubrication: synthetic polyester oil, ? °C
Failure code1: 00.15.2 False brinelling on contact surface
Failure code2: 00.06.1.3 Primary carbide
Failure code3: -
Failure code4: -

DESCRIPTIONS
FAILURE DESCRIPTION: Removal of matrix material by false brinelling type of fretting. Primary carbides in martensitic stainless steel are large and very hard, thus fret less and protrude. This gyroscope gimbal bearing undergoes slow intermittent motion, overlaid by small amplitude oscillation (hunting). EHD film cannot form, fretting occurs over entire overrolled surface. The bearing looses precision and friction control is impaired.

IMAGE DESCRIPTION: Image shows fretted contact surface. S 2/3 of image shows E–W ridging from false-brinelling type of

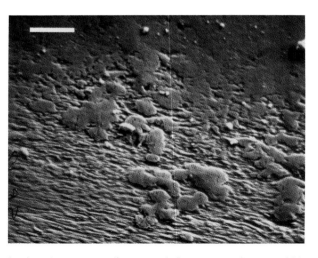

fretting. Large protruding smooth lumps are primary carbides. N image edge appears less fretted, but finishing lines have been obliterated.

SUSPECTED CAUSES: Gyroscope gimbal bearings have extremely fine finish and require high precision. They are often made of martensitic stainless steel. Due to small amplitude oscillation (hunting), superimposed on intermittent slow motions, fretting (false brinelling) conditions exist. Fretted matrix material is interspersed with primary carbides.

DATA
Plate No: 9.15
Archive No: 093-15.2.1
Image type: view
Scalebar = 15 mm (micros: ±20%, others: +100%, -50%)
Component: SABB; OR, transported, run
Speed:
Load:
Lubrication:
Failure code1: 00.15.2 False brinelling on contact surface
Failure code2: 00.12.3.2.1.1 Wear track centered in contact
Failure code3: 00.15.1 Fretting (fretting corrosion)
Failure code4: -

DESCRIPTIONS
FAILURE DESCRIPTION: Circular false brinell marks at ball spacing in the spherical ball path of the OR. Wear tracks from subsequent running connect the false brinell marks. Fretting corrosion on OD. False brinell marks, when severe, as here, cause noisy running and early spalling. May also damage separator through high ball contact loads. Visible wear track and OD fretting are not failures.

IMAGE DESCRIPTION: OD surface of OR shows circumferential black streaks of fretting corrosion over at least 1/2 circumference. Ring may have shifted in housing. ID surface is spherical ball path, with regularly spaced dark and light circular marks in both ball rows, as at A and B, from false brinelling. Change in luster of ball path between false brinell marks is wear track, presumably from running before or after stationary damage.

SUSPECTED CAUSES: Bearing was probably radially preloaded since false brinell marks extend over at least 1/2 circumference. Bearing was exposed to vibratory motion in stationary condition, probably during transport of the machine containing the bearing. Later, bearing was run, causing the wear path (aggravated by false brinell marks), and fretting bands on OD.

DATA
Plate No: 9.16
Archive No: 107-002a&b&c
Image type: SEM
Scalebar = a: 300, b: 100, c: 10 μm
(micros: ±20%, others: +100%,
-50%)
Component: ACBB; IR, mounted,
transported, run
Speed:
Load:
Lubrication: grease, 30 °C
Failure code1: 00.15.2 False brinelling
on contact surface
Failure code2: 00.17.1.2 Microspalling
(advanced surface distress)
Failure code3: -
Failure code4: -
See also PLATEs: 9.11 & 9.12 & 11.16

DESCRIPTIONS
FAILURE DESCRIPTION: False brinelling, that is, fretting of stationary ball/race contact under vibration. Finishing marks completely obliterated, extremely fine microspalling of asperity contacts, constituting surface distress. This wheel bearing,
transported on a vehicle, was subject to angular oscillation.
False brinell marks cause noisy running and may lead to early
macro-spalling. See Plate 9.11 and 9.12 for overview of false
brinelling.

IMAGE DESCRIPTION: (a): Overview of false brinelled patch,
appearing shot blasted. A few N–S finishing lines outside
patches. (b): Medium magnification view of false brinell. Dense
cluster of black 'pits' in featureless plastically worked, worn
surface. (c): High magnification of the 'pits' shows them to be
microspall craters. These individual craters cannot be distinguished from surface distress microspalls (See Plate 11.16).
Macro-configuration is diagnostic.

SUSPECTED CAUSES: False brinelling occurs in stationary Hertzian contacts under load, subject to vibration which causes
motions on the asperity scale. Subsequent running may have
superimposed surface distress (FC 00.17).

a
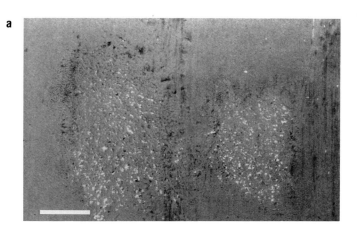

b
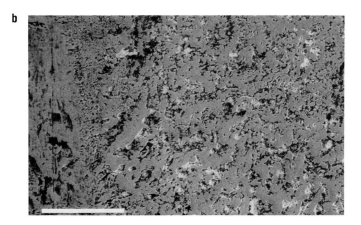

c
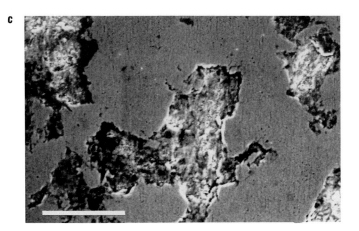

DATA
Plate No: 9.17
Archive No: 018-120
Image type: view
Scalebar = 20 mm (micros: ±20%, others: +100%, -50%)
Component: SRB; OR, run
Speed: Load:
Lubrication:
Failure code1: 00.15.2 False brinelling on contact surface
Failure code2: 00.20.1 Corrosion stain
Failure code3: -
Failure code4: -

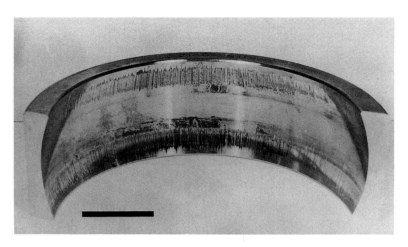

DESCRIPTIONS
FAILURE DESCRIPTION: Dense parallel axial marks of false brinelling in both roller paths, concentrated in a load zone. Scattered corrosion stains in bands on spherical ID of OR, mostly in two bands accompanying fretted strips. Dense rows of false brinell marks indicate vibration superimposed on rotation, as in a vibratory application. Water ingress into the lubricant may explain the corrosion. Early spalling expected.

IMAGE DESCRIPTION: In the spherical ID of the cut OR, two circumferential bands of light and dark-colored sharp axial marks are from false brinelling. Black patches in the ID, concentrating in two bands inboard from false brinell marks are corrosion stains. At image S, center, these overlap false brinell marks, suggesting corrosion at a later time. Contrast with electric erosion fluting (FC 00.21) showing molten surface craters.

SUSPECTED CAUSES: Vibratory machinery (for example, shaker screens), subject shaft support bearings to heavy vibratory forces which are not synchronous with roller passage. False brinell marks can initiate at random locations. A self-reinforcing process is postulated to explain serrated, rather than smooth fretting. Shaker screens often operate wet, and water ingress into the lubricant can cause corrosion.

DATA
Plate No: 9.18
Archive No: 087-031
Image type: view
Scalebar = 10 mm (micros: ±20%, others: +100%, -50%)
Component: CRB: OR, transported
Speed: 0 dN
Load:
Lubrication:
Failure code1: 00.15.2 False brinelling on contact surface
Failure code2: 00.20.1.3 Contact corrosion
Failure code3: 00.12.3.2 Wear in rolling surface
Failure code4: -

DESCRIPTIONS
FAILURE DESCRIPTION: Bearing stored (in mounted condition) with insufficient rust protection suffered patchy corrosion staining on roller path, indicating corrosive lubricant or preservative. Rollers oscillated through several degrees, removing stain under them. In some positions, oscillation sufficed to cause false brinelling. The bearing is expected to fail from wear, or spalling, if operated.

IMAGE DESCRIPTION: Black patches in the roller path are corrosion (label). Wide rectangles at roller spacing are worn clear of corrosion. False brinelling (label) consists of narrow rectangles with a luster different from the intact surface. Bearing, mounted when transported, shifted position to wear away corrosion over the wide rectangles. In some position(s), false brinelling occurred.

SUSPECTED CAUSES: Mounted bearing transported with insufficient rust protection and exposed to substantial oscillation, some of which persisted long enough to create false brinelling.

DATA
Plate No: 10.8
Archive No: 007-112
Image type: light macro
Scalebar = 5 mm (micros: ±20%, others: +100%, -50%)
Component: TRB; IR, run
Speed: 50 KdN
Load: 2.1 GPa
Lubrication: mineral oil based grease, 0–40 °C
Failure code1: 00.16.01.2.2 Spalling at contact edge, from geometry error
Failure code2: 00.16.02.4 Incipient spalling, multiple spalls
Failure code3: 00.18.1.3 Multi-fragment dent (brittle contaminant)
Failure code4: 00.18.1.2 Sharp individual dent(s) from metal debris, asperities
See also PLATE: 12.3

DESCRIPTIONS
FAILURE DESCRIPTION: Several independently initiated spalls are widest at the small-end undercut of IR (cone) roller path and taper to a point. Extensive debris denting of roller path, with larger dents from spall debris and many point-size dents probably from external contaminant (dust). Denting does not appear to be the failure cause; edge loading is. Bearing will soon fail by progressive spalling. See PLATE 12.3 for denting detail.

IMAGE DESCRIPTION: Roller path of TRB IR (cone) is seen as a shiny surface between undercuts and flanges. N side is 'small end.' Innumerable fine indentations, as from dust, are visible on the roller path; numerous larger (1 mm) dents appear to be from spall debris. From small-end undercut extend several spall craters, widest at edge and tapering, indicating origination from edge load.

SUSPECTED CAUSES: Taper error, from manufacturing or from mounting on tapered shaft, can concentrate load at one roller path edge. Insufficient roller crowning (edge relief) of roller and/or too wide undercut accentuate edge contact. Contaminant denting from dust ingress occurred in this truck wheel bearing and was aggravated by larger debris as from spalls.

DATA
Plate No: 10.9
Archive No: 003-010
Image type: view
Scalebar = 5 mm (micros: ±20%, others: +100%, -50%)
Component: CRB; R&IR&S, run
Speed: 60 KdN
Load: 1.5 GPa
Lubrication: synthetic polyester oil, 110 °C?
Failure code1: 00.16.01.2.2 Spalling at contact edge, from geometry error
Failure code2: 00.16.02.5 Advanced spalling
Failure code3: -
Failure code4: -

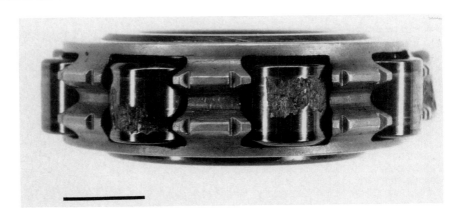

DESCRIPTIONS
FAILURE DESCRIPTION: Two rollers with extensive spalls extending from a line near the roller corner radius to the roller midplane. Rolled-in lines appear on other rollers. The relatively sharp edge of the spalls near the roller corner indicates (and IR examination confirms) edge loading from IR undercuts of excess width. Lines on rollers at IR undercut edge also may indicate undercut edge contact or separator prong wearmarks. A progression of spalls to gross failure is likely.

IMAGE DESCRIPTION: In the machined separator, rollers are held by staked prongs. S half of second roller from W shows large spall with relatively straight S edge. Third roller from W shows spall with straight N edge. First and fourth roller from W both show circumferential light and dark lines located approximately under the separator prongs. Location of the IR undercut (not shown) was observed to match spall edge.

SUSPECTED CAUSES: Excessively wide undercuts on IR roller path of CRB create edge loading because crowning (edge relief) of the roller is not dimensioned to confine contact this far from roller corners. Edge loading initiates spalls that spread toward roller center plane. Either IR edge contact or separator prong contact can mark roller with circumferential lines. Study of separator wear and of roller wearmarks is needed to differentiate the cause.

DATA
Plate No: 10.10
Archive No: 122-6&7
Image type: a,b: SEM
Scalebar = a: 500, b: 100 μm
(micros: ±20%, others: +100%,
-50%)
Component: CRB; IR, run
Speed: 46 KdN
Load: 1.8 GPa
Lubrication: mineral oil, ? °C
Failure code1: 00.16.01.2.2 Spalling at
contact edge, from geometry error
Failure code2: 00.16.03.2 Spall
propagating by re-initiation at surface
Failure code3: -
Failure code4: -

DESCRIPTIONS
FAILURE DESCRIPTION: Contact extending to edge of undercut
on IR, with heavy stress concentration at edge (probably from
edge geometry error), forms dense band of shallow spalls near
edge, with deeper, larger craters extending into the contact
area. The bearing has failed.

IMAGE DESCRIPTION: (a): E–W band with dark and light lines
at image N is undercut. S thereof is a densely microspalled and
rolled down surface. Next adjacent to S are larger spalls of
normal depth, which originated from the microspalled band.
(b): Microspalled band with featureless surface between craters,
at higher magnification. Appearance is similar to advanced surface distress but some craters, 250 μm long, would be untypical of surface distress.

SUSPECTED CAUSES: Improperly dressed grinding wheel may
leave prominent lip adjacent to undercut. When rolled over, the

a

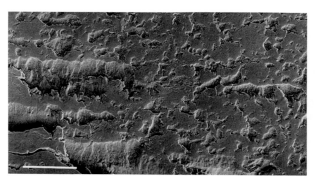

b

lip is heavily overloaded, plastically rolled down and spalls at
the (shallow) depth of high Hertz shear stress in this edge contact. Small depth of stress field makes such spalls virtually indistinguishable from surface distress. Spalled lip initiates normal depth spalls in adjacent normal contact area.

DATA
Plate No: 10.11
Archive No: 027-247
Image type: view
Scalebar = 10 mm (micros: ±20%,
others: +100%, -50%)
Component: ACBB; OR, run
Speed: 160 KdN
Load:
Lubrication: grease, 60 °C
Failure code1: 00.16.01.2.2 Spalling at
contact edge, from geometry error
Failure code2: 00.16.1.1 Subsurface
origin spall (high Hertz shear stress)
Failure code3: 00.15.1.1 Generalized
fretting, radial fit surface
Failure code4: -
See also PLATEs: 10.3 & 10.42

DESCRIPTIONS
FAILURE DESCRIPTION: Narrow, elongated line of spalls on
edge between low land (dam) of the OR, and ball groove. The
dam must remain unloaded for proper function but becomes
loaded if bearing is installed in reverse, so the dam faces the
thrust direction. Prompt spalling and damage to balls occurs.
PLATES 10.3, 10.11 and 10.42 show different spalling modes
in similar bearings.

IMAGE DESCRIPTION: On the inner surface of this OR, the low
land (dam) area is to image E from the groove. A sharp edge
separates it from the (glossy) ball path which extends W to the

dark grey land at the thrust side. Slightly S of image center, is
a row of dark spall craters at the edge. They lie in a circumferential wear track suggesting that the ball rolled over onto the
land. Normal fretting visible on OD.

SUSPECTED CAUSES: If an unsymmetrical ACBB (one land high
for thrust, the other low for assembly) is installed in reverse
and thrust loaded, the load overrides the groove edge and
spalling failure at, or just over the edge occurs.

DATA
Plate No: 10.12
Archive No: 001-8
Image type: light microgram
Scalebar = 500 μm (micros: ±20%, others: +100%, -50%)
Component: ACBB; IR, run
Speed: 1 MdN
Load: 1.4 GPa
Lubrication: synthetic polyester oil, 120 °C
Failure code1: 00.16.01.2.2 Spalling at contact edge, from geometry error
Failure code2: 00.16.1.1.1 Steep entry spall (subsurface origin)
Failure code3: 00.18.2.1 Rolled-in line at contact edge
Failure code4: -
See also PLATE: 10.5

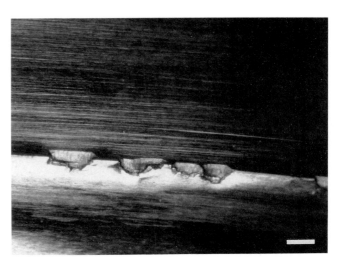

DESCRIPTIONS
FAILURE DESCRIPTION: Rolled-up groove edge from edge contact under heavy load. The edge has spalled from subsurface origin fatigue due to the high edge-stresses. The spalls may inflict further damage on balls (See PLATE 10.5). The bearing has failed.

IMAGE DESCRIPTION: A bright E–W band S of image center divides the ball track lying to the S from the land lying to the N. The sharp edge of the land is the N boundary of the bright area. Four spall craters with steep walls are visible at the edge. The shadow cast to the N of the edge indicates that the edge is elevated (plastically "rolled up") above the land surface.

SUSPECTED CAUSES: A geometry error in the bearing caused heavy contact between balls and the sharp edge of the IR groove. This edge loading produced a rolling up of the edge above the land surface and subsequent spalling of the IR (see PLATE 10.5) by subsurface-origin fatigue due to the high edge stresses.

DATA
Plate No: 10.13
Archive No: 005-17
Image type: SEM, backscatter
Scalebar = 400 μm (micros: ±20%, others: +100%, -50%)
Component: C; CM, run
Speed: 7 m/sec
Load:
Lubrication: mineral oil, 115 °C
Failure code1: 00.16.01.2.2 Spalling at contact edge, from geometry error
Failure code2: 00.18.2.1 Rolled-in line at contact edge
Failure code3: 00.17.1.2 Microspalling (advanced surface distress)
Failure code4: 00.17.1.1 Glazing (incipient surface distress)

DESCRIPTIONS
FAILURE DESCRIPTION: Narrow band of small, shallow spalls at contact edge, in and near a rolled-in line at the edge. Incipient glazing surface distress appears within the contact; advanced glazing and micro-spalling becomes visible as edge is approached. The band of small shallow spalls resulting from sharp edge contact is indistinguishable from surface distress microspalling in the edge area. Large-scale spalling and failure are likely.

IMAGE DESCRIPTION: Finishing marks run E–W. The N image half is outside the contact. A sharp edge delineates N side of dark rolled-in line at contact edge, in which multiple, small (50 μm wide), shallow spall craters are visible. To the S, adjacent to the rolled-in edge, finishing lines are obliterated by surface distress glazing and a few spalls are seen. S 1/3 of image shows incipient glazing.

SUSPECTED CAUSES: Cam follower was not crowned (it was a true cylinder up to the corner radius). This, possibly combined with misalignment, causes sharp edge contact with high stresses, resulting in rolled-in line, followed by spalling. General surface distress due to low EHD film is typical of edge contact.

DATA
Plate No: 10.14
Archive No: 087-021
Image type: light view
Scalebar = 20 mm (micros: ±20%, others: +100%, -50%)
Component: BB (maximum complement); IR & OR, run
Speed:
Load: axial
Lubrication:
Failure code1: 00.16.01.2.3 Spalling at contact edge from thrust load
Failure code2: 00.16.02.5 Advanced spalling
Failure code3: -
Failure code4: -

DESCRIPTIONS
FAILURE DESCRIPTION: Extensive spalling around circumference of IR ball groove, offset axially, as under thrust load and running over loading slot edge. Failure from edge contact at that point has spread over most of the ball groove during extended additional running. This is a gross failure.

IMAGE DESCRIPTION: OR surrounds IR in image. On IR ball path, a band of spall craters covers much of the groove bottom, but is offset to the W side, where the loading slot, ground into the land, is seen. The edge of the slot (labeled "loading notch") extends into the ball groove and was over-

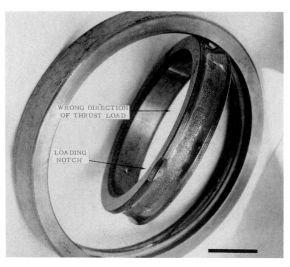

rolled. Direction of thrust load on innerring, as deduced from offset of contact path to the W, is labeled.

SUSPECTED CAUSES: Maximum-complement ball bearings contain more balls than can be assembled without a loading slot for the insertion of the last balls. Such bearings can take thrust load only on the IR face away from the loading slot, so that the contact does not overroll the slot edge. This bearing was mismounted, resulting in load application towards the loading slot, causing edge spalling.

DATA
Plate No: 10.15
Archive No: 031-005&012
Image type: a, b: view
Scalebar = a, b: 25 mm (micros: ±20%, others: +100%, -50%)
Component: DGBB; IR, run
Speed:
Load:
Lubrication:
Failure code1: 00.16.01.2.3 Spalling at contact edge from thrust load
Failure code2: 00.16.02.5 Advanced spalling
Failure code3: 00.22.01.3 Rolling element (ball, roller) crack
Failure code4: 00.22.1 Overstress crack

DESCRIPTIONS
FAILURE DESCRIPTION: Advanced compound failure of more than one mode. Thrust loaded groove is half spalled; land edge is overrolled. Large chip has broken out of the land and another adjacent chip out of the groove (bulk fracture). There are spalled and fractured balls. Probable bearing seizure. Bearings in heavy industrial machinery often run to severe compound failure before diagnosis and removal.

IMAGE DESCRIPTION: (a): IR, covered with heavy grease (on lands and in chipped areas). S half of ball groove spalled and spalls rolled down. In SE half of S land, a large chip is broken off. Near ring center, chip broken out of track; the cavities of the 2 fractures merge. (b): Spalls on several balls. 2 balls at NW, shattered. Second ball from N has a row of spalls along a great circle suggesting edge loading.

SUSPECTED CAUSES: Groove spalling appears due to axial

a

b

overload (spalls extend past groove edge). After continued running, some balls spalled; one or two shattered and jammed. They chipped the ball path and a land.

DATA
Plate No: 10.16
Archive No: 001-25&26
Image type: light macro
Scalebar = a, b: 4 mm (micros: ±20%, others: +100%, -50%)
Component: DGBB; IR&OR, run
Speed: 700 KdN
Load: 1 GPa
Lubrication: synthetic polyester oil, 120 °C
Failure code1: 00.16.01.2.3 Spalling at contact edge from thrust load
Failure code2: 00.23.1.1 Contact path rolldown in bearing
Failure code3: 00.16.02.5 Advanced spalling
Failure code4: 00.12.4 Wear of guiding-component support surface

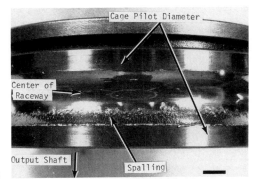

a

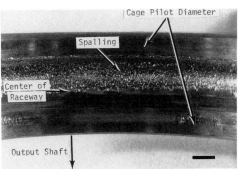

b

DESCRIPTIONS
FAILURE DESCRIPTION: Rings of a DGBB under heavy thrust load show extensive spalling on opposite edges of ball grooves. On both rings, the spalling extends to one (sharp) groove edge and has serrated that edge. A thrust load sufficient to produce severe edge contact caused plastic rolldown at the edges and early spalling from the stress concentration at the edge. Some circumferential wear marks are on separator (cage) guide surfaces of IR.

IMAGE DESCRIPTION: (a) IR ball groove extensively spalled S of label: "Center of raceway". (b) Similar spalling on OR ball groove, N of "Center of raceway". These are the two diagonally opposite groove halves under thrust load. Edges of spalled groove-halves are serrated by rollout and spalls extending to

the edges. Faint circumferential wear marks on separator guide surfaces labeled "Cage Pilot Diameter".

SUSPECTED CAUSES: Excessive thrust load for the design and looseness selected cause contact ellipse to override groove edges significantly. Stress concentration at edge initiates early spalling. Wear at separator guide surfaces may be due to debris from spalls.

DATA
Plate No: 10.17
Archive No: 080-123
Image type: light macro
Scalebar = 10 mm (micros: ±20%, others: +100%, -50%)
Component: SG; W, case hardened, run
Speed:
Load:
Lubrication:
Failure code1: 00.16.01.3 Tooth spalling
Failure code2: 00.13.3 Tooth contact galling
Failure code3: -
Failure code4: -

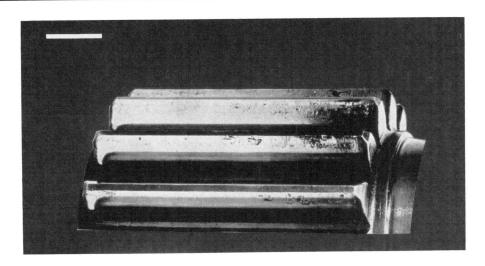

DESCRIPTIONS
FAILURE DESCRIPTION: Multiple galling marks (scoring) running radially over addendum act as sources for fatigue spalls. In its present condition, the gear is still operable, but continued spalling may lead to tooth fracture (FC 00.22.01.4).

IMAGE DESCRIPTION: Light-colored radial galling streaks in many locations on the addendum, on first and second fully visible tooth from N. On all tooth flanks, dark spall craters are interspersed with the galling marks. Microscopy would indicate that spalls originate from galling marks as defects.

SUSPECTED CAUSES: Galling (scoring) of gear teeth may occur due to overload, insufficient EHD film, excessive operating speed, surface defects or excessive roughness. Galling streaks are significant sources of spalling fatigue. Occasionally gear galling may "heal" when operating conditions become subsequently less severe. However, spall initiation may have taken place while the galling was fresh and spall formation may proceed afterward.

DATA
Plate No: 10.18
Archive No: 099-107&102
Image type: a: light macro, b: light microgram
Scalebar = a: 30 mm, b: 3 mm (micros: ±20%, others: +100%, -50%)
Component: HG; W, medium hard, run
Speed:
Load:
Lubrication:
Failure code1: 00.16.01.3 Tooth spalling
Failure code2: 00.16.02.4 Incipient spalling, multiple spalls
Failure code3: 00.12.5.2 Smooth tooth wear
Failure code4: -
See also PLATEs: 10.21 & 10.26

DESCRIPTIONS
FAILURE DESCRIPTION: In medium-hard gears, small spalls may appear on much of the dedendum area during early running. Spalling is believed to be more sliding-direction sensitive in medium-hard steel (enhanced when sliding is co-directional to rolling, as in dedendum). Such spalls may wear away and stop to proliferate, allowing the gear to continue running. See also PLATE 10.21. In other cases, failure progresses: See PLATE 10.26.

IMAGE DESCRIPTION: (a): All visible tooth contact surfaces show many small spall craters aligned from pitchline down into dedendum. Cratering is more pronounced in E half of tooth image (possible misalignment). (b): Dedendum surfaces of two consecutive teeth are mottled dark grey areas at N and S of image. Intervening tooth root, tip and addendum are light grey. Craters are rounded by wear in dedendum; no new craters. White rectangles are artifacts.

SUSPECTED CAUSES: Highly loaded medium-hard gears, often

a

b

with as-machined and relatively rough surfaces, tend to wear during run-in. Near pitchline, toward dedendum, where sliding is low, but co-directional to rolling, small spalls tend to appear, rather than wear. Spalling may be arrested in this class of material as surfaces become smoother in run-in.

DATA
Plate No: 10.19
Archive No: 099-116
Image type: light macro
Scalebar = 25 mm (micros: ±20%, others: +100%, -50%)
Component: WG; W, bronze, run
Speed:
Load:
Lubrication:
Failure code1: 00.16.01.3 Tooth spalling
Failure code2: 00.16.02.5 Advanced spalling
Failure code3: 00.12.3.3.2 Wear, centered in sliding contact
Failure code4: -

DESCRIPTIONS
FAILURE DESCRIPTION: Spall cratering covering most of tooth contact surface in worm gear wheel. Wear marks are on all unspalled areas. Worm gear wheels, generally of bronze, remain functional with extremely heavy spalling and wear. Data on spall progression in bronze are scarce but it appears slow under these conditions.

IMAGE DESCRIPTION: Worm gear wheel is viewed on flank,

with axis E–W. Two full teeth and part of a third (N image edge) show generally spalled contact surface, except at W and NW edges, which show kinematic wear marks. High areas between spall craters are also worn smooth.

SUSPECTED CAUSES: Severe surface destruction, including wear, spalling and possibly galling is encountered in worm gear contacts which undergo high sliding. Large contact area keeps stresses sufficiently low that functioning can be maintained (at slow worm gear speeds) even in the presence of significant surface destruction.

DATA
Plate No: 10.28
Archive No: 093-16.3.7
Image type: replica TEM of etched section
Scalebar = 2.5 μm (micros: ±20%, others: +100%, -50%)
Component: DGBB; IR, run
Speed: 420 KdN
Load: 3.4 GPa
Lubrication: mineral oil, 100 °C
Failure code1: 00.16.02.1.1
Microplastic deformation bands or 'butterflies'
Failure code2: -
Failure code3: -
Failure code4: -
See also PLATE: 10.30

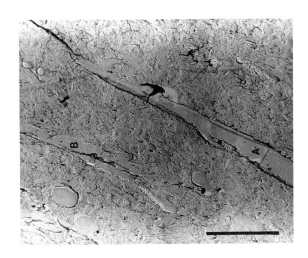

DESCRIPTIONS
FAILURE DESCRIPTION: Shown is the structure within a deformation band. The cold worked martensitic structure with dislocation cells is interspersed with newly formed lenticular carbides and some untransformed globular carbides. The lenticular carbide interfaces are believed weak and prone to channeling existing cracks in their direction. See also PLATE 10.30.

IMAGE DESCRIPTION: Grey background with multiple short dark swirls and lines is cold worked martensite in the deformation band. Smooth, lighter grey oblong structures running SE–NW as at *A* and *B* are lenticular carbides. Round structure in SW image corner is an original globular carbide. Black, crack-like lines and spots near lenticular carbides may be microcracks formed in cycling, but more likely arise from etching.

SUSPECTED CAUSES: Deformation bands are sheets of martensite with many dislocation cells from cyclic cold working in the observably defect-free matrix. Carbon migrates to the boundaries of these sheets and forms lenticular carbides. Weak interfaces between deformation bands, lenticular carbides and matrix may channel cracks in spall bottoms.

DATA
Plate No: 10.29
Archive No: 107-027a&b
Image type: SEM of Nital etched section
Scalebar = a: 10, b: 5 μm (micros: ±20%, others: +100%, -50%)
Component: ACBB; IR, run
Speed:
Load:
Lubrication: grease, 50 °C
Failure code1: 00.16.02.1.1
Microplastic deformation bands or 'butterflies'
Failure code2: 00.06.1.1 Hard micro-inclusion
Failure code3: -
Failure code4: -
See also PLATE: 10.30

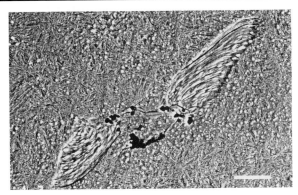

a

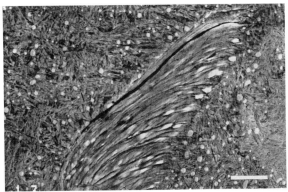

b

DESCRIPTIONS
FAILURE DESCRIPTION: Microplastic deformation band (*butterfly*) from fatigue cycling has formed around a cluster of small (about 5 μm) hard non-metallics between two "wings" of the band. Possible micro-crack at one wing edge. Deformation bands contain heavily cold-worked martensite bands separated by lamellar carbides formed during deformation.

IMAGE DESCRIPTION: (a): Mottled background is a martensitic structure with carbides as white points. In image center, several black jagged spots are non-metallics. Two wing-shaped patches of curved lines, extending SW–NE are 60 μm long deformation bands (butterflies). Black lines within the wings are lenticular carbides and/or dislocation tangles. (b) Wing, higher magnification. Heavy black line at N wing border is probably a crack, enhanced by etching.

SUSPECTED CAUSES: Repeated high-stress contact cycling of steel causes cumulative local plastic deformation which may produce deformation bands, either in the defect-free matrix or at defects. Deformation banding increases with stress and total cycle count but is not necessarily a crack originator. Cracks, if formed, may follow deformation band direction. (See PLATE 10.30.)

DATA
Plate No: 10.30
Archive No: 093-16.3.6
Image type: light metallogram, Picral etched section
Scalebar = 10 μm (micros: ±20%, others: +100%, -50%)
Component: DGBB; IR, run
Speed:
Load:
Lubrication:
Failure code1: 00.16.02.1.1 Microplastic deformation bands or 'butterflies'
Failure code2: 00.16.02.5 Advanced spalling
Failure code3: -
Failure code4: -
See also PLATE: 10.28

DESCRIPTIONS
FAILURE DESCRIPTION: In circumferential section of spalled ring, many parallel straight traces of matrix deformation bands (not at observed defects). The spall bottom follows deformation bands intermittently, with breaks from band to band. Deformation bands are microplastic events from contact stress cycling. They increase with stress and cycle count. They are not known to *initiate* cracks, but will channel existing cracks. See also PLATE 10.28.

IMAGE DESCRIPTION: Dark grey mottled background is Picral etched martensitic matrix. Multiple SW–NE running straight white-and-black lines are sections of laminar deformation bands. Jagged line near N image edge is the section through the spall bottom. Segments of bottom rising to NE follow deformation bands (at about 25° 'Martin angle').

SUSPECTED CAUSES: Repeated high-stress contact cycling of steel causes cumulative local plastic deformation which may produce deformation bands in the observably defect-free matrix. Deformation banding increases with stress and total cycle count but is not known to be a crack originator. Cracks, once formed, may follow deformation band direction jumping from band to band to create serrated spall bottom.

DATA
Plate No: 10.31
Archive No: 075-103&111
Image type: a, b: SEM
Scalebar = a: 60, b: 30 μm (micros: ±20%, others: +100%, -50%)
Component: CRB; R, carburized steel, run
Speed:
Load:
Lubrication:
Failure code1: 00.16.02.1.3 Microsphere spalling debris
Failure code2: -
Failure code3: -
Failure code4: -

DESCRIPTIONS
FAILURE DESCRIPTION: This PLATE shows the SEM appearance of spherical debris formed in spalling cracks. The generation of such debris is believed characteristic of spalling fatigue. The material is the same as the matrix steel, but is possibly oxidized at the surface. Alternating micro-motions between crack faces are suspected causes. The spheres range 10–200 μm in size: (a): is 200 μm, (b): 50 μm.

IMAGE DESCRIPTION: (a): The large dark hemisphere at image center, with adhering laminae, is a partly formed spherical debris particle. Other laminae surround it in the crack face. Greyscale reflects thinness of the lamina (thinner is lighter). The background area is a crack face. (b): Large white sphere at image center is fully formed spherical debris particle. Texture and hue indicate the presence of oxides (confirmed by X-ray analysis).

SUSPECTED CAUSES: Most debris formed by micro-motion of

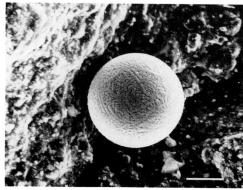

surfaces under load is laminar (example: fretting debris). Spherical (not merely cylindrical) debris have been observed only under rolling contact fatigue spalling conditions. The specific mechanism of their generation is not understood.

DATA
Plate No: 10.32
Archive No: 107-026a&b
Image type: SEM of Nital etched
section
Scalebar = a: 5, b: 3 μm (micros:
±20%, others: +100%, -50%)
Component: DGBB; B, run
Speed:
Load:
Lubrication: grease, 50 °C
Failure code1: 00.16.02.2 Contact
fatigue cracking
Failure code2: 00.16.1.1.2 Spall from
subsurface defect
Failure code3: 00.06.1.2 Sulfide
inclusion
Failure code4: -
See also PLATE: 10.29

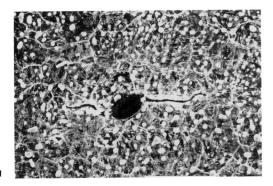

a

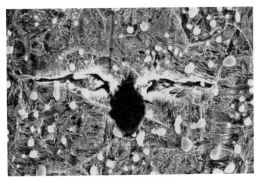

b

DESCRIPTIONS
FAILURE DESCRIPTION: Initiation of microscopic fatigue cracks
from subsurface manganese sulfide inclusions of (a) 5 μm, (b)
3 μm diameter, under high load and prolonged cycling. Sulfide
inclusions are believed to be less severe spall originating defects than are hard inclusions, and 3 or 5 μm inclusions are
minimum size to cause spalling. The possibility exists that
these microcracks (12–15 μm long) will not propagate.

IMAGE DESCRIPTION: (a): Nital etched metallographic section
at high magnification in SEM. White dots are carbides in dark
matrix, with martensite needles as faint outlines. The black oval
in the center is a manganese sulfide inclusion. Black horizontal
lines in white bands are microcracks (SEM shows sharp edges
as white.) (b): Similar image of another inclusion. Cracks are
horizontal dark openings extending from N end of inclusion.

SUSPECTED CAUSES: The microcracks originate from the
small subsurface manganese sulfide inclusion acting as a stress
raiser (low strength soft material in void). Load and cycling
time must be extreme to cause the fatigue cracking (see PLATE
10.29).

DATA
Plate No: 10.33
Archive No: 002-005a&c
Image type: a: view, b: light
metallogram, etched
Scalebar = a: 6 mm, b: 300 μm
(micros: ±20%, others: +100%,
-50%)
Component: ACBB; B, tool steel, run
Speed: 0.8 MdN
Load: 2.2 GPa
Lubrication: synthetic polyester oil,
149 °C
Failure code1: 00.16.02.2 Contact
fatigue cracking
Failure code2: 00.16.1.1.2 Spall from
subsurface defect
Failure code3: 00.16.02.1.1
Microplastic deformation bands or
'butterflies'
Failure code4: 00.04.3.1.1 Incipient
melting from forging at excessive
temperature
See also PLATE: 10.47

a

b

DESCRIPTIONS
FAILURE DESCRIPTION: (a): Several radial cracks from contact
loading of crack-prone tool steel forged at excessive temperature. Secondary spalls exist at three of the cracks. Great-circle
wear marks (FC 00.12.4) (probably separator contact).
(b): Spall. Deformation bands (butterflies) at micro-porosity and

elsewhere. Cracks growing into material from spall bottom are
due to crack-prone material. See also PLATE 10.47.

IMAGE DESCRIPTION: (a): Three radial cracks (light-colored
straight lines at arrow pairs). Spall craters exist on each crack.
Light-colored haloes decorate spall edges from reduced EHD
film. Several circular wear marks run E–W, one NW–SE (possibly from separator contact). (b): Cross-section. Rolling direction E to W. Spall bottom at N, crack at W edge (arrows).
Dark hairline cracks and white deformation bands (butterflies)
SE–NW. Micro-voids visible at *A*.

SUSPECTED CAUSES: Tool steel is sensitive to excessive forging temperature, which causes local melting and porosity.
Structure is damaged. Such material is spall and crack-prone.
This explains the radial cracking under contact load with subsequent spalling in an element (ball) not subject to tensile hoop
stress.

DATA
Plate No: 10.34
Archive No: 018-604&606&607
Image type: a: light micro; b: SEM;
c: light micro, Nital etch
Scalebar = a, b, c: 100 μm (micros:
±20%, others: +100%, -50%)
Component: DGBB; IR, hard turned,
honed, run
Speed: 100 KdN
Load: 3.7 GPa
Lubrication: mineral oil, 66 °C
Failure code1: 00.16.02.2 Contact
fatigue cracking
Failure code2: 00.18.1.2 Sharp
individual dent(s) from metal debris,
asperities
Failure code3: 00.16.1.2.1 Shallow
entry spall from surface point-defect
Failure code4: 00.16.02.1.2 Dark-
etching microplastic deformation zone

a

b

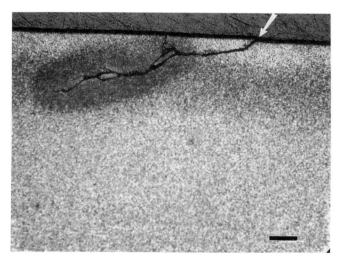

c

DESCRIPTIONS
FAILURE DESCRIPTION: (a,b): Debris dent on surface is followed by shallow-entry spall initiation through surface-origin fatigue crack entering at approximately 10° to surface.
(c): Etched section shows altered (dark-etching), microplasti-
cally worked structure surrounding crack, indicating concentrated stress acting over a substantial cycle count. Note the intact ridge between dent and spall. The ring has failed.

IMAGE DESCRIPTION: (a): Rolling surface with E–W finishing
lines. Dent (NE of arrowhead) is the angular structure, dark at
W, and lighter than surroundings at E. V-shaped crack extends

NW and SW from a point W of dent. N–S crack further W.
(b): Rolling surface is to the N of sharp edge; section is to the
S. Crack seen on both. Black vertical rectangle is artifact.
(c): Etched section. Rolling surface with crack (arrow) is at N.
Dark-etching structure is visible around crack tip.

SUSPECTED CAUSES: Dent is a common cause of early spalling by creating stress concentration, loss of EHD film and possibly material damage. Typically, a spalling crack starts a small
distance away from dent edge, leaving an intact ridge, since
maximum shear stress concentration is not at the very edge.

DATA
Plate No: 10.35
Archive No: 093-16.1.10
Image type: SEM
Scalebar = 25 μm (micros: ±20%,
others: +100%, -50%)
Component: NRB; R, run
Speed: 40 KdN
Load: 1.3 GPa
Lubrication: mineral oil, 60 °C
Failure code1: 00.16.02.5 Advanced
spalling
Failure code2: -
Failure code3: -
Failure code4: -

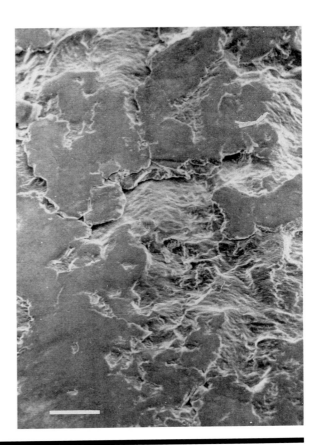

DESCRIPTIONS
FAILURE DESCRIPTION: Spall cratering on needle roller. Craters
are shallow, show multiple origins and propagation directions
(striations). Some unspalled areas appear undermined by
cracks. Spalling of small (3 mm) diameter needle rollers is
shallow due to small depth of Hertz shear stresses and is not
generally a gross failure, but bearing is noisy and inaccurate.
Roller fracture may eventually result.

IMAGE DESCRIPTION: Spall craters are irregularly shaped
areas with a striated fracture surface as bottom. Unspalled, featureless rolling surface of roller finished by tumbling is undermined by fatigue cracks at its edges (see dark shadows along
curved N–S edge just E of image center).

SUSPECTED CAUSES: Spalling is due to high-stress cycling,
with low EHD film, contamination and rough mating surface
(shaft as innerring) as likely contributors.

DATA
Plate No: 10.36
Archive No: 031-701
Image type: view
Scalebar = 30 mm (micros: ±20%,
others: +100%, -50%)
Component: TRB; R, run
Speed:
Load:
Lubrication:
Failure code1: 00.16.02.5 Advanced
spalling
Failure code2: 00.16.1.1.3 Subcase-
fatigue spall
Failure code3: 00.22.1 Overstress
crack
Failure code4: 00.23.2 Plastic
distortion of bulk shape

DESCRIPTIONS
FAILURE DESCRIPTION: Advanced compound failure of several
modes. Several deep spalls formed on each roller, probably due
to overload and subcase fatigue (contact stressing of core below case/core boundary). Edges of craters were then chipped
off due to overrolling of debris. General roller shape was lost
due to plastic working. Bearings in heavy industrial machinery
often run to severe compound failure before diagnosis and removal.

IMAGE DESCRIPTION: Several rollers of a TRB show deep cavities, which are spall craters battered and rolled over after formation. Edges of all rollers except those in the NE and SW end
positions are chipped. Overall roller shapes are destroyed by
overrolling of debris, and/or sliding after seizure of the roller in
the separator.

SUSPECTED CAUSES: The origin of the roller spalls is unclear
in the absence of the other components. Severe debris denting
(perhaps from ring spall debris) or material defects may have
initiated them. Further destruction of rollers is due to long running after failure inception.

DATA
Plate No: 10.37
Archive No: 026-6
Image type: view (partial)
Scalebar = 60 mm (micros: ±20%, others: +100%, -50%)
Component: CRB (multirow); IR, run
Speed:
Load:
Lubrication: mineral oil mist, ? °C
Failure code1: 00.16.02.5 Advanced spalling
Failure code2: 00.16.1.2.1 Shallow entry spall from surface point-defect
Failure code3: 00.20.1.3 Contact corrosion
Failure code4: 00.12.0.2 Abrasive mild wear
See also PLATE: 10.45

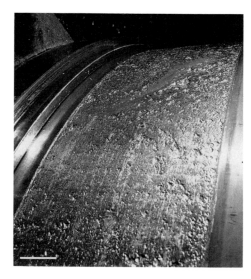

DESCRIPTIONS
FAILURE DESCRIPTION: The roller path on this CRB IR is spalled over the entire area. The bearing suffered roller failure (see PLATE 10.45), producing sharply irregular contact surfaces and copious debris which indented the IR roller path everywhere. Application is known to suffer from ingress of aggressive steel-rolling oil into bearing, which damages rolling surfaces and thus promotes spalling.

IMAGE DESCRIPTION: Roller path extends from S image edge to N and NE and is flanked by undercuts and guide flanges. Entire roller path is covered by spall craters of somewhat uniform depth, except near N end where a SW–NE running curved deep spall is followed by a relatively unspalled ridge. This feature may be due to an accident of overrolling or possibly a local material hardness difference.

SUSPECTED CAUSES: The initial failure of this large multirow steel mill roll neck bearing is the roller fatigue shown in PLATE 10.45. This IR failure may be secondary. Loads, speed, inertia and noise in a mill stand are great. Mills are not instrumented to detect early bearing failure. Mills cannot be stopped abruptly without serious consequences. Accordingly, the bearing was run long after initial failure, causing this severe secondary damage.

DATA
Plate No: 10.38
Archive No: 107-025a&b&c
Image type: SEM
Scalebar = a: 1 mm, b, c: 400 μm (micros: ±20%, others: +100%, -50%)
Component: ACBB; OR, run
Speed:
Load:
Lubrication: grease, 50 °C
Failure code1: 00.16.1.1 Subsurface origin spall (high Hertz shear stress)
Failure code2: 00.16.02.2 Contact fatigue cracking
Failure code3: 00.16.02.3 Incipient spalling, single spall
Failure code4: -

a

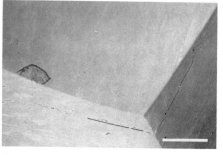
b

c

DESCRIPTIONS
FAILURE DESCRIPTION: Spalling originated in subsurface (surface-parallel) crack which exfoliated via a number of concentric surface cracks. The subsurface defect which originates the failure is not shown. This mechanism of spalling results from high load and subsurface defects in the absence of surface distress or other severe surface spall originators.

IMAGE DESCRIPTION: (a): Concentric (light color) elliptical cracks surround two incipient spalls. (b): NW image half is rolling surface; SE: circumferential section. Subsurface crack (in section) undermines surface and penetrates to it in four cracks. (c): Other location. N image quadrant is the rolling surface; E quadrant: circumferential cut; SW quadrant: axial cut. Subsurface crack in SW and E quadrants. Dark spot at W is artifact.

SUSPECTED CAUSES: Spall-initiating subsurface defect caused surface-parallel crack, at the approximate maximum Hertz shear stress level, which broke through to the surface in several cracks. Exfoliation of the spall crater has begun.

DATA
Plate No: 10.39
Archive No: 074-22&23
Image type: a,b: light macro
Scalebar = a,b: 80 mm (micros: ±20%, others: +100%, -50%)
Component: DGBB; B, run
Speed:
Load:
Lubrication:
Failure code1: 00.16.1.1 Subsurface origin spall (high Hertz shear stress)
Failure code2: 00.16.03.1 Spall propagating by cracking at spall bottom
Failure code3: 00.16.1.1.2 Spall from subsurface defect
Failure code4: 00.06.2 Inclusion stringer
See also PLATE: 10.52

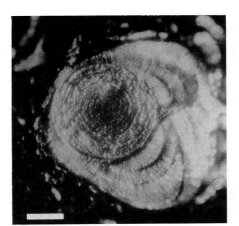

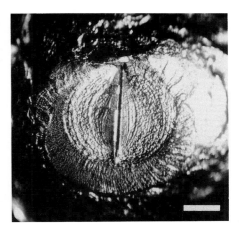

a   b

DESCRIPTIONS

FAILURE DESCRIPTION: Subsurface origin spalls on a ball, propagating by symmetrical extension of the spall bottom, as the ball changes orientation and the spall is overrolled from different directions. (a) originates from point defect, (circular symmetry), (b) from a linear inclusion (bilateral symmetry). The ball has failed. See PLATE 10.52 for surface origin ball spalling.

IMAGE DESCRIPTION: (a): Bull's-eye-shaped spall crater, initiating at the center of concentric circular striations, just W of image center. Two further arcs of crack propagation extend NE and SE beyond the original spall. (b): N–S black line at image center is inclusion stringer. Bilateral (orange slice) spall propagation to circular shape and beyond. Due to small depth of focus, outermost areas of spall are ill resolved in (a) and (b).

SUSPECTED CAUSES: Balls in radially loaded bearings change axis of rotation frequently. After a spall has initiated, it may be overrolled in any direction and thus grow circularly. Once the spall becomes sizeable it may exert an orienting effect on the ball so that axis changes become more rare and further spall extension proceeds only in two directions.

DATA
Plate No: 10.40
Archive No: 122-3
Image type: SEM
Scalebar = 400 μm (micros: ±20%, others: +100%, -50%)
Component: DGBB; B, run
Speed: 140 KdN
Load: 2.8 GPa
Lubrication: mineral oil, ? °C
Failure code1: 00.16.1.1.2 Spall from subsurface defect
Failure code2: 00.04.2 Forming seam
Failure code3: 00.16.03.1 Spall propagating by cracking at spall bottom
Failure code4: -

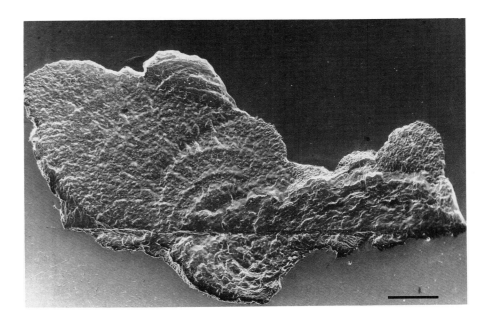

DESCRIPTIONS

FAILURE DESCRIPTION: Spall originating from a forming seam has propagated in concentric striations, primarily downstream in direction of contact travel. Some spall formation has occurred upstream from the seam. Continued spalling from this subsurface defect is likely to cause functional failure of the ball. In its present condition, the ball is noisy.

IMAGE DESCRIPTION: Seam runs E–W across image at one-third image height from S edge, forming dark straight line, with ledge at several locations. To N of seam (downstream in overrolling direction), the spall extends in several concentric striations into the NW image quadrant, propagating by continued spall bottom cracking. Spall edge has collapsed just S of seam, continuing crater about 500 μm in that direction.

SUSPECTED CAUSES: Seams are discontinuous interfaces arising during rolling (or drawing) of ball wire, and are often oxidized. They are weak interfaces, causing severe stress concentration that is likely to lead to early spalling.

DATA
Plate No: 10.41
Archive No: 122-5
Image type: SEM
Scalebar = 100 μm (micros: ±20%, others: +100%, -50%)
Component: TBB; IR, run
Speed: 40 ? KdN
Load: 5 GPa
Lubrication: grease, ? °C
Failure code1: 00.16.1.1.2 Spall from subsurface defect
Failure code2: 00.06.1.1 Hard micro-inclusion
Failure code3: 00.16.02.2 Contact fatigue cracking
Failure code4: 00.18.02.1 Light or incipient denting

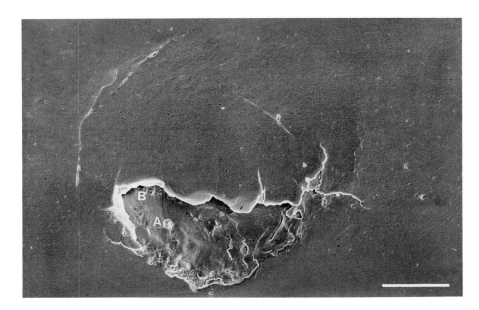

DESCRIPTIONS
FAILURE DESCRIPTION: Incipient spall originating at a (cluster of) hard subsurface micro-inclusions. Circular crack edges emerging on contact surface, with small exfoliation. Small (10 μm) hard inclusion at spall bottom, with others probable. Un-spalled surface has many fine debris dents. Spall is likely to propagate, causing functional failure.

IMAGE DESCRIPTION: Image center is occupied by cracks extending three-fourths of a circle from E through S and W to N. S half circle has spalled out. A lamina of material is under-mined by crack at the E–W diameter. White globular body with black outline and white halo at A is believed to be a hard non-metallic inclusion. An inclusion probably spalled out near N spall edge (B), Debris dents are visible on contact surface.

SUSPECTED CAUSES: Clusters of hard non-metallics may remain in steel from steelmaking and are a classical source of early spalling failure. The inclusions shown are relatively small (3 μm) but may still be significant stress concentrators under very heavy load.

DATA
Plate No: 10.42
Archive No: 027-167
Image type: light macro
Scalebar = 10 mm (micros: ±20%, others: +100%, -50%)
Component: DGBB; IR, run
Speed: 130 KdN
Load:
Lubrication: grease, 60 °C
Failure code1: 00.16.1.1.2 Spall from subsurface defect
Failure code2: 00.16.02.3 Incipient spalling, single spall
Failure code3: 00.16.01.1.1 Centered spalling, normal track width
Failure code4: 00.12.3.2.0.5 Wear track for centered axial load
See also PLATEs: 10.3 & 10.11

DESCRIPTIONS
FAILURE DESCRIPTION: Elliptical, steep-edged spall near center of ball path (under thrust load), with a line-depression in the spall bottom, suggesting an inclusion stringer as origin. PLATES 10.3, 10.11 and 10.42 show various spalling modes in similar bearings for comparison. The wear track offset to one side indicates axial load. This bearing is noisy and has failed in the quiet running application.

IMAGE DESCRIPTION: Oblong spall crater with major axis in axial direction, at arrow. Short black axial line centered in spall bottom may indicate inclusion stringer (requires metallographic

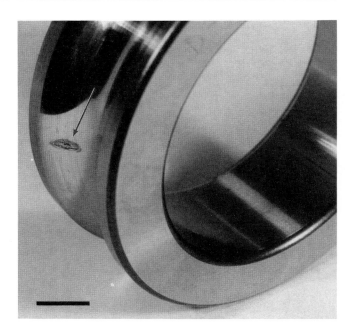

examination). Two faint dark circumferential lines run near spall tips indicating the rolling track. Note the clean, undented surface away from the spall.

SUSPECTED CAUSES: An inclusion stringer under the surface is a likely cause of this single spall in a normally loaded bearing operated in clean environment.

DATA
Plate No: 10.51
Archive No: 107-024a&b
Image type: SEM
Scalebar = a: 30, b: 5 μm (micros: ±20%, others: +100%, -50%)
Component: ACBB; IR, run
Speed:
Load:
Lubrication: grease, 50 °C
Failure code1: 00.16.1.2.1 Shallow entry spall from surface point-defect
Failure code2: 00.16.02.2 Contact fatigue cracking
Failure code3: 00.18.1.1 Rounded dent (from soft contaminant)
Failure code4: 00.17.2 Localized surface distress (halo at defect)

a

b

DESCRIPTIONS
FAILURE DESCRIPTION: Small (120 μm long) crack running normal to rolling direction and incipient spall formed from alumina microinclusion at the surface. (Calcium and aluminum was verified by microprobe analysis.) This is the earliest phase of spall crater formation. A rounded dent (15 μm) is unrelated to spalling, but shows a halo of surface distress. The bearing is likely to fail from progressive spalling.

IMAGE DESCRIPTION: (a): N—S finishing lines; in NE corner, rounded dent from soft contaminant particle, decorated by (darker) surface distress halo in which finishing lines are partly obliterated. At mid-image, two E—W cracks are black E—W lines with white rim (sharp edge). They meet in three dark patches which are the alumina inclusions. (Spalling may have begun at the inclusions). (b): Inclusions and cracks originating from them, at higher magnification.

SUSPECTED CAUSES: Hard (for example, alumina) inclusions are sources of spalling. A surface inclusion is a severe spall in-itiator, especially when surface distress is present due to low EHD film thickness. This inclusion is close to the minimum size that has been reported to cause spalling.

DATA
Plate No: 10.52
Archive No: 074-27
Image type: view
Scalebar = 20 mm (micros: ±20%, others: +100%, -50%)
Component: DGBB; B, run
Speed:
Load:
Lubrication:
Failure code1: 00.16.1.2.1 Shallow entry spall from surface point-defect
Failure code2: 00.16.03.1 Spall propagating by cracking at spall bottom
Failure code3: -
Failure code4: -
See also PLATE: 10.39

DESCRIPTIONS
FAILURE DESCRIPTION: Extensive spalling of ball surface, by removal of a uniform-depth layer. The spall is believed to originate from a surface defect (dent, nick, etc.) and then propagates in all directions as the ball changes axis of rotation. The ball has failed. Compare with PLATE 10.39, showing subsurface origin spalls.

IMAGE DESCRIPTION: Large oval spall extends from NW to SE. The spall is comparatively shallow and the spall bottom is rela-tively smooth, indicating extensive overrolling. From striations in spall bottom, origin is probably near N center of spall. Smooth, even bottom and relative shallowness suggest surface origin.

SUSPECTED CAUSES: Damage to the ball surface by surface distress, denting or other causes may precipitate spalling. Balls in radially loaded bearings change axis of rotation frequently. After a spall has initiated, it may be over-rolled in different directions and thus grow in more than one direction.

DATA
Plate No: 10.53
Archive No: 087-120
Image type: view
Scalebar = 30 mm (micros: ±20%, others: +100%, -50%)
Component: ACBB; OR, run
Speed: 1 ? MdN
Load:
Lubrication: synthetic polyester oil, ? °C
Failure code1: 00.16.1.2.1 Shallow entry spall from surface point-defect
Failure code2: 00.16.03.2 Spall propagating by re-initiation at surface
Failure code3: 00.12.3.2.0.2 Wear track when load rotates over outerring
Failure code4: 00.18.1.2 Sharp individual dent(s) from metal debris, asperities

DESCRIPTIONS
FAILURE DESCRIPTION: Two 'Heathcote bands' or circumferential wearmarks indicate zero-slip zones in ball/groove contact. A large spall, consisting of many shallow spalls, confined essentially between the Heathcote bands, indicates surface origin promoted by sliding. The bearing has failed.

IMAGE DESCRIPTION: Glossy surface of ball groove is divided by two sets of circumferential grey lines: the Heathcote bands. Large spall in SW quadrant is confined essentially between Heathcote bands. Jagged side edges and shallow depth of spall

indicate re-initiation at surface. Significant debris denting (dark points) are visible elsewhere in the groove.

SUSPECTED CAUSES: This OR of a high-speed bearing has high centrifugal loading, producing 360° load zone (see Heathcote bands). Surface initiated spalling may have been aided by debris denting and concentrated in the high-stress, high-sliding zone between Heathcote bands.

DATA
Plate No: 10.54
Archive No: 006-18&19
Image type: a: light macro, b: SEM
Scalebar = a: 10 mm, b: 200 μm (micros: ±20%, others: +100%, -50%)
Component: C; CF (sliding), run
Speed:
Load:
Lubrication: mineral oil based Diesel engine oil, ? °C
Failure code1: 00.16.1.2.1 Shallow entry spall from surface point-defect
Failure code2: 00.16.03.2 Spall propagating by re-initiation at surface
Failure code3: 00.16.01.1 Spalling centered in contact
Failure code4: 00.12.3.3.2 Wear, centered in sliding contact

DESCRIPTIONS
FAILURE DESCRIPTION: (a): Extensive surface-initiated spalling of cam follower rod end in sliding-rolling Hertzian contact with cam. (b): Fatigue spalls from (a). Spalling fatigue in Hertzian contact with predominant sliding is less common than wear (FC 00.12) or galling (FC 00.13), but does occur as shown here. Unspalled areas are featureless from wear.

IMAGE DESCRIPTION: (a): Circular endface of non-roller cam follower. Roughly circular dark worn areas are near OD and at mid-radius. Circle of light-colored spalls at center and 1/4 in from edge. (b): S quarter of image is an unspalled area with a

a

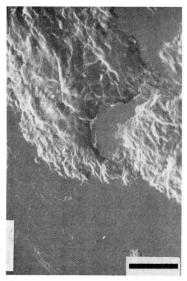

b

few faint NW–SE wear marks. N three-fourths of the image comprises two spall crater areas with interposed lamina preparing to spall out.

SUSPECTED CAUSES: Non-roller cam followers are sphere capped rod-ends in contact with a slightly tapered cam surface which is placed so as to induce rotation of the follower rod around its own axis, while the rod-end slides over the follower. During the lift phase, high pressures and (due to the sliding) high tractive forces exist which may cause spalling.

DATA
Plate No: 10.55
Archive No: 014-520a&b&c
Image type: a, b, c: light macro
Scalebar = a, b, c: 10 mm (micros:
±20%, others: +100%, -50%)
Component: TRB; IR, carburized, run
Speed:
Load:
Lubrication: mineral oil (low viscosity),
135 °C
Failure code1: 00.16.1.2.1 Shallow
entry spall from surface point-defect
Failure code2: 00.16.1.2.2 Shallow
entry spall from surface line-defect
Failure code3: 00.16.03.2 Spall
propagating by re-initiation at surface
Failure code4: -
See also PLATE: 10.44

a

b

DESCRIPTIONS
FAILURE DESCRIPTION: Three examples of spalling originating
from surface interaction (low EHD film, rough or dented surfaces). In (a), the initiator is a dent; in (b) a furrow; and in (c)
two dents. Spalls propagate in the shape of an arrowhead
opening in the rolling direction. The entry area is a shallow-angle crack. Contrast with PLATE 10.44: subsurface origin spall.

IMAGE DESCRIPTION: (a), (b) and (c): TRB IR (cone) roller
track with E–W finishing lines and undercuts at image N and
S. (a): Rolling is E to W; spall initiates at dent (arrow), progresses to NW, then to SW and again to NW. (b): Rolling is E
to W; spall initiates at furrow (deep finishing line at arrow) and
progresses to SW. (c): Rolling is W to E; two initiations at
dents (arrows), progress in an arrowhead shape. All initiating
angles are shallow.

SUSPECTED CAUSES: Low viscosity oil (high temperature)
causes low EHD film thickness; any surface defect (dent, furrow) depletes EHD film and may initiate spalling. Spall edge
acts as a secondary initiating defect.

c

DATA
Plate No: 10.56
Archive No: 093-022
Image type: a, b, c, d: view
Scalebar = a:12,b:20,c:16,d:20 mm
(micros: ±20%, others: +100%, -50%)
Component: DGBB; IR, run
Speed:
Load:
Lubrication:
Failure code1: 00.16.1.2.1 Shallow
entry spall from surface point-defect
Failure code2: 00.17.1.1 Glazing
(incipient surface distress)
Failure code3: 00.17.1.2 Microspalling
(advanced surface distress)
Failure code4: 00.16.02.5 Advanced
spalling

a

b

c

DESCRIPTIONS
FAILURE DESCRIPTION: Progression of surface-distress (FC
00.17.1) origin spalling on four IR-s from the same test group
of bearings. (a): glazing only; (b): surface distress microspalling; (c): incipient spalling; (d): advanced spalling. (a): and (b):
serviceable; (c): noisy but may run, (d): failed. If operating
conditions causing surface distress (insufficient EHD film, aggressive lubricant, rough surface) persist, progression from (a)
to (d) may be rapid.

IMAGE DESCRIPTION: Four views of different rings from the
same bearing test group (note the slightly different magnifica-
tions), after progressively longer running. (a): centered band of
changed luster in ball groove is early surface distress.
(b): frosted appearing areas (one-fourth W of ring center) are
microspalls. (c): series of spall craters, independently initiated.
(d): generalized spall cratering.

SUSPECTED CAUSES: Surface distress occurs when asperity interactions in contact are excessive, such as from insufficient
EHD film, rough surfaces, or possibly from aggressive lubricant. Microspalls develop that serve as severe initiating defects
for macroscopic spalling fatigue. Progression rate varies sharply
with conditions. Carburized parts may be more resistant than
through-hardened parts.

d

DATA
Plate No: 10.57
Archive No: 122-8&9
Image type: SEM
Scalebar = a: 1 mm, b: 100 μm
(micros: ±20%, others: +100%,
-50%)
Component: DGBB; IR, run
Speed: 170 KdN
Load: 2.8 GPa
Lubrication: mineral oil, ? °C
Failure code1: 00.16.1.2.1 Shallow
entry spall from surface point-defect
Failure code2: 00.18.1.2 Sharp
individual dent(s) from metal debris,
asperities
Failure code3: 00.16.02.2 Contact
fatigue cracking
Failure code4: -

a

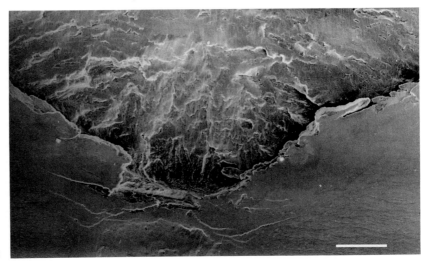

b

DESCRIPTIONS

FAILURE DESCRIPTION: Several sharp-edged shallow dents, as from rolled-in flakes (possibly from plating); some formed before, (some possibly after) spall initiation. A fan-shaped spall originated from one dent. Concentric cracks are visible downstream of the spall crater (in the rolling direction). Spalling is likely to propagate causing functional failure.

IMAGE DESCRIPTION: (a): Fan-shaped spall crater covers image center. At tip of fan, at image S, the angular, shallow depression in the surface is a dent from a thin, ductile, hard contaminant. At N edge of crater, concentric cracks are ready to exfoliate additional material. Several dents, possibly from spall debris, cross crack lines N of the crater. (b): A detail view of spall origin shows edge of initiating dent S of spall tip, followed by cracks.

SUSPECTED CAUSES: Debris dents cause (1) loss of EHD film, (2) local stress concentrations near dent edges, (3) damage to material underlying dent. These factors contribute to make dents spall initiators. Spall typically originates some small distance downstream (in the direction of contact travel) from the dent, leaving an unspalled lip between dent and crater.

DATA

Plate No: 10.58
Archive No: 018-104
Image type: view
Scalebar = 20 mm (micros: ±20%, others: +100%, -50%)
Component: SRB; IR, run
Speed:
Load:
Lubrication:
Failure code1: 00.16.1.2.1 Shallow entry spall from surface point-defect
Failure code2: 00.20.1.3 Contact corrosion
Failure code3: 00.12.3.2.1.1 Wear track centered in contact
Failure code4: 00.12.4 Wear of guiding-component support surface

DESCRIPTIONS

FAILURE DESCRIPTION: (1) Contact corrosion streaks spaced at roller spacing, on one roller path, which caused (2) extensive spalling in that roller path with cratering most severe at corrosion streaks. (3) Debris denting and wear on other roller path, caused at least one spall. (4) Center guide flange wear from debris trapped between separator and flange. The bearing was used in heavy, slow speed machinery and may have run a long period to reach this failure.

IMAGE DESCRIPTION: Roller path to image N shows five dark axial corrosion streaks at roller spacing, underneath generalized spall cratering. The cratering band is widest around the streaks.

Roller path to image S is finely dented and matte from debris denting and abrasive wear. One spall is near the center flange at W. Central guide-flange shows a step worn in the center plane, where two separator halves meet.

SUSPECTED CAUSES: Contact corrosion arises from water in the lubricant (probably grease) of the mounted bearing, or possibly from water in the package during shipment prior to mounting. Severe contact corrosion (with pitting) is a serious spall initiating defect. Spall debris from the extensive cratering act as abrasives and denting particles.

DATA

Plate No: 10.59
Archive No: 116-003&002
Image type: a: view, b: light metallogram, Nital etch
Scalebar = a: 4 mm, b: 60 μm (micros: ±20%, others: +100%, -50%)
Component: DGBB; IR, run
Speed: oscillating
Load: 2 GPa
Lubrication: grease w. silica thickener, $H_2O + CO_2$ atmosphere
Failure code1: 00.16.1.2.1 Shallow entry spall from surface point-defect
Failure code2: 00.22.4 Chemical origin (stress corrosion, embrittlement) crack
Failure code3: 00.12.0.2 Abrasive mild wear
Failure code4: 00.18.02.2 Severe or advanced denting

a   b

DESCRIPTIONS

FAILURE DESCRIPTION: (a): Bearing operated in high-pressure atmosphere of CO_2 and water vapor, with oscillating motion. Failure occurred at one-tenth of the catalog calculated life from massive spalling and circumferential bulk cracking. Chemical effect of grease on failure mechanism is assumed but not explained. The surface between spalls is worn and dented by spall debris. (b): Cracks at the spall bottom are unusual, radial-going, and branched (may be intergranular).

IMAGE DESCRIPTION: (a): IR viewed on ball groove. The con-

tact area is covered with independent origin spalls in a worn and dented surface. A jagged circumferential bulk crack runs through mid-groove. (b): Etched metallographic section through a spall. Radially inward-going heavily branched cracks suggest intergranular cracking of chemically weakened material.

SUSPECTED CAUSES: Unusual chemical environment of this bearing application produced (in repeated runs) the catastrophic spalling and cracking failure shown. If water condenses in grease under these conditions, failure may be explained thereby. Chemical effect is also suggested by unusual spall-bottom cracks and bulk fatigue failure. Corrosive effect of CO_2 on bearings is not reported by other sources.

DATA
Plate No: 10.60
Archive No: 093-16.6.6
Image type: SEM
Scalebar = 50 μm (micros: ±20%, others: +100%, -50%)
Component: DGBB; IR, honed, run
Speed: 450 KdN
Load: 3.5 GPa
Lubrication: mineral oil, 100 °C
Failure code1: 00.16.1.2.2 Shallow entry spall from surface line-defect
Failure code2: 00.02.1 Grinding, honing, lapping furrow
Failure code3: 00.16.02.2 Contact fatigue cracking
Failure code4: -

DESCRIPTIONS
FAILURE DESCRIPTION: Two honing furrows lead into a fatigue cracked and spalled region. Surface cracking has begun at one furrow end. The other furrow apparently initiated existing surface-origin spall. Furrows are serious fatigue initiating defects, especially when high EHD film thickness otherwise offers long life. The film breaks down at a furrow and high stress concentrations arise.

IMAGE DESCRIPTION: Grey background with faint N–S lines is the honed surface. At A and B, N–S running furrows with rolled-down feather edges at B, suggesting *honing* origin. At C, surface crack initiates from furrow A which ends at the bend in crack. D is the spall bottom area (only about 40 μm below the surface), a shallow spall entry. Very small (2–3 μm) contaminant dents on the surface. The large light-colored object at image SW is an artifact.

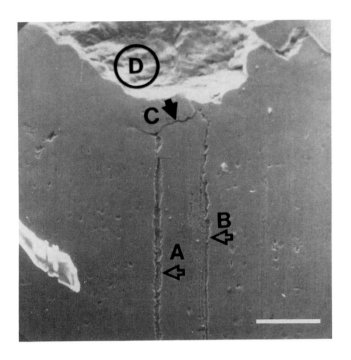

SUSPECTED CAUSES: Grinding furrows may be left in honed surface if too deep to be removed in honing. Detached honing grit may also create furrows of its own. Since the area adjacent to the furrows shown is undisturbed and the furrow has feather edges suggesting no subsequent finishing, these seem to be honing furrows.

DATA
Plate No: 10.61
Archive No: 018-608
Image type: SEM
Scalebar = 20 μm (micros: ±20%, others: +100%, -50%)
Component: DGBB; carburized tool steel, run
Speed: 100 KdN
Load: 3.7 GPa
Lubrication: mineral oil, 54 °C
Failure code1: 00.16.1.2.2 Shallow entry spall from surface line-defect
Failure code2: 00.02.1 Grinding, honing, lapping furrow
Failure code3: 00.18.1.3 Multi-fragment dent (brittle contaminant)
Failure code4: 00.18.1.2 Sharp individual dent(s) from metal debris, asperities

DESCRIPTIONS
FAILURE DESCRIPTION: Several finishing furrows, the deepest of which initiates spalling. Very small multi-fragment dents; some small debris dents. The ring has failed.

IMAGE DESCRIPTION: S two-thirds of image is rolling surface, with finishing marks running SE to NW. About mid-image, a white heavy line marks furrow with sharp point leading to the edge of the (dark) spall crater in the N one-third of the image.

The crater has a sharp edge extruded toward the furrow tip. Several lesser furrows are in NE quadrant. Dark clustered points with light haloes are multi-fragment dents. Wide depressions, with finishing lines at bottom, are debris dents.

SUSPECTED CAUSES: Contact surface was ground and subsequently honed. The grinding left several deep furrows not removed by honing, one of which caused the spall. Multi-fragment dents arise from brittle contaminant. Debris dents could be caused by spall debris. The crater edge appears raised in this SEM but probably is not.

DATA

Plate No: 10.62
Archive No: 002-018b
Image type: light macro
Scalebar = 30 mm (micros: ±20%, others: +100%, -50%)
Component: CRB; OR, run
Speed: 1.9 MdN
Load: 0.9 GPa
Lubrication: synthetic polyester oil, 176 °C
Failure code1: 00.16.1.2.2 Shallow entry spall from surface line-defect
Failure code2: 00.16.02.5 Advanced spalling
Failure code3: -
Failure code4: -

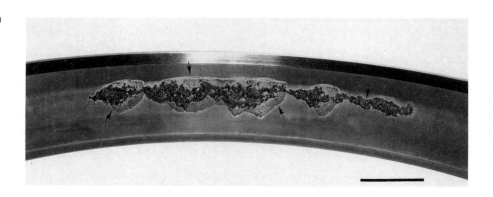

DESCRIPTIONS

FAILURE DESCRIPTION: Long circumferential spalled area on one side of OR roller path, but away from edge, formed by multiple spall craters. External evidence suggests a wire gasket element may have been rolled over (before being expelled) to create severe denting. Denting is no longer identifiable. Shallow spalls surround deep craters at several points, possibly due to overrolled spall debris creating secondary spalling.

IMAGE DESCRIPTION: Long area of contiguous deep spall craters is lined up circumferentially (arrows). The area is surrounded in several places by shallowly spalled fringes, as from secondary spalls due to overrolling of spall debris.

SUSPECTED CAUSES: From evidence of rolled-over wire gasket element, it is suspected that the wire became trapped in the roller path and created a long heavy dent before being expelled in running. Such a dent explains the long line of deep spalls. The shallow peripheral spalling may be due to debris.

11   SURFACE DISTRESS

11.1. Definition

Surface distress is defined as micro-scale spalling fatigue. It is failure of rolling contact metal surfaces by the formation of (a) *glazed* (burnished) surface areas; (b) asperity scale *microcracks*; and (c) asperity scale *micro-spall* craters, in that sequence. It is the result of predominantly *normal* contact stresses acting in asperity dimensions. Surface distress is distinguished from:

• *Spalling* (FC 00.16), which is Hertzian contact fatigue in *macroscopic* dimensions.
• *(Mild) wear* (FC 00.12), which is the ablation of surface material in the form of loose particles, under the influence of predominant tractive contact stresses acting in asperity dimensions.
• *Pit* formation, as porosity (FC 00.03) from material casting or processing, as pitting wear (FC 00.12), as a result of corrosion (FC 00.20), or of electric erosion (FC 00.21).

11.2. Nomenclature

"Surface distress" is widely used to designate this failure mode in rolling bearing technology. Another designation for the early, plastic flow stage of surface distress failure is *glazing*.

The later, microspalling stage is also designated: *peeling, fatigue wear, delamination wear, micro-pitting* or *micro-spalling*. The term "frosting" has been used for surface distress as well as for skidmarking (see FC 00.15). Due to the possibility of confusion, the term "frosting" is not used to designate the failure mode of surface distress in this Atlas. (However, a surface appearance may be described as "frosted.")

11.3. Failure Process

Surface distress has been reported almost exclusively on steel rolling contact surfaces.

NOTE: See Plate 11.10 for evidence of surface microspalling distress occurring in non-metal surfaces.

Two current theories describing surface distress in metal are by Tallian [4] and Suh [20]. Both define the failure process as fatigue in asperity dimensions but differ in details of the failure mechanism. Suh's delamination theory is described in detail in [20]. Tallian's [4] description of surface distress development, used in this Atlas, follows.

When two surfaces are in predominant rolling contact under load and with lubrication, their asperities approach each other in a direction close to the surface normal. Depending on the average thickness and rheology of the (liquid or solid) lubricant layer between the surfaces, stresses substantially exceeding the macroscopic local Hertzian stress may develop in asperity encounters.

If the lubricant is an EHD film and its thickness is three or more times the composite RMS surface roughness height, then the extra asperity stresses are statistically negligible. As the EHD film becomes thinner, or if only a boundary film is present, then the asperity stresses (which can be modeled as microscale Hertzian stress fields) become dominant in an increasing fraction of the asperity encounters.

The magnitude of asperity stresses increases with the composite "sharpness" of the asperities participating in the encounter. This sharpness can be measured by composite RMS slope or composite RMS tip curvature.

NOTE:
The parameter determining the sharpness of an asperity encounter is the *composite* slope or curvature of the two surfaces at the encounter point. Combining a very smooth surface with a rough one (ball in rough groove) does not protect the smooth surface from surface distress.

For asperity encounters in which the alternating shear stresses exceed a limit that depends on material properties, the following failure sequence is initiated:

1. *Asperity-scale plastic flow.* Both cumulative and alternating plastic flow occur in the asperities.

   • The *cumulative* plastic deformation occurs early in cycling and leads to flattening of asperity tips, especially the sharp "feather edges" that often decorate the crests of asperities in ground surfaces. The appearance of the surface will become progressively more burnished (*glazed*), as the topography left from surface finishing is gradually leveled and only smooth low-frequency waviness and scratches at the bottom of deeper finishing marks remain. The surface and immediate subsurface material are heavily cold worked.
   • The *alternating* plastic flow produces structural changes on the asperity scale which are qualitatively

195

similar to those suffered by macroscopic Hertz contacts under fatigue stressing.

2. *Micro-cracking.* With continued cyclic stressing, the plasticity of the material is exhausted and microcracks form. These tend to run surface-parallel, at depths comparable to that of the high *asperity-scale* shear stresses. They may or may not be open to the surface. A heavily distressed surface is densely populated with these microcracks.

3. *Micro-spalling.* As microcracks grow and proliferate, the surface becomes undermined in asperity dimensions, and multiple microscopic spalls form.

11.4. Distinctive Appearance

Macroscopically, plastically worked and microcracked surfaces both appear glazed. A microspalled surface appears pitted. All three may be present side-by-side on the same specimen.

A *glazed* surface differs from an as-finished surface in that finishing lines are crisp and evenly distributed on the latter, and partly or wholly obliterated on the former. When viewed under different angles of illumination from a small light source, an as-finished surface gives a "brushed" light reflection from the combined reflections of many parallel finishing marks. A glazed surface tends to show a mirror-like reflection.

NOTE: Extremely smooth original finishes (in rolling bearings, especially balls) may show a virtual mirror reflection even if not surface-distressed.

Under low magnification (scanning electron) microscopy, a glazed surface shows the smoothing of asperity ridges into almost featureless flat areas (with valleys still discernible), possibly with some incidental wear marks or dents. In contrast, mild wear produces a pebbled, profusely scratch-marked or micro-dented surface.

Glazed areas may be *generalized* on the contact surface (generalized surface distress); or, they may be *local,* in the form of *halos* around local depressions (dents, nicks) or glazed bands following furrows.

A *microcracked* surface is not usually distinguishable from a glazed one by the unaided eye. However, microcracking and microspalling most often appear together. See below for unaided-eye identification of microspalling.

Under low magnification (scanning electron) microscopy, microcracks opening to the surface may be visible in glazed areas. Microcracks can be seen in carefully prepared metallographic sections if the intersecting edge at the original surface is preserved by surface overplating.

A *microspalled* surface appears frosted to the unaided eye, possibly with barely visible black spots representing the microspalls. No safe differentiation between a microspalled distressed surface and one with skidmarking is possible by the unaided eye. However, it is suggestive of skidmarking, if the frosted surface is a circumscribed patch on the rolling surface, and suggestive of surface-distress if it runs more or less circumferentially around the rolling track following finishing lines.

Under low magnification (scanning electron) microscopy, microspalls in a glazed surface show a typical *peeling* pattern reminiscent of smooth wet soil which underwent freezing and thawing. The "mesas" are burnished and flat, (unless there was subsequent mild wear, when they are scratch-marked); the pits are fracture-surfaced spall craters. Pit rims are sharp, and often feather-edged.

Microspalls tend to "decorate" finishing lines remaining within (generalized) glazed areas and cluster within the halos of local surface distress.

Microspalls can be seen in carefully prepared metallographic sections if the intersecting edge at the original surface is preserved by surface overplating.

11.5. Causes

The two dominant variables controlling surface distress are:

EHD film thickness to roughness ratio. In the presence of a sufficiently high EHD film thickness to surface roughness height ratio surface distress does not occur because the film prevents high microstresses in asperity interactions.

NOTE: Film thickness may be sufficient to prevent *generalized* surface distress, but not *local* distress in the vicinity of surface features such as depressions which locally depressurize and thereby thin the film.

Surface microgeometry. Both the *height* and *sharpness* of asperities (RMS roughness height and slope), influence surface distress.

- Composite *roughness height* (RMS) enters the EHD film thickness to roughness height ratio. Above a ratio of 3, *generalized* surface distress does not occur. The likelihood of surface distress increases as the ratio drops below this value. Local surface distress can occur where local surface features are high compared to the average, or where the film is depleted by a "sink", such as a sharp surface depression or edge.

- Composite sharpness (RMS slope, tip curvature) of asperities influences asperity stress levels for a given film thickness to roughness ratio. Since slope and roughness height are correlated for a given finishing method, surface distress is unlikely between very smooth, unblemished surfaces.

Other factors influential in surface distress are:

Surface material fatigue resistance. Matrix properties which enhance spalling fatigue resistance also improve resistance to surface distress.

The boundary lubricating ability of the lubricant can retard surface distress, although this effect is not very strong. This means that boundary lubricating additives are a much less potent remedy to surface distress than a thicker EHD film or smoother surfaces. However, a lubricant with very poor boundary lubricating ability (some unformulated synthetics) may promote surface distress.

Some solid lubricant coatings appear to retard surface

distress. In high-speed rolling bearings, black-oxide coatings (and tin coatings) have been found to be of some help.

The use of strongly adherent, crack-free *globular chromium plating* or other hard plating (not the common hard chrome plating) may be helpful in preventing surface distress under operating conditions where effective EHD lubrication cannot be achieved.

Notes On Retarding Surface Distress

• Lubricant chemistry does not offer as potent and flexible a remedy as EHD film and surface roughness control. In fact, surface distress differs from mild wear (FC 00.12) and galling (FC 00.13), in that lubricant chemistry is a prime controlling variable for wear and galling, but not for surface distress. Some benefit from solid lubricant coatings has been observed.

• Material fatigue strength is not generally a variable available for the control of surface distress. In the interest of spalling prevention, design choices for bulk material fatigue strength have already been made and can rarely be improved upon to retard surface distress.

• Due to many application problems, the use of currently available hard coatings is reserved for special requirements.

11.6. Effects of Surface Distress

The most hazardous consequence of surface distress is *spalling fatigue*. In the absence of pre-existing surface defects (nicks, grinding burns, etc.), surface-origin spalling initiates from surface distress, through the process of asperity-scale fatigue.

The rapidity with which surface distress leads to surface-origin spalling varies greatly. The principal operating factor influencing the rate of spalling from surface distress is *tractive* interface stress. When traction is high, spalls form rapidly and profusely from surface distress. The spalls are likely to appear from many initiation sites and can destroy a component in short order. See [5] for details.

If early spalling does not terminate the operation of a component that has suffered surface distress, then surface material delamination may occur. The original surface is thereby lost over wide areas and the component becomes unserviceable through loss of dimensional accuracy, through noise, or through secondary failures.

It is possible for surface distress to be arrested, especially in the glazing stage, without further deterioration. This may occur if mild wear (FC 00.12) is present and surfaces are successfully run-in to a smoother finish or if lubrication is subsequently improved. In this case, the surface distress may not prevent functionality. However, it is unsafe to count on surface distress to be consistently benign, even in similar applications or in repeated runs of the same application.

Gears and cams appear less sensitive to the consequences of surface distress than rolling bearings. This may be due to the greater ductility of lower-hardness gear and cam steels. However, surface distress is observed on both of these machine elements.

FAILURE CODE: 00.17

Cross-index of Secondary Failure Codes

Failure code	PlateNo
00.17.01	11.4
	11.15
	11.16
	11.17
00.17.02	11.18
	11.19
	11.20
	11.21
	11.22
	11.23
00.17.1	11.28
00.17.1.1	10.13
	10.56
	12.8
	12.15
	14.19
	14.23

Failure code	PlateNo
00.17.1.2	7.12
	7.13
	8.8
	9.16
	10.13
	10.20
	10.56
	11.5
	11.6
	11.26
	11.27
	12.8
	12.21
	16.21
	18.2
00.17.2	6.5
	10.44
	10.51
	15.28

Plates

DATA
Plate No: 11.1
Archive No: 014-32
Image type: light macro
Scalebar = 10 mm (micros: ±20%, others: +100%, -50%)
Component: TRB; OR, run
Speed:
Load:
Lubrication:
Failure Code1: 00.17.1 Generalized surface distress
Failure code2: -
Failure code3: -
Failure code4: -

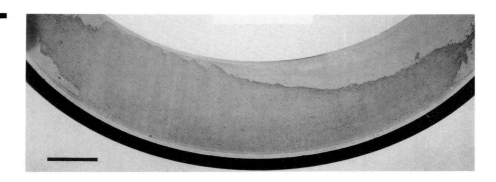

DESCRIPTIONS
FAILURE DESCRIPTION: On the roller path of the OR (cup), an extensive area in the load zone shows "frosted" ("peeled") appearance of generalized surface distress. The macro image does not permit distinction between glazing (FC 00.17.1.1) and the more advanced damage of microspalling (FC 00.17.1.2), but microspalling is more likely to correlate with the frosted appearance. Surface distress may lead to early spalling failure.

IMAGE DESCRIPTION: View is into the roller path of a TRB OR (cup). The dark circle on the S edge is the (large) endface. To the N is the light grey roller path with a sharply delineated darker grey area occupying most of the S part of the roller path. This is the surface distressed area which has a "frosted" ("peeled") appearance. Under (low) magnification, microspalls are likely to be visible.

SUSPECTED CAUSES: Insufficient EHD film thickness, combined with relatively rough surfaces, may cause surface distress (fatigue in asperity dimensions). Plastic deformation of asperities is followed by microspalling. The frosted surface appearance is typically the result of the many microspalls. (A 'glazed' surface is lustrous.)

DATA
Plate No: 11.2
Archive No: 027-240
Image type: view
Scalebar = 10 mm (micros: ±20%, others: +100%, -50%)
Component: DGBB; IR, run
Speed: 130 KdN
Load:
Lubrication: grease, 60 °C
Failure Code1: 00.17.1.1 Glazing (incipient surface distress)
Failure code2: 00.12.3.2.0.1 Wear track when load rotates over innerring
Failure code3: 00.18.1.2 Sharp individual dent(s) from metal debris, asperities
Failure code4: -

DESCRIPTIONS
FAILURE DESCRIPTION: Normal centered ball track in IR, overlaid in center plane, by narrow, surface-distressed and debris-dented band. Narrowness of band suggests profile geometry error. Bearing may have become noisy but has not failed.

IMAGE DESCRIPTION: The center 1/3 of ball groove shows different luster from outside areas, marking a ball track, extending probably to the Heathcote bands. At the center of this ball track is a narrow, darker grey band, apparently surface distressed. Just S of the light-reflection band crossing the ring are several small debris dents in the surface distressed band.

SUSPECTED CAUSES: Insufficient EHD film thickness, possibly combined with relatively rough surface finish in ball path, can lead to surface distress in the contact zone. Distress in a narrow central band within the ball track may arise if surface finish or profile geometry in that area are defective. Debris denting, caused by contamination, can promote surface distress.

DATA
Plate No: 11.3
Archive No: 027-234
Image type: light macro
Scalebar = 10 mm (micros: ±20%, others: +100%, -50%)
Component: ACBB; OR, run
Speed: 130 KdN
Load:
Lubrication: grease, 60 °C
Failure Code1: 00.17.1.1 Glazing (incipient surface distress)
Failure code2: 00.12.3.2.0.7 Wear track for misaligned outerring
Failure code3: -
Failure code4: -
See also PLATE: 7.3

DESCRIPTIONS
FAILURE DESCRIPTION: Early indication of surface distress in misaligned ball track of OR. The bearing may be noisy but has not failed. Continued surface distress may lead to spalling.

IMAGE DESCRIPTION: Ball groove of OR, with high land at image W and low land at E. From S extremity, over approximately a 90° arc, the E half of the ball groove shows a grey, finely frosted appearance suggesting surface distress. The ball track shifts to E, towards the low-land edge, as it proceeds to the N, suggesting OR misalignment.

SUSPECTED CAUSES: Insufficient EHD film thickness, possibly combined with relatively rough surface finish in ball path can lead to surface distress in the contact zone. OR misalignment can cause the contact zone to shift to one side of the groove. See drawings in PLATE 7.3.

DATA
Plate No: 11.4
Archive No: 007-101&102
Image type: a, b: SEM
Scalebar = a: 10, b: 12 μm (micros: ±20%, others: +100%, -50%)
Component: ACBB; a: OR, b: B, (stainless steel), run
Speed:
Load:
Lubrication: synthetic polyester oil, ? °C
Failure Code1: 00.17.1.1 Glazing (incipient surface distress)
Failure code2: 00.17.01 Surface distress, no sliding
Failure code3: 00.15.2 False brinelling on contact surface
Failure code4: 00.06.1.3 Primary carbide

DESCRIPTIONS
FAILURE DESCRIPTION: Extreme plastic flow of surface asperities from surface distress without microspalling. Removal of material (possibly along grain boundaries) by the false brinelling type of fretting wear. This gyroscope gimbal bearing undergoes small amplitude oscillation (hunting). EHD film cannot form and fretting of weaker material elements occurs over the entire overrolled surface. The texture is characterized by blocky hard primary carbides of 440C steel.

IMAGE DESCRIPTION: (a) & (b): Image covered with flattened,

a   b

deformed areas with irregular contours (plastically deformed asperities with underlying blocky carbides). Darker gaps are believed to be fretted depressions along grain boundaries.
(a): Finishing lines are visible as one continuous and one partially rolled-over furrow near W edge. (b): Random thin dark lines may be lapping marks. (a) & (b): Irregular white spots are imaging artifacts.

SUSPECTED CAUSES: Gyroscope gimbal bearings have an extremely fine finish and require high precision. Their motion is often oscillation (hunting). Surface distress and fretting conditions both exist. In the case shown, extreme plastic asperity deformation without microspalling is interspersed with fretted zones (perhaps grain boundaries). Blocky carbides distort surface topography.

DATA
Plate No: 11.5
Archive No: 107-019a&b
Image type: SEM
Scalebar = a: 500, b: 100 μm
(micros: ±20%, others: +100%, -50%)
Component: ACBB; IR, run
Speed:
Load:
Lubrication:
Failure code1: 00.17.1.1 Glazing
(incipient surface distress)
Failure code2: 00.17.1.2 Microspalling
(advanced surface distress)
Failure code3: -
Failure code4: -

DESCRIPTIONS
FAILURE DESCRIPTION: Ball groove of ACBB extensively glazed by surface distress. One circumferential band, located in the contact center, shows microspalling. The bearing is not failed.

IMAGE DESCRIPTION: (a): At E image edge, IR land is rough grey N–S band. Adjacent toward W is ball groove, starting with unrun area (dark), then glazed ball path (shaded grey), in which, about image center, a band of microcracks and microspalls decorates the contact center (maximum pressure, relatively high sliding). (b): Higher magnification. Featureless grey glazed background, E–W running microcracks and incipient microspall craters.

SUSPECTED CAUSES: On relatively smooth surfaces, with insufficient EHD film, surface distress produces uniform plastic working yielding a high-luster 'glazed' surface. In a ball groove, the contact pressure and sliding are high in the contact center. This aggravates surface distress into microspalling. Traction from sliding favors cracking perpendicular to the sliding direction.

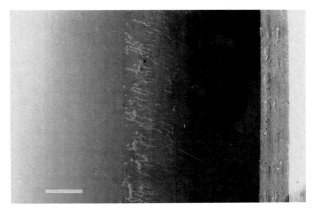

a

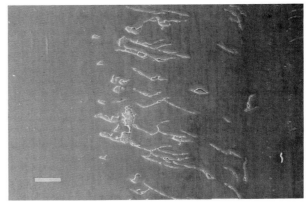

b

DATA
Plate No: 11.6
Archive No: 074-2
Image type: view
Scalebar = 10 mm (micros: ±20%, others: +100%, -50%)
Component: TRB; R, run
Speed:
Load:
Lubrication:
Failure Code1: 00.17.1.1 Glazing
(incipient surface distress)
Failure code2: 00.17.1.2 Microspalling
(advanced surface distress)
Failure code3: 00.01.2 Scratch,
toolmark, scuffmark
Failure code4: -

DESCRIPTIONS
FAILURE DESCRIPTION: On both rollers shown, patches of surface distress near center plane. In one roller, the patch is angularly confined (not a band). Overall cause of distress is severe asperity contact through insufficient EHD film. Axial localization of distress suggests excessive profile crowning. Circumferential localization suggests uneven surface roughness. Scratches may contribute. Rollers may fail in spalling but are not yet failed.

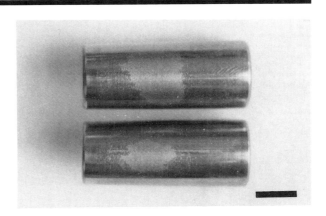

IMAGE DESCRIPTION: Patch or band of "frosted" surface distress centrally on N roller. Confined frosted patch W of center on S roller. Both rollers show several minor scuffmarks: on N roller, near E end of centerline; on S roller, near E end, S of centerline.

SUSPECTED CAUSES: Surface distress is generally due to insufficient EHD film. Heavy load contributes, hence suspicion of load concentration on roller center by "overcrowning," that is, excessive relief of the profile toward the edges. Sharp localization of surface distress suggests uneven roughness, possibly combined with scuffing or nicking to initiate the distress.

DATA
Plate No: 11.7
Archive No: 093-17.1.4&5
Image type: a, b: SEM
Scalebar = a: 35, b: 10 μm (micros: ±20%, others: +100%, -50%)
Component: DGBB; IR, run
Speed: 450 KdN
Load: 3.5 GPa
Lubrication: mineral oil, 100 °C
Failure Code1: 00.17.1.1 Glazing (incipient surface distress)
Failure code2: 00.18.1.1 Rounded dent (from soft contaminant)
Failure code3: 00.18.1.2 Sharp individual dent(s) from metal debris, asperities
Failure code4: 00.12.3.2.2 Scratch marks, kinematic wear marks in rolling surface

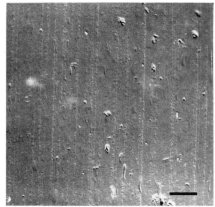

a

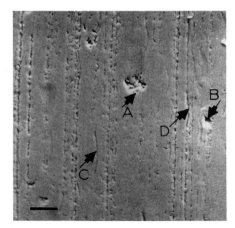

b

DESCRIPTIONS
FAILURE DESCRIPTION: Multiple changes in an as-run surface under mild surface distress conditions. Glazing has obliterated many finishing lines. Kinematic wear marks from ball spin. Dents are from soft and hard contaminants, the latter decorated by surface distress halo and some microspalling. Condition diagnostic for ball bearing operating under marginal EHD film, with some contamination in the presence of some ball sliding (Heathcote slip).

IMAGE DESCRIPTION: (a), (b): Finishing lines run N–S and are extensively glazed over by plastic flow (areas where lines are interrupted, missing, or dotted). Micro-spalled dents and kinematic wear marks (see (b)). In (b): Kinematic wear mark at C and D, slightly micro-spalled debris dents at A and B.

SUSPECTED CAUSES: Insufficient EHD film thickness compared to roughness leads to asperity contact under higher stress causing plastic flow of asperity ridges, initiating surface distress glazing, which gradually covers finishing lines by smoothing them or folding material over them. Denting on microscale is universal from contaminants below filtering level, which are larger than the film thickness.

DATA
Plate No: 11.8
Archive No: 005-18a&b
Image type: a, b: SEM (backscattered electron)
Scalebar = a, b: 40 μm (micros: ±20%, others: +100%, -50%)
Component: C; CM, run
Speed: 4.5 m/sec
Load: 1.4 GPa
Lubrication: mineral oil, 115 °C
Failure Code1: 00.17.1.1 Glazing (incipient surface distress)
Failure code2: 00.18.1.2 Sharp individual dent(s) from metal debris, asperities
Failure code3: -
Failure code4: -

a

b

DESCRIPTIONS
FAILURE DESCRIPTION: Comparison of finished unrun and run surface of cam. Unrun surface (a) has even grinding lines with an occasional line running at a low angle to the others. On run surface (b), many grinding lines are plastically obliterated by surface distress (glazing), leaving only the deeper lines. Fine dents are due to rolled-in contamination. Glazing and fine denting to the degree seen are not failures, but merely warning indications.

IMAGE DESCRIPTION: (a): Normal grinding lines proceed E–W and are smooth and sharp-edged. A few lines are at shallow angles to the others. The backscattered electron SEM image exaggerates contrast and shows lines steeper than they are. (b): Several wide horizontal strips with little texture, where grinding lines are plastically obliterated. Deeper lines remain. Several round dents are caused by rolled-over debris.

SUSPECTED CAUSES: Surface distress of the magnitude shown is common when rolling contacts operate without full EHD film. Debris dents of this magnitude (2–3 μm diameter) are inescapable in all but the most extreme cleanness conditions, from debris carried in even well filtered lubricant.

DATA

Plate No: 11.9
Archive No: 099-202
Image type: light macro of fractured tooth
Scalebar = 20 mm (micros: ±20%, others: +100%, -50%)
Component: SG; W, med. hard, run
Speed:
Load:
Lubrication:
Failure Code1: 00.17.1.1 Glazing (incipient surface distress)
Failure code2: 00.22.01.4 Gear tooth crack or fracture
Failure code3: -
Failure code4: -
See also PLATE: 11.11

DESCRIPTIONS

FAILURE DESCRIPTION: Tooth contact surface with surface distress glazing in a relatively rough finish on a medium-hard gear. Gross tooth fracture, unrelated to the glazing. The relatively rough surfaces of medium-hard gearing are subject to surface distress in insufficient EHD film conditions. This damage is not usually a cause for component failure.

IMAGE DESCRIPTION: The rough fracture surface of the broken tooth is at image S and E. At image N, is a tooth flank with dark mottling in the addendum and dedendum and, a clear band at the pitchline (and stains, probably from corrosion). The mottling represents glazed areas interspersed with unaffected areas or microspalls. Some sliding was required for surface distress, leaving pitchline band clear.

SUSPECTED CAUSES: The tooth broke from causes unrelated to surface distress. Surface distress glazing, which in finer surfaces extends to asperity peaks and many valleys, may be limited to peaks (ridges) in the relatively soft, relatively rough surface of medium hardness gears. Compare with high hardness gear in PLATE 11.11.

DATA

Plate No: 11.10
Archive No: 004-16
Image type: SEM
Scalebar = 100 μm (micros: ±20%, others: +100%, -50%)
Component: DGBB; B, silicon nitride, run
Speed: >600 KdN
Load:
Lubrication: Sputtered molybdenum disulfide coating
Failure code1: 00.17.1.2 Microspalling (advanced surface distress)
Failure code2: 00.05.1 Micro-porosity
Failure code3: -
Failure code4: -

DESCRIPTIONS

FAILURE DESCRIPTION: Ball from experimental bearing with steel rings and hot pressed silicon nitride ceramic balls, with molybdenum disulfide based lubricant coating and polymer separator. After running, the ceramic ball surface shows local microspalling as from surface distress, possibly at a pre-existing pore. Whole surface is pitted, as from damaged coating. (No plastic flow is visible.) X-ray analysis indicates incomplete solid lube coating remaining.

IMAGE DESCRIPTION: Background is grey coated surface of ball, peppered with lighter-color micropits, as from incomplete coating. At image center is a cluster of microspalls as from

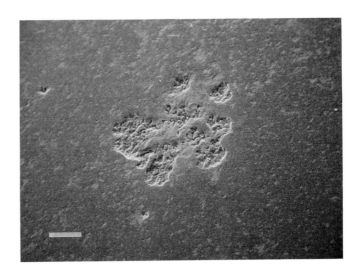

surface distress. One small crater each to W and S of large cluster.

SUSPECTED CAUSES: Dry lubricated ball bearings with ceramic balls are a unique component. Normal contact fatigue failures occur, as in the surface distress microspalling shown. Role of solid lubricant in preventing surface distress is not well understood. Hot pressed silicon nitride is prone to some porosity, serving to nucleate (micro or macro) spalling.

DATA
Plate No: 11.11
Archive No: 080-201&202
Image type: a, b: SEM (backscatter)
Scalebar = a: 1 mm, b: 400 μm
(micros: ±20%, others: +100%, -50%)
Component: SG; W, high hardness, run
Speed:
Load:
Lubrication:
Failure Code1: 00.17.1.2 Microspalling
(advanced surface distress)
Failure code2: 00.16.01.3.1 Tooth
pitchline or dedendum spalling
Failure code3: 00.12.5.2 Smooth tooth
wear
Failure code4: 00.16.02.4 Incipient
spalling, multiple spalls
See also PLATE 11.18

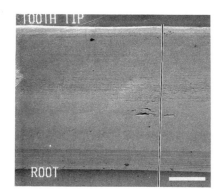

a

b

DESCRIPTIONS
FAILURE DESCRIPTION: Surface distress microspalling (often designated "pitting") has occurred near the pitchline. A few macroscopic spalls are in the dedendum, at the edge of the surface distressed area. Addendum and dedendum are worn down in the high-sliding areas causing high pressure near the pitchline. The gear was found to be of insufficient hardness. It has not failed, but is expected to fail in spalling. See PLATE 11.18 for detail.

IMAGE DESCRIPTION: (a): View of tooth contact surface from tip to root (labeled). The black line crossing, from N to S, marks plane of subsequent sectioning (see PLATE 11.18), Microspalls, in E–W rows transverse to sliding direction cover addendum near pitchline. Smooth wear near tip and root. Four macroscopic spalls with straight E–W edge near image center (pitchline) appear originating from distress. (b): Details of micro- and macrospalls.

SUSPECTED CAUSES: Gear was found to have insufficient surface hardness. Wear occurred in high-sliding zones away from pitchline, leaving the pitchline raised, and under excessive contact pressure. Surface distress occurred in the material, followed by spalling. (In normal gear, spalling is more common in dedendum, where sliding traction reduces fatigue life.)

DATA
Plate No: 11.12
Archive No: 005-22&26
Image type: a: SEM, b: metallogram,
Nital etch
Scalebar = a: 10, b: 8 μm (micros:
±20%, others: +100%, -50%)
Component: C; CM, run
Speed: 8 m/sec
Load: 1.8 GPa
Lubrication: mineral oil, 115 °C
Failure Code1: 00.17.1.2 Microspalling
(advanced surface distress)
Failure code2: 00.16.02.2 Contact
fatigue cracking
Failure code3: -
Failure code4: -

a

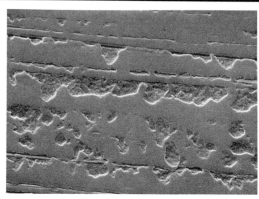

b

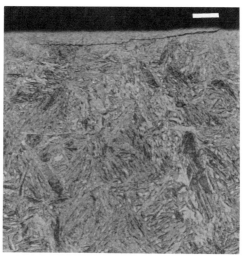

DESCRIPTIONS
FAILURE DESCRIPTION: (a): Surface distress, with plastically worked material retaining some finishing lines. Microspalling follows finish lines. (b): Section through surface distressed area, showing microcrack (4 μm deep). Continued running under similar conditions leads to early spalling failure of cam.

IMAGE DESCRIPTION: (a): Contact surface. Rolling direction is E–W along finishing lines, which appear as black furrows with intervening ridges. Surface distress glazing by plastic flow between finishing lines. Extensive micro-spalling of glazed ridges, confined between furrows. (b): Etched section through surface distressed material. Rolling direction E to W. Dark line of shallow-angle microcrack runs from surface to 3 μm depth.

SUSPECTED CAUSES: Heavily loaded cam/follower contact in high speed engine undergoes high pressure and traction at entry point to lift lobe. With inadequate EHD film, surface distress arises.

DATA
Plate No: 11.13
Archive No: 074-1
Image type: view
Scalebar = 10 mm (micros: ±20%, others: +100%, -50%)
Component: DRBB; IR, run
Speed:
Load:
Lubrication:
Failure Code1: 00.17.1.2 Microspalling (advanced surface distress)
Failure code2: 00.16.1.2.1 Shallow entry spall from surface point-defect
Failure code3: 00.12.3.2.0.5 Wear track for centered axial load
Failure code4: -

DESCRIPTIONS
FAILURE DESCRIPTION: Double-row ball bearing IR operated under heavy axial load shows ball track on one side of both grooves. The ball track area is surface distressed ("frosted") by a profusion of asperity scale microspalls. In one groove, a row of macroscopic spalls has formed in the groove bottom. The bearing has failed.

IMAGE DESCRIPTION: Double-row ball bearing IR, with two

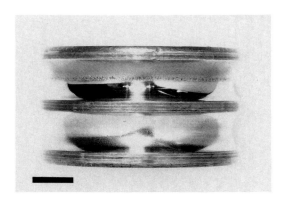

symmetrical ball grooves and three lands. Original finish of grooves is high luster as seen on S half of N groove. N half of both grooves appears frosted. A centered band of spall craters in N groove. Dark and light colored reflections in S half of both grooves are due to lighting.

SUSPECTED CAUSES: Insufficient EHD film, possibly combined with rough surfaces or aggressive lubricant may produce surface distress, that is, plastic flow and microspalling on an asperity scale. Under continued running, surface distressed areas are prone to macroscopic spalling, where load is heaviest. In this case that location is the bottom of one groove.

DATA
Plate No: 11.14
Archive No: 074-28&29
Image type: a: view, b: light microgram
Scalebar = a: 10 mm, b: 100 μm (micros: ±20%, others: +100%, -50%)
Component: DGBB; B, run
Speed:
Load:
Lubrication:
Failure Code1: 00.17.1.2 Microspalling (advanced surface distress)
Failure code2: 00.16.1.2.1 Shallow entry spall from surface point-defect
Failure code3: 00.18.1.2 Sharp individual dent(s) from metal debris, asperities
Failure code4: -

DESCRIPTIONS
FAILURE DESCRIPTION: Ball with band of spalls around a great circle, indicating operation without indexing of ball axis (a). Numerous surface distress microcracks and microspalls exist in the vicinity of the spalls, serving as initiating defects (b). Ball may have suffered surface distress when contacting a rough ring surface under low EHD film. Spalling was secondary. The ball has failed.

IMAGE DESCRIPTION: (a): Numerous spall craters along E-W great circle of a ball. Elsewhere, the ball surface is debris dented, probably from spalling debris. (b): Background is light grey glazed ball surface from surface distress; finishing lines are still visible. There are many jagged N-S running microcracks and black appearing microspalls.

SUSPECTED CAUSES: In producing surface distress, the composite surface roughness in the contact governs. A smooth sur-

a

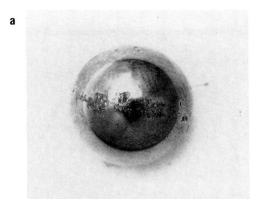

b

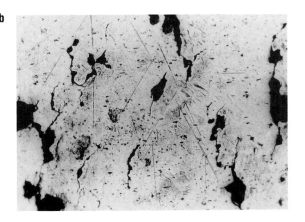

face (ball) combined with a rough one (ring) can produce surface distress. Often the smooth surface suffers the distress, possibly because the work hardened asperities of the rough surface progressively overroll all areas on the smooth surface.

DATA
Plate No: 11.15
Archive No: 107-015a&c
Image type: SEM
Scalebar = a: 100, b: 10 μm
(micros: ±20%, others: +100%,
-50%)
Component: ACBB; IR, run
Speed:
Load:
Lubrication: grease, 50 °C
Failure Code1: 00.17.1.2 Microspalling
(advanced surface distress)
Failure code2: 00.17.01 Surface
distress, no sliding
Failure code3: -
Failure code4: -
See also PLATE: 11.21

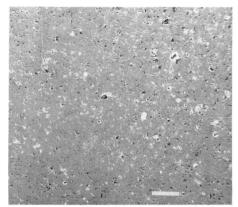

a

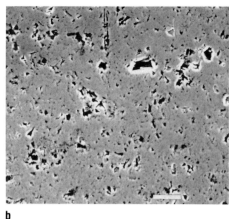

b

DESCRIPTIONS
FAILURE DESCRIPTION: Advanced generalized surface distress.
All finishing lines are obliterated by plastic working of the surface; a dense distribution of fine (1–5 μm dia.) microspalls has
formed. No preferred orientation in microspalling. This characterizes absence of sliding. See PLATE 11.21 for sliding. Rapid
macro-spalling is likely upon continued running, due to the profusion of microspalls acting as surface defects.

IMAGE DESCRIPTION: (a), (b): Background is featureless grey
surface of plastically smoothed asperities. Sharp-edged black
shapes are microspalls. Some of them have a white halo indi-

cating a "feather edge" of lamina undermined by cracks. The
non- directionality of crater shapes is more clearly seen at
higher magnification in (b).

SUSPECTED CAUSES: Surface distress is contact fatigue in asperity dimensions, arising when asperity interaction stresses are
excessive, as from insufficient EHD film and sharp asperity
slopes (rough surface). Plastic 'glazing' of surface, with obliteration of finishing lines occurs first, microspalling of heavily
worked asperities follows. The area shown is in or near a
Heathcote band where sliding is minimal (PLATE 11.21 shows
contact edge).

DATA
Plate No: 11.16
Archive No: 093-17.1.11&13
Image type: a, b: SEM
Scalebar = a: 140, b: 10 μm
(micros: ±20%, others: +100%,
-50%)
Component: DGBB; IR, run
Speed: 450 KdN
Load: 2.8 GPa
Lubrication: synthetic polyester oil,
130 °C
Failure Code1: 00.17.1.2 Microspalling
(advanced surface distress)
Failure code2: 00.17.01 Surface
distress, no sliding
Failure code3: -
Failure code4: -

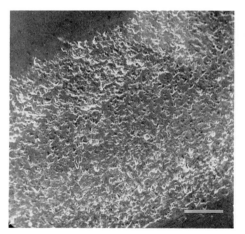

a

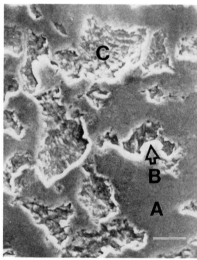

b

DESCRIPTIONS
FAILURE DESCRIPTION: Band of surface distress microspalling
with a dense population of spall craters on a background of
glazed, plastically flown surface. "Feather edges" are rolled
over crater rims. Spall bottoms show a typical fracture surface.
Adjacent to the spalled bands is a surface area which is glazed
only. The bearing will soon spall in continued running.

IMAGE DESCRIPTION: (a): Wide, SW–NE band following rolling
direction, covered with microspall craters in a featureless glazed
surface. In NW and SE image corners, are glazed but uncra-

tered surfaces. (b): High magnification shows: a featureless
glazed surface at *A*, the feather edge of plastically flowed material at *B* and a spall bottom fracture surface at *C*. Feather
edges are not worn off.

SUSPECTED CAUSES: Synthetic oils used in high speed (aerospace) applications at high temperature often have low working
viscosity, forcing thin EHD films and promoting surface distress. Chemical aggressiveness of formulated lubricants, which
may arise after long use, appears to accelerate surface distress
microcracking and microspalling.

DATA
Plate No: 11.17
Archive No: 107-017a&c
Image type: a, b: SEM
Scalebar =: a: 100, b: 10 μm
(micros: ±20%, others: +100%,
-50%)
Component: CRB; IR, run
Speed:
Load:
Lubrication:
Failure Code1: 00.17.1.2 Microspalling
(advanced surface distress)
Failure code2: 00.17.01 Surface
distress, no sliding
Failure code3: 00.18.2.2.2 Stippled
line(s) or band(s) from rolled-in debris
Failure code4: -

DESCRIPTIONS
FAILURE DESCRIPTION: Rolling-in of solid contamination produced 'stippled' bands of indentations of varying density. Surface distress microspalling is initiated, chiefly at dents. Many
smaller craters form in densely dented bands; fewer, larger craters form in less densely dented bands. Some areas are virtually free of dents and microspalls. Severe surface distress is
likely to lead to early macro-spalling failure.

IMAGE DESCRIPTION: (a): Image divided by N–S lines into five
main zones. 1st and 4th zones from W are relatively undamaged. 2d zone is densely dented, with small craters. 3d and
5th zones are less densely dented, with larger craters.
(b): transition, zones 2 to 3. In W half, multiple dents with
traces of N–S finishing marks change to sharp-edged microspalls interspersed with featureless surface. E half: fewer dents,
larger craters.

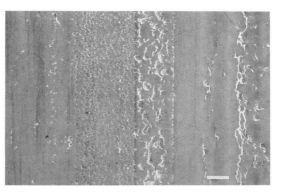

a

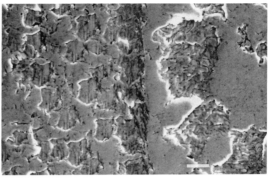

b

SUSPECTED CAUSES: Operation with solid contamination at low
sliding creates rolled-in denting first. It may then undergo surface distress under insufficient EHD film, causing glazed surfaces and microspalls. (Surface distress can arise without denting.)

DATA
Plate No: 11.18
Archive No: 080-206&207
Image type: a, b: SEM (with section)
Scalebar = a: 100, b: 20 μm
(micros: ±20%, others: +100%,
-50%)
Component: SG; W, high hardness, run
Speed:
Load:
Lubrication:
Failure Code1: 00.17.1.2 Microspalling
(advanced surface distress)
Failure code2: 00.17.02 Surface
distress, with sliding
Failure code3: -
Failure code4: -
See also PLATE: 11.11

DESCRIPTIONS
FAILURE DESCRIPTION: In a case-hardened gear, surface distress microspalling (often designated 'pitting'). (a) shows multiple microspalls formed fish-scale fashion from microcracks
transverse to rolling/sliding direction. In (b), a few microspalls
with their initiating cracks extending about 10 μm deep into
cross section, toward sliding direction. Macro-spalls have not
formed in this area. See PLATE 11.11 for overview.

a

b

IMAGE DESCRIPTION: (a), (b): W image half is tooth flank
surface, E half polished cross-section. E–W running dark lines
in tooth flank surface are microcracks transverse to rolling/slid-
ing direction. Some exfoliation into microspalls. (b): section
through two microcracks shows their propagation at about 30°
to contact surface, progressing toward the pitchline, located toward image N, that is, opposite to the sliding direction.

SUSPECTED CAUSES: Gear was found to have insufficient surface hardness. Wear occurred in high-sliding zones away from
pitchline, leaving the pitchline raised, under excessive contact
pressure. Surface distress occurred in (soft) material, followed
by spalling.

DATA

Plate No: 11.19
Archive No: 107-020a&c
Image type: a, b: SEM
Scalebar = a: 100, b: 10 μm
(micros: ±20%, others: +100%, -50%)
Component: SRB; IR, run
Speed:
Load:
Lubrication:
Failure Code1: 00.17.1.2 Microspalling (advanced surface distress)
Failure code2: 00.17.02 Surface distress, with sliding
Failure code3: -
Failure code4: -

a

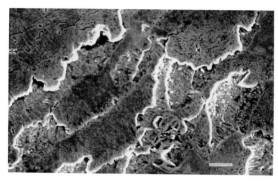

b

DESCRIPTIONS

FAILURE DESCRIPTION: Surface destroyed by generalized microcracking and incipient microspalling due to surface distress in the presence of high tractive stresses from sliding under poor EHD lubrication. Imminent gross failure from macroscopic spalling or bulk cracking is likely.

IMAGE DESCRIPTION: (a): Surface consists of dense SW–NE rows of microcracks and microspalls. Original surface is no longer discernible. Near center of image N edge, a few faint N–S lines may be remnants of circumferential finishing lines.
(b): Higher magnification. Complex winding microcracks running in an overall SW–NE direction overlap and create a "fish-scale" surface pattern, which, without magnification, appears "frosted".

SUSPECTED CAUSES: The as-manufactured surface was proba-

bly rather rough. Heathcote sliding, combined with axial slip, created a net SE to NW sliding direction. Microcracking from poor lubrication has a main direction perpendicular to sliding. This surface has much reduced long-term spalling resistance.

DATA

Plate No: 11.20
Archive No: 018-301&304
Image type: a: light microgram, b: SEM
Scalebar = a: 200, b: 20 μm
(micros: ±20%, others: +100%, -50%)
Component: DGBB; IR, tool steel, run
Speed: 400 KdN
Load: 3.1 GPa
Lubrication: synthetic polyester, 150 °C
Failure Code1: 00.17.1.2 Microspalling (advanced surface distress)
Failure code2: 00.17.02 Surface distress, with sliding
Failure code3: 00.06.1.3 Primary carbide
Failure code4: -

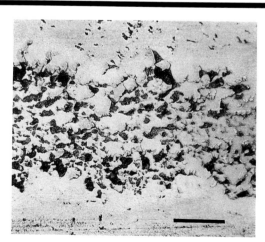

a

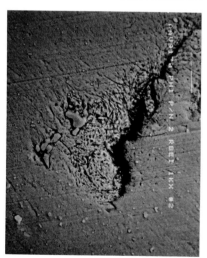

b

DESCRIPTIONS

FAILURE DESCRIPTION: Generalized surface distress microspalling with directionality caused by sliding. Initiation of microspalls tends to be associated with hard carbides of the tool steel. Calculated EHD film thickness was 0.08 μm, resulting in film thickness/RMS roughness ratio below 1, which is conducive to surface distress. Early macro-spalling failure is likely.

IMAGE DESCRIPTION: (a): Area on IR ball path. Band of surface distress microcracking and angular microspall craters runs E–W at image center. Rolling and ball spin are E–W.

(b): Shows apex of one angular microspall. Rolling, ball spin and finishing lines all run W–E. Microspalled area is an irregular fracture surface extending E from angular, smooth-surfaced carbides, to a sharp step shown as black due to shadowing.

SUSPECTED CAUSES: Low EHD film thickness/roughness ratio, and kinematically required sliding of ball in groove (Heathcote slip), have produced surface distress. Hard, somewhat prominent carbides act as microspall initiators.

DATA
Plate No: 11.21
Archive No: 107-016a&c
Image type: SEM
Scalebar = a: 100, b: 10 μm
(micros: ±20%, others: +100%, -50%)
Component: ACBB; IR, run
Speed:
Load:
Lubrication: grease, 50 °C
Failure Code1: 00.17.1.2 Microspalling (advanced surface distress)
Failure code2: 00.17.02 Surface distress, with sliding
Failure code3: 00.12.3.2.2 Scratch marks, kinematic wear marks in rolling surface
Failure code4: -
See also PLATE: 11.15

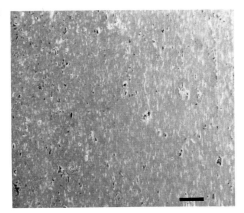

a

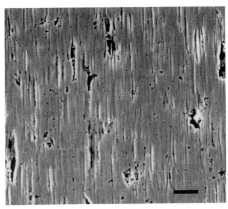

b

DESCRIPTIONS
FAILURE DESCRIPTION: Advanced generalized surface distress. All finishing lines are obliterated by plastic working of the surface; a dense distribution of fine (1–5 μm dia.) microspalls has formed. There is a strong preferred orientation in microspalls and many parallel kinematic wear marks. This characterizes the *presence* of sliding. See PLATE 11.15 which shows the *absence* of sliding. Macroscopic spalling is likely in further running, due to microspalls as surface defects.

IMAGE DESCRIPTION: (a): Background is featureless grey surface of plastically smoothed asperities. Sharp-edged black shapes are microspalls, some with a white halo indicating 'feather edge.' (b): Higher magnification shows dense population of straight N–S lines, which are kinematic wear marks in the *sliding* direction. Also, N–S elongated microspalls. Both with white haloes. Wear marks create asperities which initiate microspalling.

SUSPECTED CAUSES: Surface distress is contact fatigue in asperity dimensions arising when asperity interaction stresses are excessive, as from insufficient EHD film and sharp asperity slopes (rough surface). Kinematic wearmarks, from sliding under asperity contact conditions, create additional microspall-initiating defects. The area shown is near the contact edge where sliding is substantial (PLATE 11.15 is at or near Heathcote band.)

DATA
Plate No: 11.22
Archive No: 074-6&7
Image type: a: light microgram, b: metallogram (etched)
Scalebar = a: 100, b: 50 μm
(micros: ±20%, others: +100%, -50%)
Component: DGBB; IR, run
Speed:
Load:
Lubrication:
Failure Code1: 00.17.1.2 Microspalling (advanced surface distress)
Failure code2: 00.17.02 Surface distress, with sliding
Failure code3: 00.16.02.2 Contact fatigue cracking
Failure code4: 00.16.1.2 Surface origin spall

a

b

DESCRIPTIONS
FAILURE DESCRIPTION: (a): Extreme microcracking of surface transverse to rolling and sliding direction. (b): Microcracks progress down in rolling direction at about 30° angle from surface. At least one deep (over 100 μm) crack in same direction, suggesting unusually high tractive forces driving macrocrack deeper without preliminary microspalling.

IMAGE DESCRIPTION: (a): Microgram shows a generally distressed surface with only a few E–W finishing lines remaining, and numerous jagged N–S microcracks. (b): metallogram (section) with several microcracks NE to SW, to about 20 μm depth. One crack progressed to about 100 μm depth, which is macroscopic in contact dimensions. Cracks proceed into material at approximately 30° angle with E to W rolling direction.

SUSPECTED CAUSES: Surface distress microcracking is usually limited to asperity dimensions (a few μm depth). Under heavy tractive forces (sliding with poor lubrication), shear stresses are high at all depths, from the surface to the normal depth of the max. Hertz shear stress. This may drive cracks down to macroscopic depth, producing macro-spalling.

DATA
Plate No: 11.23
Archive No: 018-124&125
Image type: view
Scalebar = a, b: 30 mm (micros: ±20%, others: +100%, -50%)
Component: SRB; a: R&G&IR; b: R, run
Speed:
Load:
Lubrication:
Failure Code1: 00.17.1.2 Microspalling (advanced surface distress)
Failure code2: 00.17.02 Surface distress, with sliding
Failure code3: 00.16.1.2.1 Shallow entry spall from surface point-defect
Failure code4: -

a

b

DESCRIPTIONS
FAILURE DESCRIPTION: Glazed and microspalled ("frosted," "peeled") bands with macro-spalling near ends of all rollers, due to inadequate lubrication aggravated by the higher sliding velocity at roller ends. IR contact conformity may be too high, causing stress concentration near ends, resulting in spalling near the edges. The bearing has failed.

IMAGE DESCRIPTION: (a): IR/R/separator assembly of separator-guided SRB. Frosted appearance on all roller OD-s, with micro and macrospall craters in two sharply defined bands at roller ends. Shallow craters as from surface origin. (b): Similar failure to (a) in rollers of another SRB. Frosted appearance extends in patches, from edges to contact center. Macrospalling from axial surface cracks due to traction in sliding. Edge spalling in both images.

SUSPECTED CAUSES: Edge loading in SRB suggests excessive

contact conformity. Thin EHD film, possibly with rougher surfaces, initiates surface distress, aggravated by higher sliding near roller ends and leading to surface initiated spalls.

DATA
Plate No: 11.24
Archive No: 122-1&2
Image type: SEM composite
Scalebar = 100 μm (micros: ±20%, others: +100%, -50%)
Component: SABB; IR, run
Speed: 120 KdN
Load: 3.7 GPa
Lubrication: mineral oil, ? °C
Failure Code1: 00.17.2 Localized surface distress (halo at defect)
Failure code2: 00.02.1 Grinding, honing, lapping furrow
Failure code3: 00.16.1.2.2 Shallow entry spall from surface line-defect
Failure code4: -
See also PLATE: 5.3

DESCRIPTIONS
FAILURE DESCRIPTION: Grinding furrow flanked by a glazed halo on both sides, shows several surface distress microspalls and leads into a line-defect origin spall. Grinding furrows are spall-initiating surface defects, both by causing collapse of EHD film (surface distress) and as direct stress raisers. The resulting spall is an incipient functional failure.

IMAGE DESCRIPTION: Image is a composite of two SEM micrograms. At image W is the initiation of a spall crater which

originated from the grinding furrow running E–W across image center. The furrow starts deepening just W of E image edge and progresses to the crater. N and S of furrow, grinding lines are obliterated by glazing halo. Microspalls in N half of halo. Furrow ends just short of spall crater edge, leaving a lip of metal.

SUSPECTED CAUSES: Grinding furrows are caused by detached grinding grit and are often "comet-tail" shaped (see PLATE 5.3). This furrow deepens toward the spall, but its endpoint is obliterated by rolldown at spall edge. Surface distress arises at the furrow since the lubricant drains into the furrow out of the EHD film. Local stress concentration tends to initiate spalling.

DATA
Plate No: 11.25
Archive No: 093-17.2.2&3
Image type: a, b: SEM
Scalebar = a: 40, b: 12 μm (micros: ±20%, others: +100%, -50%)
Component: DGBB; IR, run
Speed: 450 KdN
Load: 3.5 GPa
Lubrication: mineral oil, 65 °C
Failure Code1: 00.17.2 Localized surface distress (halo at defect)
Failure code2: 00.02.1 Grinding, honing, lapping furrow
Failure code3: 00.18.1.4 Multiple irregular denting from fine, loose hard debris
Failure code4: -
See also PLATE: 11.26

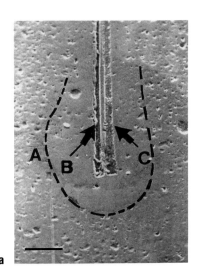

a

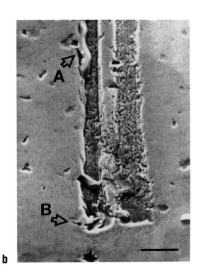

b

DESCRIPTIONS
FAILURE DESCRIPTION: A pair of furrows (FC 00.02) with abrupt ending, probably produced by detached grains of grinding or honing grit. The surrounding surface shows minimal remnants of finishing lines, extensive glazing and denting. There is severe plastic working of surface material along furrows, with folding and cracking, due to a drained EHD film. The surface distress is due to insufficient EHD film, the denting to contaminants. Early spalling is likely.

IMAGE DESCRIPTION: (a): Two furrows, apparently formed simultaneously in finishing by two grains of grinding or honing grit, extend from N image center to an abrupt end. There are many sharp-cornered debris dents on the surface. Faint N–S finishing lines are visible near S edge. Entire surface is glazed, most severely near dent edges, within contour A. Material is folded at B and C. (b): Same furrows, at higher magnification, show cracked, folded material at A and B. Some dents.

SUSPECTED CAUSES: Grinding or honing furrows, when severe, drain the EHD film in their vicinity, causing severe asperity contact. In the debris-contaminated, low EHD film environment evidenced in this PLATE, severe plastic working of material in furrow vicinity results. Sharp furrow edges fold and crack under plastic working. Surface distress also modifies dents by flowing the edges and possibly spalling the bottoms. See also PLATE 11.26.

DATA
Plate No: 11.26
Archive No: 018-311
Image type: light microgam
Scalebar = 100 μm (micros: ±20%, others: +100%, -50%)
Component: DGBB; IR, tool steel, run
Speed: 400 KdN
Load: 2.3 GPa
Lubrication: synthetic polyester, 150 °C
Failure Code1: 00.17.2 Localized surface distress (halo at defect)
Failure code2: 00.17.1.2 Microspalling (advanced surface distress)
Failure code3: 00.02.1 Grinding, honing, lapping furrow
Failure code4: -
See also PLATE: 11.25

DESCRIPTIONS
FAILURE DESCRIPTION: Grinding furrow, possibly caused by detachment of a primary carbide in grinding. Halo of surface distress with microspalls along the furrow. Surface distressed furrows are serious surface defects likely to cause premature spalling failure.

IMAGE DESCRIPTION: Background is contact surface with E–W finishing lines. In image center, heavy black E–W line with sharp ends is grinding furrow. N and S of furrow, oblong 'halo,' where finishing lines are partly obliterated. Irregular, sizeable black spots in halo are microspalls. Black spotting and staining elsewhere on image may be due to etching and is not diagnostic.

SUSPECTED CAUSES: Finishing of tool steel components is more difficult than for 52100 type bearing steel, in part because of many larger carbides. Such carbides may become detached and gouge the surface in finishing to make a furrow. (See also PLATE 11.25.) EHD film collapses near a furrow, causing asperity contact and surface distress glazing and microspalling.

DATA

Plate No: 11.27
Archive No: 107-023a&b
Image type: SEM
Scalebar = a, b: 100 μm (micros: ±20%, others: +100%, -50%)
Component: DGBB; IR, run
Speed:
Load:
Lubrication:
Failure Code1: 00.17.2 Localized surface distress (halo at defect)
Failure code2: 00.17.1.2 Microspalling (advanced surface distress)
Failure code3: 00.18.1.2 Sharp individual dent(s) from metal debris, asperities
Failure code4: -

DESCRIPTIONS

FAILURE DESCRIPTION: Sharply delineated debris dent causes a glazing 'halo' of surface distress, within which surface distress microcracking and microspalling occurs. The bearing is not failed.

IMAGE DESCRIPTION: (a): Background with N–S finishing lines is undamaged surface. In image center is a footprint-shaped debris dent, with finishing lines preserved in bottom. Rim of dent shows obliterated finishing lines (halo) gradually fading outward. Microspall NW of dent. (b): Microspall from (a) is S of image center, surrounded by 'glazed' surface, with folds along finishing lines. Glazed dent rim runs E from S spall edge.

SUSPECTED CAUSES: Debris dent may have raised edges acting as stress concentrators. In EHD film, a local depression

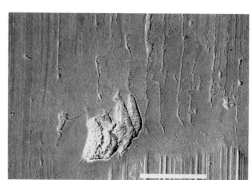

concentrates stress around edges even if these are not raised as a result of the collapse of the film. Surface distress halos result, which may initiate microspalling.

DATA

Plate No: 11.28
Archive No: 093-17.2.5
Image type: SEM
Scalebar = 55 μm (micros: ±20%, others: +100%, -50%)
Component: DGBB; IR, run
Speed: 450 KdN
Load: 3.5 GPa
Lubrication: mineral oil, 100 °C
Failure Code1: 00.17.2 Localized surface distress (halo at defect)
Failure code2: 00.18.1.2 Sharp individual dent(s) from metal debris, asperities
Failure code3: 00.17.1 Generalized surface distress
Failure code4: -

DESCRIPTIONS

FAILURE DESCRIPTION: Circular debris dent of about 240 μm diameter with finishing lines in the dent bottom. Raised material rim around dent is plastically worked by surface distress, especially at trailing edge (in rolling direction) where EHD film tends to be thinner. There is some generalized glazing of the surface. Dents with distressed haloes are significant spall originating defects.

IMAGE DESCRIPTION: Finishing lines are dark, dotted N–S lines. At *A*, a circular dent is illuminated obliquely, causing light-colored wall in S and dark in N. Finishing lines continue in

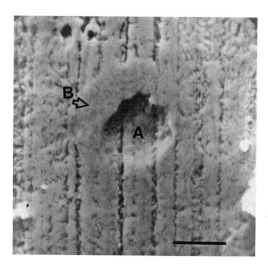

the dent. At *B*, circular elevated rim without finishing lines is surface distress halo. Rolling direction is S to N.

SUSPECTED CAUSES: Insufficient EHD film thickness compared to roughness occurs preferentially at defects such as the dent at *A* where the film drains. Asperities contact under higher stress and flow plastically, initiating surface distress in the rim surrounding the dent, whether elevated in denting (as here) or not. Film thickness cannot build up promptly downstream from dent in rolling direction, hence more asperity contact occurs there.

12 DENTING

12.1. Definition

A dent is a plastic depression (short gash, rounded-edged hollow, sharp-edged single- or multifaceted impression, depressed solid or stippled line) caused in a *working* surface by a relatively incompressible object pressed into it by the passage of a contacting rolling element. Denting is the process by which dents form. It is often combined with wear-marks (FC 00.12). Denting, by the definition used in this Atlas, occurs *in service.*

Dents are distinguished from:

• *Nicks,* which are plastic indentations formed prior to service (FC 00.01);
• *Wear marks,* that is, scratch marks made by an opposing asperity or a third body in a sliding contact (FC 00.12);
• *Pits,* which are point depressions made by means other than plastic indentation (FC 00.03, FC 00.12, FC 00.20, FC 0.21);
• *Spalls,* which are craters caused by contact fatigue (FC 00.16).

12.2. Nomenclature

Denting is a commonly used designation for this failure mode. The most common alternative designation is *nicking* wherein the distinction between pre-service and in-service failure is lost. In this Atlas, the distinction will be maintained wherever it can be established. A designation found in some gear literature is *peening,* although the definition of peening does not clearly exclude wear.

12.3. Failure Process

Denting is the result of a plastic impression made on a surface when a sharp asperity or an entrapped foreign body is pressed into the contact surface under *normal* load. It is most distinct on rolling contact surfaces, where the relative motion in the contact is predominantly normal to the surface. (Sliding motion in the contact results in wear marks (FC 00.12)). The process of forming dents resembles an indentation hardness test: The indenter penetrates the surface in an approximate normal direction, carries surface material down with it and generally throws up significant raised edges. The rounded dents formed by soft

debris however, have no raised edges. An indented line can form by plastic flow beneath a rolling indenter (an edge on an opposing rolling element).

The detailed morphology of the failure depends on the nature of the indenter, as follows:

1. *Debris (hard particle) dent.* A single, sharply outlined dent, mostly with raised edges, is made by a hard (metal) particle passing *once* through the contact. In the process, the particle is generally flattened, but retains its distinctive outline, often with sharp corners and edges.
2. *(True) brinell mark.* This is a plastic depression of simple outline (ellipse, truncated ellipse, rectangle, dumbbell) made by a mating rolling body under heavy static or impact load. (See FC 00.15 for *false* brinelling.)
3. *Rounded (soft particle) dent* without sharp corners or raised edges is made by a soft, essentially incompressible particle entrapped in the contact. A Hertz contact (with EHD film) effectively confines any entrapped particle during the short contact passage so that particles of plastic or fiber fail to escape laterally and produce a dent. Some grease thickeners have been found to produce dents under shock loading of the contact.
4. *Multi-fragment dent* is produced by hard, brittle particles, such as sand or abrasive grit, if they shatter in the contact. These dents show many sharp-cornered facets and, at times, embedded grit.
5. *Rolled-in lines* are made by sharp circumferential edges on the mating rolling contact surface. They are plastically depressed lines formed by high edge-pressures. Deep circumferential scratch marks on the mating surface can also produce rolled-in lines.
6. *Stippled lines* in the rolling direction result from sharp asperities on the mating surface, including raised carbides and firmly embedded debris grains, which make a dent at every contact passage. A slight axial shift among the contacting bodies may produce bands of stippled lines.
7. *Contaminant denting,* giving a fine, matte surface with a pebbled appearance under magnification, is produced by copious loose fine hard debris, generally in the lubricant, passing through the contact.

12.4. Distinctive Appearance

A dent appears as a depression with a shiny surface. Original finishing marks generally remain visible. Raised edges often arise during denting but may be worn or rolled down in running. A line indentation has a shiny surface if formed plastically.

Classes of dents can be distinguished as follows (using a microscope, preferably scanning electron microscope, for details):

1. *Debris (hard particle) dents* are sharp-edged depressions corresponding to the shape of the indenting particle, originally with raised edges, which may be rolled or worn down in further running. The most common indenting particle is a metal chip, which forms a dent that looks roughly chip-shaped. Also common are dents secondary to spalling, with shapes reflecting spall debris that are blockier than chips.

2. *(True) brinell marks* are regularly shaped elliptic, round, rectangular or dumbbell shaped indentations. The true brinell mark on a Hertz contact surface is a plastic depression in the shape of the static Hertz contact area, and is identical in shape to a false brinell mark created by fretting wear between Hertzian contacting bodies (FC 00.15). The surface of a true brinell mark, which is formed by plastic deformation, retains the original finishing marks in the depressed surface. By contrast, the surface in the false brinell mark is a wear surface on which original finishing marks are effaced and a matte, non-directional surface appears.

3. *Soft particle dents* show rounded or drop shapes and rounded edges. They result from the entrapment of soft materials (such as plastics, fibers, or wood chips) which deform under the contact pressure. Since such materials are essentially incompressible, they can form dents in the much harder contact material because the Hertz contact configuration allows them no escape. Roughly paddle-shaped rounded dents (with an extending narrow neck) have been observed in grease lubricated contacts undergoing impact loading and are apparently the result of the delayed escape of grease (thickener) from the contact through a narrow channel.

4. *Multi-fragment dents* appear like the imprint of shattered glass into a soft surface. They consist of many sharp-faceted angular impressions clustered and overlapping in a small area. Their source is an entrapped brittle particle which shatters as the contact rolls over it. Sand (from external contamination or sand-cast parts), and also grains of abrasive, may provide the particles.

5. *Rolled-in lines* run in the rolling direction. They appear when a sharp edge on a rolling body contacts the opposing contact surface under a sufficient load to cause plastic deformation of the opposed body at the encounter with the edge. Rolled-in lines, when viewed under magnification, are distinguished from scratch marks by the absence of sharp (feather) edges on the mark and possibly by the preservation of finishing lines crossing the rolled-in mark.

A rolling element with a circumferential scratch-mark or finishing furrow of substantial depth can produce a rolled-in line in the opposing body. Commonly, cylindrical or tapered rollers of a bearing, scratched in the separator contact, produce rolled-in lines in a ring rolling-track.

6. *Stippled lines* in the rolling direction appear in contacts with very little sliding, in the presence of sharp, hard asperities or firmly embedded debris in the opposing contact surface. They consist of long series of dents of identical shape and are most common in cylindrical or tapered roller bearings in which an asperity contacts the opposing surface over and over along the same track, essentially without sliding. Stippled lines can occur as stippled bands, if the contact shifts axially or if there are many indenters.

A special case of stippled bands formed of geometrically similar dents occurs in ball bearings, from an indenter imbedded in a ball slowly changing its axis of rotation (indexing).

7. *Contaminant denting* is profuse denting from fine loose hard debris. Macroscopically, a matte surface is generated which, under magnification, appears pebbled rather than scratch-marked as in wear (FC 00.12). In the presence of some sliding, contaminant denting and scratch-marking may be intermixed on the same surface.

Distinction between *nicks* (pre-service indentations) and *dents* (in-service indentations) is aided by considering the location and direction of the indentation. Nicks can appear on any surface and run in any direction since they are the result of random impacts. Dents, by contrast, are formed on the operating component so that they are limited to contact surfaces (including separator contact surfaces) and their direction must be compatible with the kinematics of relative motion.

It may be possible to determine whether substantial running time was accumulated by the surface since denting. A fresh dent is likely to have sharp, perhaps raised edges and any finishing marks in the depression appear similar to those outside it. A dent that accumulated much running time tends to have no raised edges and finishing marks inside it may be sharper than those on the more worn surface outside the indentation. Another indicator that the component was run since denting, is surface distress decoration (FC 00.17) surrounding the dent.

12.5. Causes

Dents are caused by indigenous or exogenous particulate contaminants or sharp asperities. Common sources are listed below.

Sources Indigenous to the Machine-Element

1. *Hard particle dents:*

   - *Loose wear debris* from rolling components, metal

DATA
Plate No: 12.5
Archive No: 064-401
Image type: view
Scalebar = 40 mm (micros: ±20%, others: +100%, -50%)
Component: HG; P&W, high hardness, ground, run
Speed:
Load:
Lubrication:
Failure code1: 00.18.1.2 Sharp individual dent(s) from metal debris, asperities
Failure code2: 00.22.01.4 Gear tooth crack or fracture
Failure code3: -
Failure code4: -

DESCRIPTIONS
FAILURE DESCRIPTION: Extensive random denting of contact surfaces on both mating gears, from coarse hard debris. A chipping fracture on one tooth may have contributed to the debris. The chipping itself may have originated from overrolling of a large hard piece of debris. The gear has failed.

IMAGE DESCRIPTION: Pinion is at image center. Near W and E edges, are mating gears. All contact surfaces of both gears in W-side mesh show irregular (light grey) dent marks. Pinion teeth near E-side mesh appear intact with finishing lines still visible. A large chip is broken out of the tooth tip at A.

SUSPECTED CAUSES: A mass of debris was injected into the gear mesh, causing extensive denting of contact surfaces. The chip missing from the tooth, if fragmented, would contribute to the debris. It is not evident whether the chipping occurred from unrelated causes or was itself due to overrolling of a large piece of debris.

DATA
Plate No: 12.6
Archive No: 093-18.1.28&29&30
Image type: a, b, c: SEM
Scalebar = a: 20, b: 2.5, c: 3 μm
(micros: ±20%, others: +100%, -50%)
Component: DGBB; IR, run
Speed: 450 KdN
Load: 3.4 GPa
Lubrication: mineral oil, 60 °C
Failure code1: 00.18.1.3 Multi-fragment dent (brittle contaminant)
Failure code2: 00.12.0.1 Adhesive mild wear
Failure code3: -
Failure code4: -

DESCRIPTIONS
FAILURE DESCRIPTION: Multi-fragment dent in honed surface, caused by the shattering and subsequent indentation of a hard, brittle contaminant particle. Sharply cut edges are intact in some areas; elsewhere, adhesive wear has removed edges, leaving tensile fracture surfaces. Such denting can lead to abrasive wear (from embedded debris), surface distress (through interruption of EHD film) and spalling.

IMAGE DESCRIPTION: (a): In a well-preserved honed surface with N–S finishing lines, a cluster of sharp-edged dents and rounded pits occupy the image center. (b): Sharp-edged plastic deformation, visible at A and B, and a folded edge at C, indicate plastic indentation by sharp hard particles. (c): tensile fracture surface in a pit forming part of the dent cluster, probably from tearing of a raised edge in adhesive wear.

SUSPECTED CAUSES: Brittle contaminant (sand, abrasive, process material etc.) may enter a rolling contact and initiate one of three processes: 1. denting by loose particles (FC 00.18.1.4), 2. denting by embedded debris (FC 00.18.2.2), or 3. shattering and formation of multi-fragment dents as shown.

a
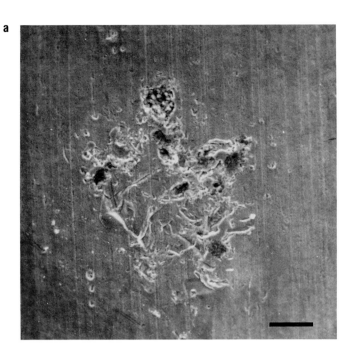

b
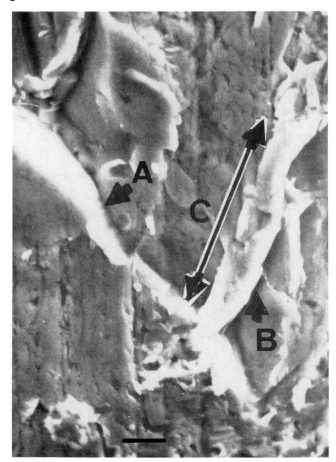

c
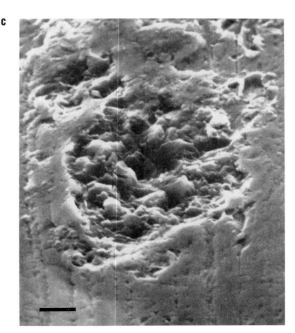

DATA

Plate No: 12.7
Archive No: 107-007a&b&c
Image type: a, b, c: SEM
Scalebar = a: 100, b: 20, c: 20 μm
(micros: ±20%, others: +100%, -50%)
Component: DGBB; IR, run
Speed:
Load:
Lubrication:
Failure code1: 00.18.1.3 Multi-fragment dent (brittle contaminant)
Failure code2: 00.18.1.1 Rounded dent (from soft contaminant)
Failure code3: 00.18.1.2 Sharp individual dent(s) from metal debris, asperities
Failure code4: 00.18.01.1.1 Denting of rolling surface, no sliding

DESCRIPTIONS

FAILURE DESCRIPTION: Present are: dents from hard contaminant, from soft deformable contaminant (20–60 μm) and a multi-fragment dent from shattered brittle contaminant. Short kinematic wear marks are from earlier running. The bearing was operated at low EHD film (kinematic wear marks FC 00.12) and in contaminated environment with abrasive (brittle), ductile (metal) and soft (organic) debris. The bearing has not yet failed.

IMAGE DESCRIPTION: (a): Overview of 1 mm² surface. Dark N–S stripes at A are lubricant deposits. The dense cluster of small indentations at B is a multi- fragment dent. There are dents from deformed (metal) debris, as at C. Gentle depressions were caused by soft particles, as at D. Feature B is magnified in (b); feature C in (c). Note prior fine dents in C. Kinematic wear marks ("fingernail marks") at E are short (due to low spin/roll ratio) and partly worn off.

SUSPECTED CAUSES: Deformable (metal) debris flatten but retain their general shape when rolled over (C). Soft material, such as plastic trapped in the contact makes a rounded dent (D). Grinding grit or other brittle abrasive may shatter upon over-rolling to make a cluster of fine (multi-fragment) dents (B). Hard (overrolled) asperities on the mating surface may make fingernail marks due to ball spin during contact.

a

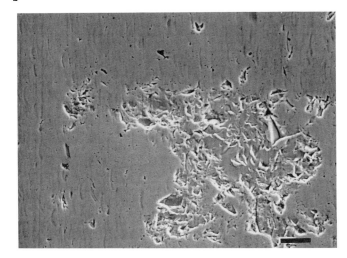

b

c

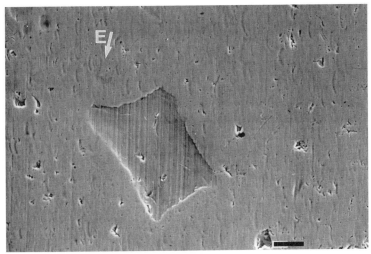

DATA
Plate No: 12.8
Archive No: 093-18.1.15
Image type: SEM
Scalebar = 15 μm (micros: ±20%, others: +100%, -50%)
Component: DGBB; IR, run
Speed: 450 KdN
Load: 3.4 GPa
Lubrication: mineral oil, 60 °C
Failure code1: 00.18.1.4 Multiple irregular denting from fine, loose hard debris
Failure code2: 00.12.3.2.2 Scratch marks, kinematic wear marks in rolling surface
Failure code3: 00.17.1.1 Glazing (incipient surface distress)
Failure code4: 00.17.1.2 Microspalling (advanced surface distress)

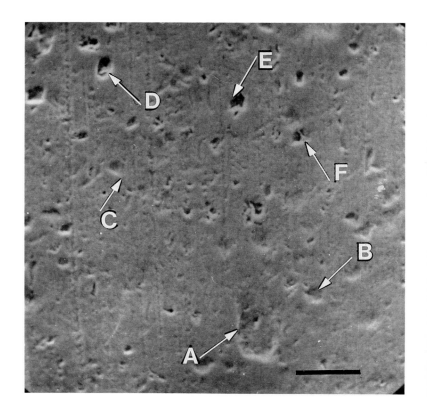

DESCRIPTIONS
FAILURE DESCRIPTION: Multiple denting has occurred on a very small scale, from fine (1–5 μm) contaminant. Light surface distress glazing is visible with obliteration of most finishing lines. Small surface distress microspalls were initiated at the dents. Kinematic wear marking. Damage of this level permits achieving normal life for industrial applications.

IMAGE DESCRIPTION: Background is a honed surface with some finishing lines running N–S, largely obliterated by glazing. Extensive scattered debris denting is visible as at A, B and C, with surface depressed but not exfoliated. At D, E and F are microspalls, from the action of surface distress on dents. Isolated kinematic wear ("fingernail marks") are present.

SUSPECTED CAUSES: Fine denting (and kinematic wear marking) of the size shown are virtually inescapable in most industrial applications with circulating oil due to contaminant ingress past the filters (filtering to less than 10 μm particle size is uncommon). Mild surface distress is not unusual but preventable if ample EHD films can be provided.

DATA
Plate No: 12.14
Archive No: 107-012a&b&c
Image type: a, b, c: SEM
Scalebar = a, b: 100, c: 10 μm
(micros: $\pm$20%, others: +100%, -50%)
Component: ACBB; B, run
Speed:
Load:
Lubrication:
Failure code1: 00.18.2.2.2 Stippled line(s) or band(s) from rolled-in debris
Failure code2: 00.09.1 Scoring from forcible assembly or mounting (no galling)
Failure code3: -
Failure code4: -
See also PLATE: 12.15

DESCRIPTIONS
FAILURE DESCRIPTION: Multiple debris denting of ball surface, including a band of identically oriented dents rolled in by a hard particle embedded in the mating surface. Damage to ball surface promotes surface distress and subsequent surface-origin spalling; with more contamination, damaging wear is also expected. Some scratchmarks are visible, probably as a result of disassembly.

IMAGE DESCRIPTION: (a): 1 mm^2 of ball surface. In N 1/3 of image, the SW–NE running light-colored lines are disassembly damage. In N–S band W of image center, are multiple debris dents (light-colored points and unresolved light-color bands). (b): Dent bands are enlarged, showing dense marking in E image half. (c): Dense part of dent band, with many identically shaped sharp-edged dents from a particle embedded in the mating surface.

SUSPECTED CAUSES: When fine, hard contaminant is present, it may embed in a rolling surface and mark the mating surface every time it is rolled over. A given grain continues to make the same shape dent. In a ball contact, in which the ball indexes against the mating surface, numerous rows of parallel dents may form. See also PLATE 12.15.

a

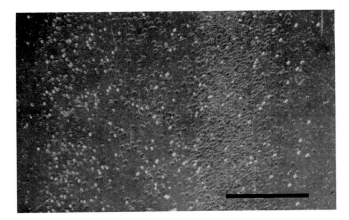

b

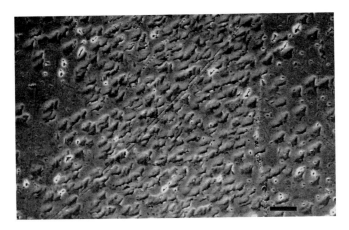

c

DATA
Plate No: 12.15
Archive No: 093-18.1.17
Image type: SEM
Scalebar = 20 μm (micros: ±20%, others: +100%, -50%)
Component: DGBB; B, run
Speed: 300 KdN
Load:
Lubrication: mineral oil, 60 °C
Failure code1: 00.18.2.2.2 Stippled line(s) or band(s) from rolled-in debris
Failure code2: 00.17.1.1 Glazing (incipient surface distress)
Failure code3: -
Failure code4: -
See also PLATE: 12.14

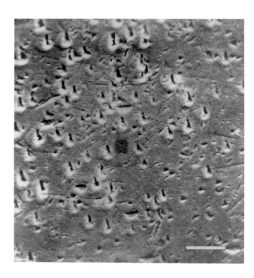

DESCRIPTIONS
FAILURE DESCRIPTION: Rows of parallel oriented sharp dents with raised edges appear, due to indentation from an abrasive particle embedded in the mating contact surface. Raised edges and undented surface are slightly glazed from surface distress. Denting of this density interrupts EHD film and promotes surface distress with subsequent spalling. Abrasive wear may also take place. See also PLATE 12.14.

IMAGE DESCRIPTION: Grey background is the slightly glazed lapped ball surface. Some lapping lines are still visible (E image edge). Rows of dark-bottomed, wedge-shaped dents are elongated in N–S direction, with tips pointing N and with light-col-ored rims (raised edges). Some differently shaped dents without raised edges (near E and S image edges) are older. The dark square in the image center is an imaging artifact.

SUSPECTED CAUSES: When fine, hard contaminant is present, it may embed in a rolling surface and mark the mating surface every time it is rolled over. A given grain continues to make the same shape dent. In a ball contact, in which the ball indexes against the mating surface, numerous rows of parallel dents may form. Any sliding velocity component will elongate the dents in one direction.

DATA
Plate No: 12.16
Archive No: 018-109
Image type: light macro
Scalebar = 20 mm (micros: ±20%, others: +100%, -50%)
Component: SRB; IR, run
Speed:
Load:
Lubrication:
Failure code1: 00.18.3 Brinelling
Failure code2: -
Failure code3: -
Failure code4: -
See also PLATEs: 12.18 & 12.20

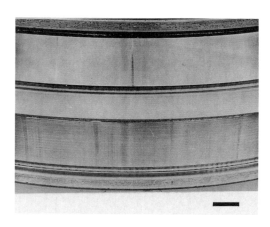

DESCRIPTIONS
FAILURE DESCRIPTION: Multiple axial brinell marks on both roller paths of SRB IR were inflicted by a high static load or impact. Marks in one path broaden toward the center flange, suggesting axial loading (possibly when pressing the ring onto the shaft through the OR and the rollers). Such marks may become more visible after running, since they wear differently from the unbrinelled area. The bearing is noisy and will spall earlier than normal. More severe brinelling appears in PLATES 12.18 and 12.20.

IMAGE DESCRIPTION: Side view of a SRB IR with flanges and undercuts at N and S edge, center flange extending E–W at mid-image. Roller paths are grey. Flaring, fuzzy-edged axial dark marks showing brinell dents extend across entire path width and, in path at image S, broad towards the center flange. Depending on lighting, a mark may appear dark or light.

SUSPECTED CAUSES: Assembly of a SRB on a tight shaft may produce static loading, especially if mounting pressure is applied across the roller contacts. A bearing so damaged is noisy, but may run for an appreciable time before failing. Since brinell marks are depressions, rollers traveling over them undergo load and traction variations which may be reflected in differential wear, highlighting the marks by a change in luster.

DATA
Plate No: 12.17
Archive No: 093-18.1.1
Image type: light microgram
Scalebar = 150 μm (micros: ±20%,
others: +100%, -50%)
Component: DGBB; IR, run
Speed: 450 KdN
Load: 3.4 GPa
Lubrication: mineral oil, 60 °C
Failure code1: 00.18.3 Brinelling
Failure code2: -
Failure code3: -
Failure code4: -

DESCRIPTIONS
FAILURE DESCRIPTION: Light brinell mark in groove of a
DGBB IR. The mark is only 0.2 μm deep (by tracing) and oblong with major axis across the ball groove. The bearing is
noisy for quiet running applications, but unlikely to fail soon
from the brinelling.

IMAGE DESCRIPTION: Honed groove surface is shown with finishing lines running E–W. At image center, a circular-appearing
depression is made visible by shading of highly directional metallographic lighting. The cross-curvature of the groove distorts
light reflection further, making part of the oblong mark appear

circular. Such marks can be detected by moving the part under
a binocular microscope and observing a break in the edge of
lighting crossing the mark.

SUSPECTED CAUSES: Impact loading or high static loading of
ball contacts cause brinelling.

DATA
Plate No: 12.18
Archive No: 087-104
Image type: light macro
Scalebar = 20 mm (micros: ±20%,
others: +100%, -50%)
Component: DGBB; IR & OR, run
Speed:
Load:
Lubrication:
Failure code1: 00.18.3 Brinelling
Failure code2: 00.12.3.2.0.7 Wear
track for misaligned outerring
Failure code3: -
Failure code4: -

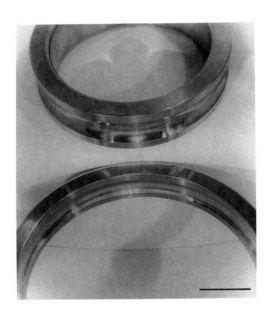

DESCRIPTIONS
FAILURE DESCRIPTION: Brinell marks are present at ball spacing, extending to ball groove edge in both OR and IR (on opposite sides). The bearing is noisy and may fail in high speed
application from separator fracture. Early spalling at brinell
marks is likely.

IMAGE DESCRIPTION: In service, visible IR sideface matches
averted OR sideface. OR ball groove edge near averted face
shows three indentations at ball spacing (at N-most point and
on each side), which are triangular, with base at the dented

edge. These are brinell marks extending across the edge. On
the IR, two elliptical brinell marks at same spacing are grey
shadows, in the groove outboard of triangular light reflections.
The shifting circumferential lines in the OR groove are the wear
track.

SUSPECTED CAUSES: Assembly or disassembly of bearing on
tight fitted shaft, by pressing on OR face, indents ball grooves
near edge. The dark wear track which varies in axial location
around the ring circumference suggests misalignment in running.

DATA
Plate No: 12.19
Archive No: 031-1501
Image type: view
Scalebar = 10 mm (micros: ±20%, others: +100%, -50%)
Component: SRB assembly, run
Speed:
Load:
Lubrication: grease, ? °C
Failure code1: 00.18.3 Brinelling
Failure code2: 00.16.1.2.1 Shallow entry spall from surface point-defect
Failure code3: 00.18.2.1.2 Rolled-in line, both contact edges
Failure code4: -

DESCRIPTIONS
FAILURE DESCRIPTION: In OR roller path, an isolated spall of elliptical contour following a brinell mark, probably sustained by impact in shipping or mounting of the bearing. Rolled-in circumferential lines are shown emanating from both ends of the spall, probably from dents made by the spall edge on the rollers. The bearing has failed.

IMAGE DESCRIPTION: Bearing is shown with IR/roller assembly swiveled out of alignment, exposing OR roller path at E–W image centerline, just S of IR side-face. At the image center is a barrel-shaped spall crater with sharp contours. It corresponds to the contour of a heavy brinell mark extending over the entire roller length. Circumferential rolled-in lines of distinct luster extend E and W of the spall.

SUSPECTED CAUSES: If a bearing is dropped during shipment, or suffers a severe impact load in mounting, heavy brinell marks may be made on both rings (and one or more rollers). Overrolling of such marks in service is likely to precipitate early spalling-out of the damaged material. The spall edge copies onto the rollers which then may roll-in circumferential lines into the ring contact path.

DATA
Plate No: 12.20
Archive No: 087-118
Image type: view
Scalebar = 15 mm (micros: ±20%, others: +100%, -50%)
Component: DGBB; IR, run
Speed:
Load:
Lubrication:
Failure code1: 00.18.3 Brinelling
Failure code2: 01.11.2 Separator fracture, cracking
Failure code3: 00.12.3.2.4 Scoring wear (macroscopic gouging without galling)
Failure code4: 11.5 Carbonized oil deposit

DESCRIPTIONS
FAILURE DESCRIPTION: The innerring ball groove is severely brinell marked at ball spacing. The brinell marks are gouged and the adjacent area is battered. These are plastic flow events. The discoloration in the groove and on the lands is presumed to arise from oil carbonized in overheating. The brinelling is attributed to fracture, entrapment and lockup of the separator under the balls.

IMAGE DESCRIPTION: In the groove bottom are four brinell marks, which balls have plowed forward circumferentially to form gouges. The adjacent groove surface is plastically battered. Blackish discoloration is visible around the groove bottom (except where worn off) and dark streaks appear on both lands, as from carbonized oil due to overheating.

SUSPECTED CAUSES: The brinell-type indentations occurred through a stamped steel separator failure. Sheet steel was entrapped between the balls and OR, and locked them against the IR. The bearing seized. In dissipating momentum, the rotor drove the locked balls along the groove, making plowed gouges. Prior to lockup, the separator material was overrolled, denting the innerring. Overheating during seizure created the black deposit marks (carbonized lubricant).

DATA
Plate No: 12.21
Archive No: 099-132
Image type: light macro
Scalebar = 30 mm (micros: ±20%, others: +100%, -50%)
Component: HG; W, medium hard, run
Speed:
Load:
Lubrication:
Failure code1: 00.18.4.1 Gear tooth peening (irregular local plastic flow)
Failure code2: 00.17.1.2 Microspalling (advanced surface distress)
Failure code3: 00.16.02.4 Incipient spalling, multiple spalls
Failure code4: -
See also PLATEs: 12.22 & 12.23

DESCRIPTIONS
FAILURE DESCRIPTION: In medium-hard gearing, local plastic flow of macroscopic dimensions occurred in the contact surface due to the interaction of geometric imperfections. This is similar to surface distress glazing except that it is on a larger scale. Surface distress microspalling and incipient macrospalling have followed. The gear may be runnable but is inaccurate, noisy and may be prone to fracture.

IMAGE DESCRIPTION: View of one flank surface in several consecutive gear teeth, with contact extending, as a lighter-grey area, from W tooth edge to within 8 mm of E tooth edge. The patchy variation of hue across the tooth width in the addendum and dedendum represents plastic peening. The dark pinpoints are spall craters, concentrated in dedendum.

SUSPECTED CAUSES: Cold working of medium-hard gear contact surfaces may occur under heavy, localized or impact loads. Geometric irregularities cause peened appearance. Plastically worked material microspalls in surface distress and subsequently develops macro-spall craters. Compare to PLATES 12.22 and 12.23, for other forms of local plastic flow in gears.

DATA
Plate No: 12.22
Archive No: 099-133
Image type: light macro
Scalebar = 8 mm (micros: ±20%, others: +100%, -50%)
Component: SG; W, high hardness, run
Speed:
Load:
Lubrication:
Failure code1: 00.18.4.2 Gear tooth rippling (transverse wavy plastic flow)
Failure code2: -
Failure code3: -
Failure code4: -
See also PLATEs: 12.21 & 12.23

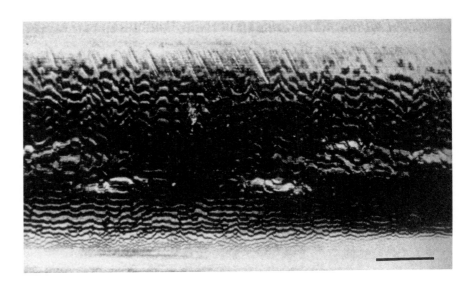

DESCRIPTIONS
FAILURE DESCRIPTION: In the gear contact surface, local plastic flow under vibratory conditions has produced transverse ripples. These are wave surfaces, with phase shifts at radial lines or in a fish-scale pattern. Rippling is believed to result when softer subsurface material flows plastically under repeated loading, distorting the harder surface. The increased roughness produces local stress concentrations which may eventually spall.

IMAGE DESCRIPTION: Gear tooth contact surface is shown, with tip at N image edge and root at S edge. Glancing lighting highlights transverse crests and troughs of waviness with radial lines delineating shifts in crest location (phase). The surface is generally glossy (burnished) in appearance.

SUSPECTED CAUSES: Rolling contact at very high stresses produces, in softer materials, plastic flow in the rolling direction at the high Hertz shear stress layer. A case hardened or work hardened surface may warp under this flow producing the ripples. The axial phase-shifts may be due to geometric imperfections in stress distribution, causing uneven flow rates. See PLATES 12.21 and 12.23 for other forms of local plastic flow in gears.

DATA
Plate No: 12.23
Archive No: 099-134
Image type: light macro
Scalebar = 30 mm (micros: ±20%, others: +100%, -50%)
Component: HYG; P, high hardness, run
Speed:
Load:
Lubrication:
Failure code1: 00.18.4.3 Gear tooth ridging (plastic ridges in sliding direction)
Failure code2: 00.12.5 Gear tooth wear
Failure code3: -
Failure code4: -
See also PLATEs: 12.21 & 12.22

DESCRIPTIONS
FAILURE DESCRIPTION: The ridge and valley pattern in a high-sliding hypoid gear set shows ridges following the sliding direction. It arises from combined plastic flow and wear, which is probably initiated by machining imperfections. This is not an imminent failure, but the roughening of the surface may lead to any form of gear failure, such as galling, spalling, wear and eventual tooth fracture.

IMAGE DESCRIPTION: Hypoid pinion teeth cover the image from NW to SE corner. Tips are light grey; flank surfaces dark with light oblique streaks which represent the ridging. These ridges are more sharply defined than the rippling of FC 00.18.4.2.

SUSPECTED CAUSES: In high-sliding gear sets such as worm gearing or hypoid gearing, a pattern of differential plastic flow and wear develops following the sliding direction. It is believed to result from a variation of contact pressure across the contact width and results in pronounced prominent ridges and valleys. Compare to PLATES 12.21 and 12.22 for other forms of plastic flow in gear tooth contacts.

13 HEAT IMBALANCE FAILURE

13.1. Definition

Heat imbalance failure is a complex sequence of failure events precipitated by a (macroscopic) temperature excursion in the Hertz contact machine element due to heat generated in excess of the heat simultaneously removed.

Heat imbalance failure is distinct from:

- *galling* (FC 00.13);
- *lubricant failure* (FC 11, FC 12);

but may be the precipitating cause and/or the result of either or both of the latter.

Heat imbalance failure is *not synonymous* with overheating, which is a temperature excursion of the machine element. The latter may or may not precipitate failure. Heat imbalance failure is diagnosed when, as a result of overheating, one or more irreversible changes occur in the contact components.

Heat imbalance failure differs from other contact component failure modes in that it is a *systems* failure. The effects may manifest themselves primarily on one or a few components, but the failure mechanism is that of loss of thermal equilibrium of the machine element as a system.

13.2. Nomenclature

Heat imbalance failure (also designated overheating failure) is a recognized failure class in rolling bearing technology (less generally in gear technology). Terms for one of the subclasses of heat imbalance failure are more commonly used, for example: hot plastic flow, temper coloring, permanent hardness loss or overheating seizure.

13.3. Failure Process

Sequence of Failure Events

The failure process in all heat imbalance failures, comprises the sequence of events described below.

1. The steady-state thermal equilibrium in a volume enclosing the Hertz contact machine element gives way to an excess of heat generation over heat removal. The heat imbalance can result from any combination of: *increased heat generation* in the machine element, and *reduced heat outflow*. See *Causes* below for operating conditions conducive to heat imbalance.
2. The temperature of some or all contact components, and often that of some other components of the machine-element (including the lubricant), rises in an excursion above the maximum design level.
3. Depending on the magnitude, location and duration of the temperature excursion, one or more of the following *intermediate* failure occurrences take place.

Lubrication failure. (See also FC 11.1 and FC 12.)

- In an organic liquid lubricant (oil, grease), rheological properties change as temperature increases. Most importantly, *viscosity drops*, and EHD film conditions correspondingly deteriorate. At a given temperature, the lubricant evaporates or burns off, before reaching high pressure in the contact, and EHD lubrication ceases. These phenomena occur with minimal time lag behind the temperature change.

The direct consequence of deteriorating EHD lubrication is further increased heat generation, providing positive feedback to the heat imbalance failure.

- Grease surrounding the machine-element may soften at the increased temperature, causing it to *slump* as a lump into the path of the contact components and undergo violent churning. As a result it may liquefy and escape through the chamber closure, leaving the machine element lubricated only with a thin adhering layer of lubricant, soon lost to decomposition (see below).
- In any lubricant, *decomposition* and oxidation occur at sufficiently high temperatures, if they act over sufficient time. (See FC 11 and FC 12 for details.) Minor changes in lubricant chemistry may have long-term deleterious effects on Hertz contact machine element performance; major changes immediately render the lubricant unserviceable, converting the system to a dry-lubricated or unlubricated system.

233

The loss of fluid lubrication in the form designed into the machine typically leads to sharply *increased heat generation*, creating rapid and often catastrophic failure of the machine-element.

Loss of Operating Clearance

Due to differential thermal expansion of components, operating clearance can be lost in any machine-element confined by its design. Examples: rolling bearings may lose internal looseness; gear pairs may lose clearance; and cam systems may lose the gap between cam and follower (tappet) at the bottom of the stroke. Clearance loss from thermal expansion is reversible with the temperature and therefore may not be observable in the stopped machine.

Loss of operating clearance generally leads to large parasitic loads on the Hertz contacts. An increased load further increases heat generation, creating rapid, often catastrophic failure.

NOTE: In steel components with metastable retained austenite, operation at elevated temperature for protracted periods may produce permanent volume growth leading to an irreversible loss of operating clearance.

Loss of component material strength may follow operation at temperatures which exceed the design maximum.

• *Plastic materials* (gears, and bearing separators) may soften or melt at temperatures tolerated by metals, leading to hot plastic flow or disintegration under load.
• The hot hardness of *steel* is less than normal ambient temperature hardness, leading to hot plastic flow under load.
• *Hardened steel* loses hardness permanently at temperatures in excess of the tempering temperature used in manufacture, permitting plastic flow under load even after operating temperature has reverted to normal.

Chemical change in structural component material may result from operation at elevated temperature:

• Some *plastic materials* become embrittled when held at elevated temperature, leading to subsequent cracking during operation.
• *Non-stainless steel* develops thin oxide layers when held at elevated temperatures in air. These *temper colors* can serve to diagnose the order of magnitude of the temperature exposure.

The ultimate failure from heat imbalance, often referred to as a *burn-up*, is a runaway temperature excursion. This occurs when lubrication has been lost and/or softening of the contact material has induced massive galling. Components may be deformed out of all recognition (balls into rollers and vice versa). Components may be welded together (rolling elements, rings and separator pieces from a rolling bearing into a block, forcing rotation at the fit interfaces). The failure process culminates in gross seizure and/or bulk fracture, often extending to the shaft, housing or machine frame.

Arrest of Heat Imbalance Failure

Heat imbalance failure can be arrested at almost any point short of gross seizure or fracture. Practically significant scenarios for the arrest of heat imbalance are:

• *Quenching of microscopic thermal instability.* Momentary load peaks, the passage of a contaminant particle or some other local disturbance may overheat *one asperity contact* during operation. If copious liquid lubricant immediately floods the surfaces upon separation, the instability can be quenched leaving, at worst, skidmarking (FC 00.14) or local galling (FC 00.13). Some lubrication methods favor quenching more than others (oil over grease, bulk oil over mist, circulating oil over splash and jet or underrace lubrication over free flow).
• *Resupply of grease through softening* (see FC 12). During moderate overheating, the grease available in the immediate contact area may deteriorate (be contaminated, harden, be expelled), resulting in a loss of lubricating effectiveness. Bulk grease in the warmed grease pack becomes softer, however, and may slump into the contact path and replenish the supply. If the heating, and thus the softening is moderate, destructive churning of the whole grease pack may be avoided.
• *Moderating operating conditions.* In machinery with variable operating conditions, a temporary overload and/or overspeed may be relieved as the operating cycle progresses, or be deliberately relieved by the operator observing a temperature excursion.

13.4. Distinctive Appearance

A heat imbalance condition may be identified directly by observing temperatures at suitable locations on the machine. Morphologically, heat imbalance failure is recognized as one of the resulting irreversible failure modes, appearing as follows.

Hot Plastic Flow

In metals and heat-softening plastics, hot plastic flow is the decisive indicator of heat imbalance failure. It can be distinguished from cold plastic flow by appearance. Hot plastic flow is generally much more extensive than cold flow; the shapes of components are drastically altered; and surface oxidation is common (but not inevitable) in metals. No causes other than overheating produce hot plastic flow. Compare this to cold flow under FC 00.23. Note also the following details:

• Hot plastic flow is a *late* consequence of heat imbalance. Due to its destructive nature, hot plastic flow is likely to obliterate signs of earlier events in the failure process.
• Whereas hot plastic flow is certainly due to overheating, the overheating itself may well be a secondary failure mode. It is advisable to search a plastically deformed component for remaining signs of other failure modes (galling or spalling of contact components, galling or fracture of a bearing separator, etc).
• In ceramics, a similarly distinctive heat imbalance failure mode is not observed. Indications of overheating may be: cracking or fracture of the ceramic or hot plastic flow of adjacent metal components.

DATA
Plate No: 13.3
Archive No: 027-143&144
Image type: a, b: color view [SEE IMAGE IN APPENDIX]
Scalebar = a, b: 10 mm (micros: ±20%, others: +100%, -50%)
Component: DGBB; duplex; IR & B, run
Speed: 100 KdN
Load:
Lubrication: grease, 60 °C ?
Failure code1: 00.19.2 Hot plastic flow
Failure code2: 00.13.02 Extensive galling
Failure code3: 00.19.1.2 Temper colors in contact surfaces
Failure code4: 00.12.3.2.1.4 Wear track at contact edge

[See Image in Appendix]

DESCRIPTIONS
FAILURE DESCRIPTION: Duplex ball bearing assembly axially over-preloaded. Contact in one IR overran the groove edge. Overheating caused temper colors, rollout and severe galling with massive material transfer to balls. The second IR was overheated and temper-colored but the contact did not overrun the edge. The bearing assembly has failed.

IMAGE DESCRIPTION: (a): Two IRs mounted in duplex as shown. E IR has a straw temper color (200°C) on the E half. W half is blue (260°C) and the groove edge is rolled out (arrows). W IR is straw colored on the E land and blue in E 1/4 of the groove. (b): Three balls matching E IR. Ball at W has a straw temper color, a blue band of higher heating and, W of this band, a rolled-in line from the edge. Balls at center and E show blue temper color and large masses of welded-on galled steel.

SUSPECTED CAUSES: Axially preloaded duplex bearing pairs may suffer excess preload if spacing of the bearings is inaccurate. Overheating, loss of lubrication and temper coloring may result. One half may suffer more damage if external axial load adds to preload or if minor profile geometry differences favor overrunning of the groove edge.

DATA
Plate No: 13.4
Archive No: 002-014a
Image type: view
Scalebar = 20 mm (micros: ±20%, others: +100%, -50%)
Component: ACBB; B, tool steel, run & unrun
Speed: 1.7 MdN
Load: 1.5 GPa
Lubrication: synthetic polyester oil, 176 °C
Failure code1: 00.19.2 Hot plastic flow
Failure code2: 00.19.3 Scale formation
Failure code3:
Failure code4:

DESCRIPTIONS
FAILURE DESCRIPTION: Four balls are substantially reduced from original diameter by hot plastic flow and wear of heat-softened surface material. One new ball is shown for reference. A bearing with such balls has lost shaft support accuracy; the balls overroll the groove edge and the separator is damaged. Material was found rehardened, which in tool steel requires local temperatures well in excess of 700 °C. This is gross failure.

IMAGE DESCRIPTION: All used balls are visibly smaller than the unused center ball shown for reference. The used balls have streaks from overrolling the groove edge, pits from galling against the separator and scaling from high temperature.

SUSPECTED CAUSES: In a high speed, high load turbine engine bearing, excessive heat was generated, presumably from excessive IR bore/shaft looseness which permitted relative rotation. The heat caused lubrication to fail; balls galled against the separator pockets, started sliding against rings, were heated to virtual forging temperature, wore greatly, scaled and underwent plastic flow.

DATA

Plate No: 13.5
Archive No: 014-28
Image type: view
Scalebar = 20 mm (micros: ±20%, others: +100%, -50%)
Component: TRB, complete, run
Speed:
Load:
Lubrication:
Failure code1: 00.19.2.1 Hot plastic flow without welding (rollout)
Failure code2: 00.13.2.1.1 Rolling surface galling, no dent or nick visible
Failure code3: 01.14.1 Separator pocket galled
Failure code4: 01.13.3 Separator wear from unintended contact

DESCRIPTIONS

FAILURE DESCRIPTION: Unstable overheating (heat imbalance failure) of bearing after loss of adequate lubrication. OR roller path, roller ends and IR thrust flange ('rib') suffered hot plastic flow (rollout). The roller ends and ODs galled. The separator is bent, its OD is worn against OR. This is a gross failure. Complete seizure is imminent.

IMAGE DESCRIPTION: At image S, IR/roller assembly is viewed from the large sideface. Part of the OR is seen at image N. OR roller path is generally battered, with irregular circumferential bands of galling (light grey) near center plane and near S edge. The roller ends are hot-rolled down, to form center protrusions. The IR thrust flange (rib) is rolled thin. Roller OD has

galling streaks. The separator is deformed; its OD has light-color wear streaks and galled metal at pocket edges.

SUSPECTED CAUSES: Loss of adequate lubrication leads to progressive overheating as heat removal fails to balance increased heat generation from friction. The material softens and deforms; the geometry is destroyed; and galling occurs. The separator bends and is pushed against OR, where it wears. The roller end/thrust flange (rib) pressure exceeds reduced yield point and both surfaces roll down, leaving protrusions at the roller axis.

DATA

Plate No: 13.6
Archive No: 018-122
Image type: view
Scalebar = 30 mm (micros: ±20%, others: +100%, -50%)
Component: SRB; IR & R, run
Speed:
Load:
Lubrication:
Failure code1: 00.19.2.1 Hot plastic flow without welding (rollout)
Failure code2: 00.16.01.1.2 Centered spalling, wide track
Failure code3: 00.12.3.2.3 Step worn in rolling surface or dimension worn off-spec
Failure code4: 00.12.4 Wear of guiding-component support surface

DESCRIPTIONS

FAILURE DESCRIPTION: Unstable overheating (heat imbalance failure) of bearing after loss of adequate lubrication. IR roller paths and roller ODs suffered severe hot plastic flow (rollout), producing deep grooves in IR and near both ends of each roller. Generalized shallow spalling, material removal by wear and continued rolldown proceeded simultaneously. Wear of IR center flange OD occurred against separator.

IMAGE DESCRIPTION: IR design with three flanges. Both roller paths and the flange faces contacting the roller ends are rolled out (depression in roller paths, sharp flange edges). Roller OD

has grooves near both end faces; corners and a circle near the edge of the visible end face (not the thrust face) are deformed. Spall craters covering roller paths on IR and roller OD are mostly shallow and rolled down. Circumferential wear scratches appear on the center flange OD.

SUSPECTED CAUSES: Loss of adequate lubrication leads to progressive overheating as heat removal fails to balance increased heat generation from friction. The material softens and deforms and the geometry is destroyed. Wear and spalling of softened material occurs, removing surface material. This may postpone or prevent gross seizure unless the separator fractures.

DATA

Plate No: 13.7
Archive No: 093-19.1.6
Image type: SEM
Scalebar = 15 μm (micros: ±20%, others: +100%, -50%)
Component: DGBB; IR, tool steel, run
Speed: 1.7 MdN
Load: 1.4 GPa
Lubrication: synthetic polyester oil, arrested, ? °C
Failure code1: 00.19.2.1 Hot plastic flow without welding (rollout)
Failure code2: 00.19.1.2 Temper colors in contact surfaces
Failure code3: -
Failure code4: -

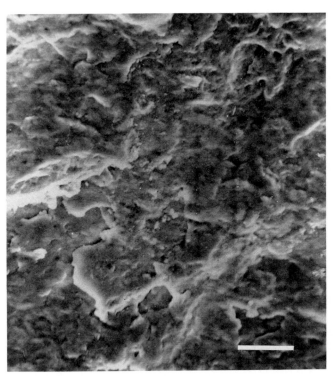

DESCRIPTIONS

FAILURE DESCRIPTION: Ball groove surface of tool steel bearing which suffered heat imbalance failure and plastic flow with total obliteration of original finish. Temper colors were observed. The bearing underwent an "oil shutoff test" to determine its survivability if lubricant is lost. It has suffered gross failure.

IMAGE DESCRIPTION: "Kneaded" surface of ball groove shows: material displaced by plastic flow over the entire surface area; laminae formed and rolled on; and total obliteration of the original surface finish. Macro appearance showed temper color. The observed condition is typical of high-temperature overheating during operation.

SUSPECTED CAUSES: Ultrahigh speed bearings, as shown, rely on lubricating action to control the rate of heat development, and on mass flow of the lubricant (or gas) for removal of gen-

erated heat. In an oil shutoff test, heat removal through lubricant convection is lost at once and lubricating effectiveness rapidly degrades. Very high temperatures arise, at which even heat resistant tool steel softens and plastically fails. Survival time is limited to minutes.

DATA

Plate No: 13.8
Archive No: 074-36
Image type: view
Scalebar = 10 mm (micros: ±20%, others: +100%, -50%)
Component: CRB; R, run
Speed:
Load:
Lubrication:
Failure code1: 00.19.2.1 Hot plastic flow without welding (rollout)
Failure code2: 00.19.3 Scale formation
Failure code3: 00.12.3.2.3 Step worn in rolling surface or dimension worn off-spec
Failure code4:

IMAGE DESCRIPTION: The roller at image W is battered by rolldown and shows blackish scale. The roller in the center is shorter and shows rounded edges and flat areas on OD from sliding wear. Ball-shaped object at image E originated as a similar roller but rolldown of edges is complete to form a sphere.

SUSPECTED CAUSES: Cylindrical roller bearings exposed to significant thrust load are prone to galling seizure between roller end-faces and guide flanges (for example by over-rolling of the flange edge). Such a seizure forces the roller to slide on the unflanged ring. Sufficient wear, rolldown and skew moment can result in turning the roller endwise in the rolling direction. It may then wear flat or, by repeated turns, be rounded into a sphere.

DESCRIPTIONS

FAILURE DESCRIPTION: Heat imbalance failure in a (cylindrical) roller bearing. All rollers underwent hot plastic rollout. One roller galled repeatedly against a guide flange and was turned in the separator pocket so that its edges were rolled and worn down to a sphere. Scale has formed on all rollers. This is a gross failure.

DATA
Plate No: 13.9
Archive No: 018-617&619
Image type: a: view, b: light macro, section, etched
Scalebar = a: 12, b: 5 mm (micros: ±20%, others: +100%, -50%)
Component: DGBB; IR, run
Speed:
Load:
Lubrication:
Failure code1: 00.19.2.1 Hot plastic flow without welding (rollout)
Failure code2: 00.19.5 Local structure damage from frictional heating
Failure code3: 00.13.02 Extensive galling
Failure code4: 00.23.2 Plastic distortion of bulk shape

a   b

DESCRIPTIONS
FAILURE DESCRIPTION: Bulk of ring overheated and softened so that rolldown in ball groove extended to deformation of one land, one side-face and the bore. A rehardened and tempered layer has formed under the ball path. Galling and scaling occurred in the ball path. The material folded over the land OD. This is a gross failure.

IMAGE DESCRIPTION: (a): Ball groove radius has increased, land OD at image E is tapered, edge is rounded and folded over. E endface is dished in. E edge of bore shows circular groove from plastic deformation. Ball path surface is battered, and shows circumferential jagged line in NW from galling. Scale patches are in the S. (b): Etched section with rolled groove edge at W. White layer at groove surface is rehardened; dark patches beneath are tempered. Light-colored arcs are produced by lighting.

SUSPECTED CAUSES: Loss of grease lubricant is the most likely failure initiator. Overheating occurs from increased friction. The relatively light load prevents seizure, permitting massive rollout of the entire ring. Galling in the ball path results from ball sliding. Rehardened layer, with underlying retempered zone in cross section indicates that the surface temperature exceeded 900 °C.

DATA
Plate No: 13.10
Archive No: 074-35
Image type: view
Scalebar = 20 mm (micros: ±20%, others: +100%, -50%)
Component: DGBB; IR&B&G, run
Speed:
Load:
Lubrication:
Failure code1: 00.19.2.1 Hot plastic flow without welding (rollout)
Failure code2: 00.22.01.3 Rolling element (ball, roller) crack
Failure code3: 01.11.2 Separator fracture, cracking
Failure code4: 00.19.3 Scale formation
See also PLATE: 13.11

DESCRIPTIONS
FAILURE DESCRIPTION: Severe heat imbalance failure, probably initiated by a separator geometry error causing the separator to become trapped under a ball. It produced: (1) separator fracture; (2) severe hot working of balls (rollout); (3) formation of a concentric hollow in the ball (See PLATE 13.11); (4) fracture of the hollowed ball; and (5) scale formation on balls. This is a gross failure.

IMAGE DESCRIPTION: Well-preserved OR is at image E (IR, probably damaged, was not available). The disintegrated stamped steel "ribbon" separator is at NW, with one ball still in a pocket. Five balls, all show hot plastic flow and degrees of scaling. One ball (arrow) has an oblong concentric hollow through which it has fractured.

SUSPECTED CAUSES: Stamped ribbon separators, if too loose or stretched by high ball forces (misalignment) may become trapped between a ball and ring, locking the ball. Sliding under high pressure occurs; the bearing overheats and the separator breaks. A metal rolling process similar to tube rolling may produce a hollow center in heavily plastically rolled balls under strong tractive surface forces. Cracking under contact load follows.

DATA
Plate No: 13.11
Archive No: 018-621
Image type: light macro
Scalebar = 3 mm (micros: ±20%, others: +100%, -50%)
Component: DGBB; B, run
Speed:
Load:
Lubrication:
Failure code1: 00.19.2.1 Hot plastic flow without welding (rollout)
Failure code2: 00.23.2 Plastic distortion of bulk shape
Failure code3: 00.22.01.3 Rolling element (ball, roller) crack
Failure code4: 00.18.2.2.1 Rolled-in continuous line from opposing edge
See also PLATE: 13.10

DESCRIPTIONS
FAILURE DESCRIPTION: Balls subject to severe plastic strain while overheated have formed a concentric hollow leading to fracture of one ball in service. (The second ball was broken for examination.) The rolling surface of the ball is severely battered, with rolled-down line from edge contact. See also PLATE 13.10.

IMAGE DESCRIPTION: The ball at image E is unbroken, with surface battered throughout, and a heavy rolled-in line running NW–SE along a great circle. The ball at image SW has a large spherical hollow in the center, which is surrounded by fracture surface showing wear (occurred in service). The ball at NW has a smaller hollow in the center, which is surrounded by chipped and cross-cracked impact fracture surface artificially produced in examination.

SUSPECTED CAUSES: A metal-rolling process similar to tube rolling produced a hollow center in heavily plastically rolled bodies under strong tractive surface forces. Cracking under contact load has followed. The uncracked ball shows plastic battering of the overheated surface and a line rolled-in by the ring groove edge, which was overrolled during uncontrolled overheated operation.

DATA
Plate No: 13.12
Archive No: 027-423
Image type: color view [SEE IMAGE IN APPENDIX.]
Scalebar = 20 mm (micros: ±20%, others: +100%, -50%)
Component: DGBB; IR, run
Speed:
Load:
Lubrication: grease, ? °C
Failure code1: 00.19.2.1 Hot plastic flow without welding (rollout)
Failure code2: 12.2 Carbonized grease
Failure code3: 00.13.2.1 Rolling surface galling
Failure code4: 00.01.1.1 Nick with raised edges

[See Image in Appendix]

DESCRIPTIONS
FAILURE DESCRIPTION: Severe heat imbalance failure has caused: (1) rolldown of groove; (2) carbonized grease; and (3) severe galling in groove (probably involving pressed steel separator and balls). Severe nicks at the groove edge may have occurred at bearing dismounting. This is a gross failure.

IMAGE DESCRIPTION: Black carbonized grease deposit on both lands and, in streaks, in the ball groove of IR. Circumferential bands of the groove were gouged free of deposit by severe sliding (possibly caused by the separator caught under a ball). At image center, there is a sharp-edged black galling mark where the separator and ball locked on the groove and made a depression later filled in with carbonized grease. E edge of groove shows nicks with raised edges near image N, perhaps from dismounting.

SUSPECTED CAUSES: Severe heat imbalance failure in bearing, probably due to loss of lubricant, caused: high friction; deviation from epicyclic ball speeds; extreme ball-to-separator forces; stamped steel separator distortion with separator caught under a ball; sliding of separator and ball over groove; galling, and possibly seizure. High temperature carbonized the grease. Difficult dismounting of the seized bearing may have caused nicks.

DATA
Plate No: 13.13
Archive No: 018-204
Image type: view, OR sectioned
Scalebar = 10 mm (micros: ±20%, others: +100%, -50%)
Component: NRB; OR & R, run
Speed:
Load:
Lubrication:
Failure code1: 00.19.2.2 Hot plastic flow with bulk welding
Failure code2: 00.13.02 Extensive galling
Failure code3: 00.12.3.2.3 Step worn in rolling surface or dimension worn off-spec
Failure code4: -

DESCRIPTIONS
FAILURE DESCRIPTION: Needle rollers misaligned during mounting of separator-less (cageless) drawn-cup needle roller bearing. Rollers have jammed during running; and galled against shaft and OR ('cup'). The bearing overheated losing lubricant; this caused gross plastic flow of rollers and cup followed by heavy galling and wear, probably ending in seizure.

IMAGE DESCRIPTION: W image half shows cross sectioned OR (drawn cup). Several skewed rollers are welded-in at S cup half. One is at N section edge. The galled, battered and worn cup rolling surface is shown in N image half. E image half shows bent, welded-together needle rollers with a large flat worn on each.

SUSPECTED CAUSES: Improper installation of cageless needle roller bearing may leave rollers skewed. When load is applied and shaft turns, rollers wedge in, requiring a high torque to turn the bearing by sliding the shaft over the locked rollers. Overheating, material softening, galling, welding and wear follow.

DATA
Plate No: 13.14
Archive No: 093-034
Image type: light macro
Scalebar = 20 mm (micros: ±20%, others: +100%, -50%)
Component: TRB; IR & R & OR, run
Speed:
Load:
Lubrication:
Failure code1: 00.19.2.2 Hot plastic flow with bulk welding
Failure code2: 00.19.2.1 Hot plastic flow without welding (rollout)
Failure code3: 11.5 Carbonized oil deposit
Failure code4: -

DESCRIPTIONS
FAILURE DESCRIPTION: Rollers are severely rolled out and welded to IR track. The OR track is severely rolled down. Dark discoloration is present, as from a carbonized lubricant. All the damage constitutes a severe heat imbalance failure due to loss of lubrication. This is a gross failure.

IMAGE DESCRIPTION: The OR section is at image N, with S half of track rolled out and battered by hot plastic flow. On the S half of the OR track is a carbonized lubricant coating. The IR section is at image S. In it are four rollers welded to the thrust flange due to heat imbalance failure. All of the IR roller track and the rollers are covered with a dark coating of carbonized

lubricant. The separator has been ejected and rollers have rolled up against each other.

SUSPECTED CAUSES: Loss of effective lubrication in a taper roller bearing is rapidly followed by overheating of thrust flange contact with a heavy sliding component under load. That contact will gall and eventually seize (weld). In the process, adjacent rolling contact areas also overheat, soften, gall and suffer rollout. The separator disintegrates during these events, permitting the rollers to roll up against each other.

DATA

Plate No: 13.15
Archive No: 027-424
Image type: color view [SEE IMAGE IN APPENDIX.]
Scalebar = 10 mm (micros: ±20%, others: +100%, -50%)
Component: DGBB; B & G, run
Speed:
Load:
Lubrication: grease, ? °C
Failure code1: 00.19.2.2 Hot plastic flow with bulk welding
Failure code2: 00.19.3 Scale formation
Failure code3: 00.13.2.1 Rolling surface galling
Failure code4: 01.11.2 Separator fracture, cracking
See also PLATE: 13.3

[See Image in Appendix]

DESCRIPTIONS

FAILURE DESCRIPTION: Heat imbalance failure of ball bearing has caused: (1) Plastic battering of balls; (2) scaling of ball surface; and (3) galling and transfer of metal laminae from groove to balls; (4) fracture of polymer separator. This is a gross failure.

IMAGE DESCRIPTION: Two darkened fragments of machined polymer (phenolic) separator at image W. Two brown-coated battered balls at image E show foil-shaped masses welded onto the balls by galling. Color may be from scaling, grease decom-position products or possibly separator material (more detailed examination needed). Contrast this with PLATE 13.3, where the ring at image E shows *moderate* overheating.

SUSPECTED CAUSES: Severe heat imbalance failure in bearing, probably due to loss of lubricant (or primary separator failure) has caused: softening of steel; galling between balls and grooves; deviation from epicyclic ball speeds; extreme ball/sep-arator forces; separator fracture; and overrolling of debris re-sulting in battering of ball surfaces. High temperature caused scale formation.

DATA

Plate No: 13.16
Archive No: 027-139
Image type: color view [SEE IMAGE IN APPENDIX]
Scalebar = 2 mm (micros: ±20%, others: +100%, -50%)
Component: ACBB; B, run
Speed: 130 KdN
Load:
Lubrication: grease, 60 °C
Failure code1: 00.19.4.3 Friction polymer on guiding part support surface
Failure code2: 12.3 Friction polymer, grease lubrication
Failure code3:
Failure code4:

[See Image in Appendix]

DESCRIPTIONS

FAILURE DESCRIPTION: Friction polymer bands of two orienta-tions on ball which has rubbed excessively against separator and was strongly heated. The ball remains serviceable. The high-friction event that produced the overheating may lead to grease loss and resulting bearing failure.

IMAGE DESCRIPTION: The southern hemisphere of ball is cov-ered with coaxial E–W circles of yellow, brown and grey fric-tion polymer bands, as ball rubbed without indexing against (phenolic plastic) separator pocket. The northern hemisphere shows NW–SE-oriented friction polymer circles from another ball orientation. The black diamond in the center of the ball im-age, and the grey rim of the image are lighting artifacts.

SUSPECTED CAUSES: Relatively high-speed rubbing of ball in separator pocket, in the absence of sharp asperities to cause wear marks, may heat the contact and promote friction polymer formation, as well as its removal by light wear. The combina-tion of the two effects creates the banded appearance. See Chapter introduction for a description of the etch test that dis-tinguishes friction polymer from temper color.

DATA

Plate No: 13.17
Archive No: 005-6
Image type: light metallogram. Nital etch
Scalebar = 100 μm (micros: ±20%, others: +100%, -50%)
Component: C; CF, run
Speed: 7.5 m/sec
Load: 1.4 GPa
Lubrication: mineral oil, 115 °C
Failure code1: 00.19.5 Local structure damage from frictional heating
Failure code2: 26 Support bearing damage (of gear, cam)
Failure code3:
Failure code4:

DESCRIPTIONS

FAILURE DESCRIPTION: High-speed, insufficiently lubricated sliding between contact surfaces has caused strong interface heating which retempered and rehardened the near-surface material. Concurrently, galling (FC 00.13) may have occurred. The retempered and rehardened structure resembles a grinding burn tending to cause early spalling failure. Contamination found in the cam follower roller/pin gap caused braking of the roller and contact sliding.

IMAGE DESCRIPTION: In this section, the rolling surface runs W–E (arrows). Extending S from this surface, whitish oblong streaks are light-etching rehardened material. Directly S of them

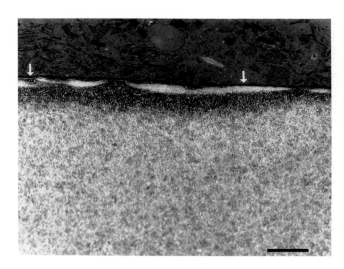

is a wide band of dark-etching overtempered material, blending gradually into the unaltered (mottled appearing) structure. The mottled dark area N of the rolling surface is specimen-mounting material.

SUSPECTED CAUSES: In cam/follower systems the follower roller separates from the cam in each cam revolution at the end of the lift ramp. If friction of the roller on its pin is high, the roller rotation then slows down and undergoes abrupt acceleration at the start of the next lift phase. The friction forces in the cam/roller interface may not suffice to prevent gross sliding, leading to contact overheating (and possible galling).

DATA
Plate No: 14.7
Archive No: 080-104
Image type: color macro [SEE IMAGE IN APPENDIX]
Scalebar = 20 mm (micros: ±20%, others: +100%, -50%)
Component: HG; P, high hardness, run
Speed:
Load:
Lubrication:
Failure code1: 00.20.1.3 Contact corrosion
Failure code2: 00.20.2 Corrosion pitting
Failure code3: -
Failure code4: -

[See Image in Appendix]

DESCRIPTIONS
FAILURE DESCRIPTION: The tooth flank surfaces of the gear are covered by small scattered corrosion pits, with clean metal surface between them. No pitting is visible on the gear OD. This type of corrosion is attributed to an aggressive substance in the lubricant, such as an aggressive EP additive, acting chiefly in the high pressure contact environment. The gear is not failed but may spall prematurely or deteriorate further if the corrosive environment continues.

IMAGE DESCRIPTION: The image is of a portion of a helical pinion with integral shaft. All contact surfaces show evenly scattered fine brown-black corrosion pits. The gear OD shows no pits, just circumferential machining marks (which may be corroded).

SUSPECTED CAUSES: EP additives in some gear oils may become aggressive if water is admixed or temperature is excessive. They corrode the steel, especially where high local temperatures arise due to contact loading and sliding.

DATA
Plate No: 14.8
Archive No: 031-1101
Image type: view (partial)
Scalebar = 20 mm (micros: ±20%, others: +100%, -50%)
Component: SRB; IR, run
Speed:
Load:
Lubrication: mineral oil, ? °C
Failure code1: 00.20.1.3 Contact corrosion
Failure code2: 00.20.2 Corrosion pitting
Failure code3: 00.16.1.2.1 Shallow entry spall from surface point-defect
Failure code4: 00.12.4 Wear of guiding-component support surface

DESCRIPTIONS
FAILURE DESCRIPTION: Numerous contact corrosion streaks are visible at roller spacings with more than one roller set position. Corrosion pits appear in and outside the contact areas. Spalls follow the contact corrosion outlines. Circumferential wear marks are on the separator guide surface (OD) of the center flange. The bearing has failed.

IMAGE DESCRIPTION: OD of SRB IR (partial view), showing both roller paths and three flanges. Rectangular axial bands extend across both roller paths where the original surface is destroyed. Black corrosion pits are in and outside the bands.

Spall craters follow straight edges of the contact bands on the roller path facing image N. Circumferential (shiny) wear marks are on the OD of the center flange.

SUSPECTED CAUSES: This bearing operated in a paper machine. Water (steam) ingress into the bearing causes contact corrosion outlining the area within the fluid meniscus adjacent to each contact. Spalls initiate at the corrosion pits concentrated within the liquid filled area near the contacts. Wear on the separator guide surface may be due to abrasion by debris.

DATA
Plate No: 14.9
Archive No: 087-117
Image type: view
Scalebar = 10 mm (micros: ±20%, others: +100%, -50%)
Component: ACBB; B, run
Speed:
Load:
Lubrication:
Failure code1: 00.20.2 Corrosion pitting
Failure code2: 00.16.1.2.1 Shallow entry spall from surface point-defect
Failure code3: 00.16.03.2 Spall propagating by re-initiation at surface
Failure code4: -
See also PLATEs: 14.4 & 14.11

DESCRIPTIONS
FAILURE DESCRIPTION: Dense corrosion pitting on balls has precipitated spalls on each. Irregular propagation suggests multiple spall starts from several corrosion pits. The balls have failed.

IMAGE DESCRIPTION: Fine corrosion pitting on all three balls, best seen near the contour, where dark spots contrast with reflection from the white background. Corrosion is most advanced on the ball at image N, least on the ball at image SE. One spall crater is visible on each ball; the most advanced is on ball at N, which shows several initiation points with ridges dividing the crater bottom.

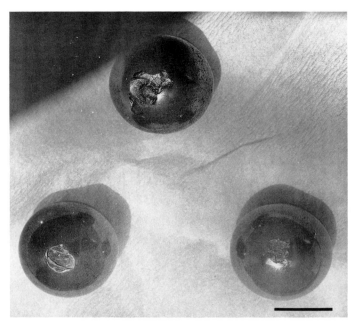

SUSPECTED CAUSES: Due to fine finish, unworn balls are more corrosion-resistant than other parts of identical material. When corrosion occurs in an environment such as water spray, condensation, salt air or acidified lubricant, small stains or pits tend to form. Pits are major sources of early spalling. See also PLATEs 14.4 and 14.11.

DATA
Plate No: 14.10
Archive No: 031-502
Image type: view
Scalebar = 40 mm (micros: ±20%, others: +100%, -50%)
Component: TRB (multirow); OR, run
Speed:
Load:
Lubrication: mineral oil, ? °C
Failure code1: 00.20.2 Corrosion pitting
Failure code2: 00.16.1.2.1 Shallow entry spall from surface point-defect
Failure code3: 00.20.1 Corrosion stain
Failure code4: 02.13 Rubbing seal counterface wear

DESCRIPTIONS
FAILURE DESCRIPTION: Generalized corrosion of free surfaces (stains) and contacts (pits) with subsequent extensive spalling composed of small craters emanating from pits. Spalling covers the rolling contact surfaces. The flange contact surface is heavily corrosion pitted, and may be galled. The bearing may still turn but has no useful life left.

IMAGE DESCRIPTION: The ring side face (facing image N) and the ID of the center flange (with oil holes) show dark corrosion stains. The roller path is densely peppered with pits and spalls (details not discernible in the image) indicating corrosion fol-

lowed by spalling. The N-facing thrust face of the center flange is corrosion-pitted, and may be galled. On the contact surface, adjacent to the N edge, circular wear bands are visible, which may be due to seal wear.

SUSPECTED CAUSES: This bearing operated in a paper machine, in wet environment. Water ingress (possibly steam) past damaged seal, caused corrosion, followed by spalling. On the flange thrust surface pits and rust are visible, and galling is suspected.

DATA
Plate No: 14.11
Archive No: 001-10
Image type: light microgram
Scalebar = 400 μm (micros: ±20%, others: +100%, -50%)
Component: ACBB; B, run
Speed: 1 MdN
Load: ? (axial)
Lubrication: synthetic polyester oil, 120 °C
Failure code1: 00.20.2 Corrosion pitting
Failure code2: 00.20.1.3 Contact corrosion
Failure code3: 00.12.4 Wear of guiding-component support surface
Failure code4: -
See also PLATEs: 14.4 & 14.9

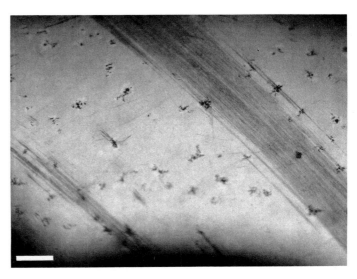

DESCRIPTIONS
FAILURE DESCRIPTION: (1) Random corrosion pits on ball surface; (2) parallel scratchmarks along a great circle and a nearby minor circle, inflicted later than the corrosion pits. Exposure to an aggressive environment caused the corrosion. The scratchmarks appear to be due to contact with abrasive particles or asperities in the separator. This is incipient failure in a high-speed bearing. See also PLATEs 14.4 and 14.9 for ball corrosion.

IMAGE DESCRIPTION: Grey background is ball surface. Lapping marks are not visible. Clusters of dark spots are corrosion pits. The band of dark parallel arcs across the NE image quadrant consists of scratchmarks. Similar bands are in the SW quadrant. Centered between the two sets of bands is one corrosion pit from which scratches in identical direction emanate, showing that scratches covering pits or emanating from a pit were made after the pits had formed.

SUSPECTED CAUSES: Due to fine finish, balls are intrinsically more corrosion-resistant than other parts of identical material. When corrosion occurs in an environment such as water spray, condensation, salt air or acidified lubricant, pits, rather than stains tend to form. The scratch marking appears to be caused independently of the corrosion, except where it originates at a pit which may have provided corroded debris.

DATA
Plate No: 14.12
Archive No: 014-13
Image type: view
Scalebar = 30 mm (micros: ±20%, others: +100%, -50%)
Component: TRB; IR & OR & R, run
Speed:
Load:
Lubrication: grease, ? °C
Failure code1: 00.20.2 Corrosion pitting
Failure code2: 00.20.1.3 Contact corrosion
Failure code3: 00.20.01.1 Generalized corrosion
Failure code4: -
See also PLATEs: 14.5 & 14.6 & 14.12

DESCRIPTIONS
FAILURE DESCRIPTION: In the OR roller path, on the rollers and (less) on the IR roller path, axial bands of macroscopic corrosion pits have formed from trapped condensation surrounding the stationary contacts. On the OR OD, general corrosion and/or fretting is visible. Corrosion is diagnosed because of the random, spotty appearance extending across the entire OD width. Contact corrosion pits form severe spall-initiating surface defects. See PLATEs 14.5, 14.6 and 14.12, for comparison.

IMAGE DESCRIPTION: An IR ('cone') at image N is flanked by two rollers. The OR ('cup') is at image S. Corrosion pit bands at roller spacing are near N (small) edge of IR track and at extreme E. Many pit bands are on the roller OD. Heavy bands appear at roller spacing in the OR track. The OR OD is diffusely rust stained. (Fretting is possible but less likely across full width and in small diffuse spots. In color view, fretting tends to be more red; corrosion more blackish.)

SUSPECTED CAUSES: This bearing was grease lubricated and used in a road vehicle wheel. Condensation may accumulate at contacts when vehicle stands in the cold, and produce the staining if grease is unsuitable to protect contacts.

DATA
Plate No: 14.13
Archive No: 014-19&20
Image type: a, b: view
Scalebar = a, b: 10 mm (micros: ±20%, others: +100%, -50%)
Component: TRB; IR & R, run
Speed:
Load:
Lubrication:
Failure code1: 00.20.2 Corrosion pitting
Failure code2: 00.20.1.3 Contact corrosion
Failure code3: 00.20.1 Corrosion stain
Failure code4: 00.15.1.1 Generalized fretting, radial fit surface
See also PLATEs: 14.6 & 14.12

DESCRIPTIONS
FAILURE DESCRIPTION: Thin wavy lines of corrosion micropitting are on the IR ('cone') and the roller contact surfaces. Compared to PLATE 14.6, the corrosion pitting indicates more aggressive (or more long-term) corrosion over small surface areas. There are some corrosion stains. Pits are spall-initiating surface defects. Early spalling failure is expected. Incidental fretting is present in IR ('cone') bore. See also PLATE 14.12 illustrating significant TRB corrosion.

IMAGE DESCRIPTION: (a): rollers with wavy axial dark lines formed by corrosion micropits (discernible under magnification). Some diffuse corrosion staining is visible near N end of rollers. (b): Thin, straight dark lines formed by corrosion pits near S roller path edge in image center and 1/5 from image E. Minor staining exists at image W. Broad curved dark band at W is artifact. Heavy dark spotting in the bore is fretting.

a

b

SUSPECTED CAUSES: If an aggressive agent (water, acidified preservative or lubricant) enters contacts in small quantity but remains in place for long, localized corrosion pitting may develop. Lesser concentrations may cause stains. Heavy bore fretting indicates that the bearing ran extensively. Corrosion may be a late occurrence; otherwise spalls would have formed.

DATA
Plate No: 14.14
Archive No: 093-20.1.4
Image type: light microgram
Scalebar = 1 mm (micros: ±20%, others: +100%, -50%)
Component: SRB; IR, run
Speed:
Load:
Lubrication:
Failure code1: 00.20.2 Corrosion pitting
Failure code2: 00.20.1.3 Contact corrosion
Failure code3: 11.2 Water in oil
Failure code4: -

DESCRIPTIONS
FAILURE DESCRIPTION: The lubricant in this SRB contained a modest concentration of water which formed fine droplets on the stationary contact surface. It appears that a small amount of relative motion took place in the contact. Where pure rolling occurred, the droplets formed round pits. Where a sliding component existed, the points were smeared out into streaks. Extensive corrosion produces many spall-initiating surface defects.

IMAGE DESCRIPTION: Image shows SRB IR roller path with rolling direction E–W. At image S, dark points densely pepper

the surface. Progressing to N, they coalesce into bands and then, near *A* into individual streaks about 600 μm long. It is assumed that water droplets in oil were wiped over the surface by sliding.

SUSPECTED CAUSES: Water in the lubricant is a serious source of corrosive attack when its concentration exceeds a maximum dependent on the ability of the lubricant's antioxidant to prevent corrosion. Corrosion pits cause loss of contact fatigue resistance.

DATA
Plate No: 14.15
Archive No: 087-102&103
Image type: a: view, b: light microgram
Scalebar = a: 10 mm, b: 500 μm
(micros: ±20%, others: +100%, -50%)
Component: CRB; IR, unrun
Speed: -
Load: -
Lubrication: -
Failure code1: 00.20.2 Corrosion pitting
Failure code2: 00.20.3 Corrosive fingerprint-mark
Failure code3: 00.20.1 Corrosion stain
Failure code4: -

DESCRIPTIONS
FAILURE DESCRIPTION: Incipient corrosion pitting on contact surface of unrun IR due to inadequate rust-preservation for existing humidity. Corrosion pits (as distinct from stains) have significant depth and form serious spall-initiating surface defects. In bore, light staining is visible, and possibly fingerprint-marks.

IMAGE DESCRIPTION: (a): Roller path of IR is at the image center; undercut and guide flange to the S. Dark spots at the image center near undercut and 1/5 from W contour are corrosion pits. Irregular fine stain is near N edge of roller path, (1/5 from W contour) and on flange contact surface, at W. Fingerprint-shaped stains are visible in the bore, near image centerline. (b): Corrosion pitting on surface. Pit contains oxides, the depth is not resolved. There are E–W finishing lines.

SUSPECTED CAUSES: Inadequate rust preventative for the humidity condition prevailing at storage permits corrosion stains or (if exposure is longer) pits. Water droplets in grease

(FC 12.4.2) are likely sources of pitting. Pits may have significant (several μm) depth, which becomes apparent in efforts to remove the corrosion by light polishing. Fingerprint marks arise from human touch of degreased steel surfaces.

DATA
Plate No: 14.16
Archive No: 014-145
Image type: light metallogram. Nital etch.
Scalebar = 40 μm (micros: ±20%, others: +100%, -50%)
Component: TRB; IR, run
Speed:
Load:
Lubrication:
Failure code1: 00.21.1 Electric erosion pitting
Failure code2: -
Failure code3: -
Failure code4: -
See also PLATEs: 14.21 & 14.22

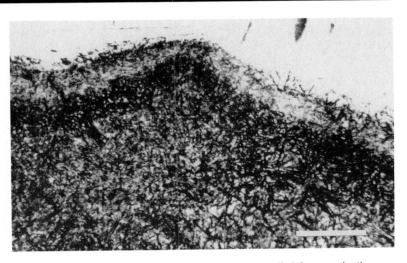

DESCRIPTIONS
FAILURE DESCRIPTION: The material was overheated in electric erosion damage. A rehardened layer has formed at the pit bottom surface; and an overtempered layer is beneath that. Electric erosion creates extremely noisy bearings which tend to fail rapidly by spalling, or (in case of fluting), seizure or separator fracture. See PLATEs 14.21 and 14.22, for the appearance of eroded surfaces.

IMAGE DESCRIPTION: The image is an etched metallographic section through the electric erosion damaged part. The white

area at image N is protective plating applied for examination. The scalloped interface adjacent to the white area represents two eroded pits. Light-etching crescents S of surface are rehardened. Dark etching crescents next S of these are overtempered. Normal material extends to S image edge.

SUSPECTED CAUSES: Electric current passing through the rolling contacts of a bearing (with insulating lubricant) makes sparks which erode (melt) the surface. Depending on current intensity, fine pitting, gross pitting or fluting may result.

DATA
Plate No: 14.17
Archive No: 027-165
Image type: light macro
Scalebar = 5 mm (micros: ±20%, others: +100%, -50%)
Component: DGBB; IR, run
Speed: 100 KdN
Load: <1.6 GPa
Lubrication: grease, 60 °C
Failure code1: 00.21.1 Electric erosion pitting
Failure code2: 00.16.1.2.1 Shallow entry spall from surface point-defect
Failure code3: -
Failure code4: -

DESCRIPTIONS
FAILURE DESCRIPTION: A band of fine electric erosion pits is in the IR ball groove. A cluster of incipient surface-origin spalls was initiated by some of the pits. Additional spalls are likely to be initiated from other pits. The bearing has failed as spalling is expected to progress rapidly.

IMAGE DESCRIPTION: The dark area of the image is the ball groove. There are reflected highlights near E and W image edges and a reflected light streak below letter B. One land faintly visible above B. An extensive band of fine electric ero-

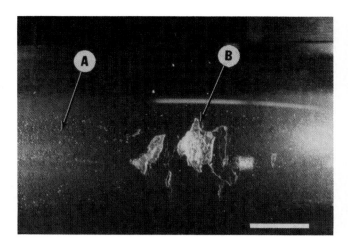

sion pits is marked by arrow A. Fan-shaped (surface origin) spall craters are at arrow B and to the W.

SUSPECTED CAUSES: Electric current passing through the rolling contacts of a bearing (with insulating lubricant) makes sparks which erode (melt) the surface. Depending on current intensity and other variables, fine pitting (as shown), large pits or 'flutes' (axial bands of pitting) may be caused. Pits are serious spall-originating surface defects.

DATA
Plate No: 14.18
Archive No: 027-179
Image type: light macro
Scalebar = 2 mm (micros: ±20%, others: +100%, -50%)
Component: DGBB; B, run
Speed: 110 KdN
Load:
Lubrication: grease, 60 °C
Failure code1: 00.21.1 Electric erosion pitting
Failure code2: 00.16.1.2.1 Shallow entry spall from surface point-defect
Failure code3: 00.16.02.4 Incipient spalling, multiple spalls
Failure code4: -

DESCRIPTIONS
FAILURE DESCRIPTION: A line of electrical pits from passage of moderate current, with possible incipient spalling, is visible along a great circle. The bearing is very noisy and the separator will wear. Spalling failure is imminent.

IMAGE DESCRIPTION: The ball appears dark in the image, with multiple bright light reflections. An E–W band of pits is indicated by two arrows. Some of the pits appear irregular as if spalls had been initiated.

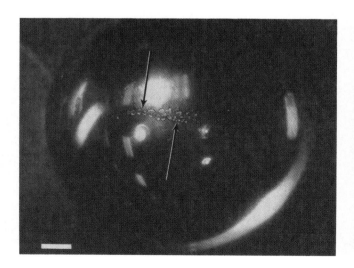

SUSPECTED CAUSES: Electric current passing through the rolling contacts of a bearing (with insulating lubricant) makes sparks which erode (melt) the surface. Depending on current intensity, fine pitting may occur (as shown). With other current densities and operating conditions, large pits or 'flutes' (pitted axial troughs) may form. Pits are serious spall-originating surface defects.

DATA

Plate No: 14.19
Archive No: 107-006a&b
Image type: a, b: SEM
Scalebar = a: 50, b: 10 μm (micros: ±20%, others: +100%, -50%)
Component: DGBB; IR, run
Speed:
Load:
Lubrication: oil, 50 °C
Failure code1: 00.21.1 Electric erosion pitting
Failure code2: 00.17.1.1 Glazing (incipient surface distress)
Failure code3: 00.12.3.2.2 Scratch marks, kinematic wear marks in rolling surface
Failure code4: -
See also PLATEs: 14.17 & 14.23

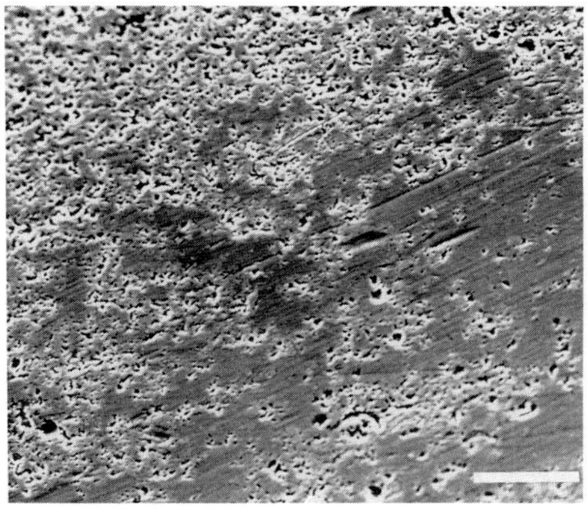

a

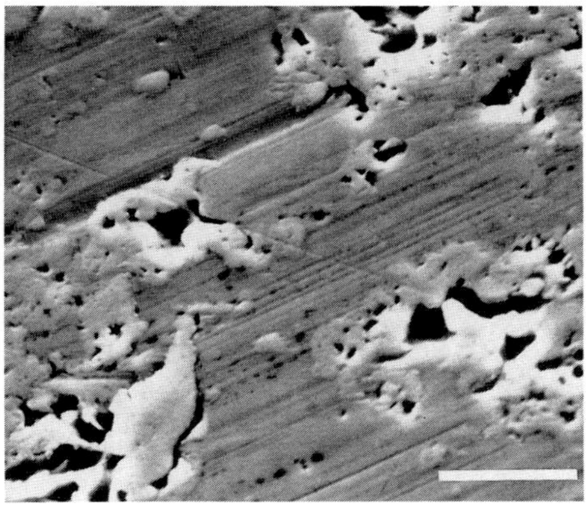

b

DESCRIPTIONS

FAILURE DESCRIPTION: Microscopic pitting of contact surface through long-time passage of small current. Raised pit edges are being rolled down (surface glazing). The surface has suffered damage comparable in its effect to surface distress (asperity-scale spalling) and is prone to early spalling failure. The few wearmarks are incidental.

IMAGE DESCRIPTION: (a): Background is dark grey rolling surface. Finishing lines run SW–NE. Many dense, small, black-centered electric erosion pits with light (raised) rims are visible. Near image center E, are two short deep wear scratches. (b): High magnification. Grey rolling surface shows darker, SW–NE running finishing lines. Black irregular electric pits with surrounding raised (light color) edges, which are rolled down by contact passage. There are no fracture surfaces as found in spalls.

SUSPECTED CAUSES: Electric current passing through the rolling contacts of a bearing (with insulating lubricant) makes sparks which erode (melt) the surface. Depending on current intensity, fine pitting (as shown, see also PLATE 14.17) or massive fluting (see PLATE 14.23) may result.

DATA

Plate No: 14.20
Archive No: 107-005a&b
Image type: a, b: SEM
Scalebar = a: 1 mm, b: 100 μm (micros: ±20%, others: +100%, -50%)
Component: DGBB; IR, run
Speed:
Load:
Lubrication:
Failure code1: 00.21.1 Electric erosion pitting
Failure code2: 00.18.1.2 Sharp individual dent(s) from metal debris, asperities
Failure code3: 00.16.1.2.1 Shallow entry spall from surface point-defect
Failure code4: -
See also PLATE: 14.23

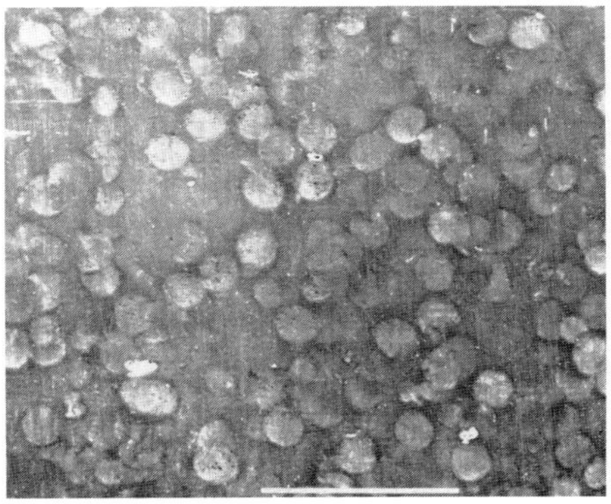

a

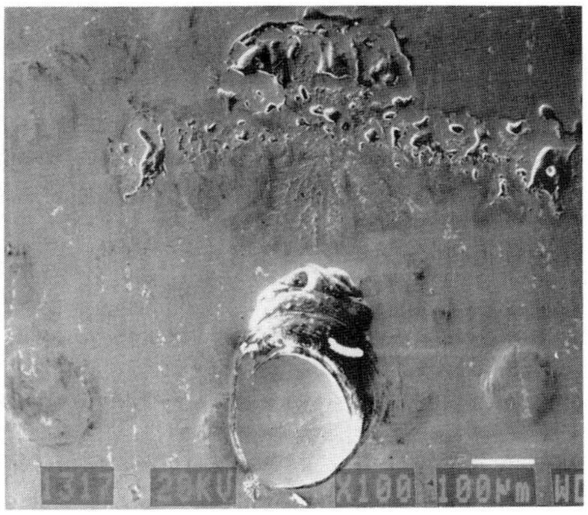

b

DESCRIPTIONS

FAILURE DESCRIPTION: (a): Circular platelets of surface material were removed by electric current passage through the contact. Sharp-edged cratering was caused by local melting. Removed platelets were rolled over to form circular dents.
(b): Erosion craters with rolled-down edges are shown, possibly starting to spall. A platelet begins to form. Pits from electric current erosion are major noise sources and tend to lead to very early spalling.

IMAGE DESCRIPTION: (a): The dark grey background is the rolling surface with finishing lines running N–S. Identical-sized circular light and dark spots are dents of about 200 μm diameter. (b): Near center of S image edge: remelted erosion pit with striated bottom and raised loosened platelet at S. Flat circular depressions in SE, NW and SW quadrants are dents. At image N are erosion pits, with rolled-down edges. These possibly initiate spalls.

SUSPECTED CAUSES: Electric current passing through the rolling contacts of a bearing (with insulating lubricant) makes sparks which erode (melt) the surface. Depending on current intensity, fine pitting (as shown) or massive fluting may result. See PLATE 14.23.

DATA
Plate No: 14.21
Archive No: 014-70&71
Image type: a: view; b: light macro
Scalebar = a, b: 5 mm (micros: ±20%, others: +100%, -50%)
Component: TRB; a: R&G; b: IR, run
Speed:
Load:
Lubrication:
Failure code1: 00.21.1 Electric erosion pitting
Failure code2: 00.20.1 Corrosion stain
Failure code3: -
Failure code4: -

DESCRIPTIONS
FAILURE DESCRIPTION: One large electric erosion pit each, is in the roller and the IR, due to one-time passage of high-intensity current in the stationary bearing. Incidental corrosion staining is visible on the IR. The bearing has failed.

IMAGE DESCRIPTION: (a): The rollers appear light grey in the dark stamped-steel separator. On the center roller, midway along the contact is a large, circular dark pit with raised rim. (b): IR ('cone') roller path with the thrust flange at N image edge. At image center, is a large pit matching that on image

a   b

(a). The rim of the pit is raised. Incidental corrosion stain streaking appears on the roller path.

SUSPECTED CAUSES: This bearing supported a rotor on which electric arc welding was performed while grounding the machine through the stator. The full welding current passed through the bearing, creating massive electric sparking and erosion pitting. The bearing is unusable.

DATA
Plate No: 14.22
Archive No: 014-68
Image type: light macro
Scalebar = 15 mm (micros: ±20%, others: +100%, -50%)
Component: TRB; IR, run
Speed:
Load:
Lubrication:
Failure code1: 00.21.2 Electric erosion fluting
Failure code2: -
Failure code3: -
Failure code4: -
See also PLATE: 14.23

DESCRIPTIONS
FAILURE DESCRIPTION: 'Fluted' electric erosion damage is shown, with transverse depressions in rolling surface, in which considerable pitting took place, alternating with relatively undamaged bands between flutes. Fluting requires continuing current flow above a minimum strength. Fluting erosion creates extremely noisy bearings which tend to fail rapidly by seizure or separator fracture. See PLATE 14.23 for detailed appearance of the fluted surface.

IMAGE DESCRIPTION: At the N image edge is the thrust flange ('large-end rib') of a TRB OR ('cone'); at the S edge is the small-end flange (rib) and undercut. Between these, the roller

path is covered by approximately periodic sharp-edged axial valleys ('flutes') of 1–3 mm width and extending completely across roller path.

SUSPECTED CAUSES: Fluting under electric erosion is not fully explained. Apparently, vibratory conditions lead to concentration of current flow at minimum surface separation points occurring during the vibration and flutes form there. Less current flows near maximum separation points. Existence of flutes apparently locks in the vibration phase so that fluting is reinforced. See magnified images of flutes in PLATE 14.23.

DATA
Plate No: 14.23
Archive No: 093-21.1.8&7
Image type: a: SEM, b: SEM with section
Scalebar = a: 250, b: 8 μm (micros: ±20%, others: +100%, -50%)
Component: DGBB; IR, run
Speed:
Load:
Lubrication:
Failure code1: 00.21.2 Electric erosion fluting
Failure code2: 00.17.1.1 Glazing (incipient surface distress)
Failure code3: -
Failure code4: -
See also PLATE: 14.22

DESCRIPTIONS
FAILURE DESCRIPTION: 'Fluted' electric erosion damage with transverse depressions in rolling surface. There is dense cratering in flutes, and no damage or damage of considerably lower depth between flutes. The crater bottoms in the flutes are molten surfaces; crater edges have been rolled over and are surface-distressed. Fluting creates extremely noisy bearings which tend to fail rapidly by seizure or separator fracture.

IMAGE DESCRIPTION: (a): Portion of a ball groove. The surface at *A* is unfluted. Finishing marks and rolling direction run along the arrow in NE corner. The leading edge of a flute is at *B–B*, with craters extending to the NW. SE of line *C–C* is the trailing edge of another flute, with cratering. There is minor damage at *D*. (b): A section plane begins at *A*; the edge of the fluted surface is at arrow *B*. A molten crater bottom is at *C*; raised, overrolled, glazed rims are at *D*.

SUSPECTED CAUSES: Fluting from electric erosion is not fully understood. Apparently a vibratory occurrence concentrates current along the thinner film areas, forming flute bottoms. The existence of flutes appears to lock in the vibratory phase so that flutes are reinforced. For appearance of the fluted surface, see PLATE 14.22.

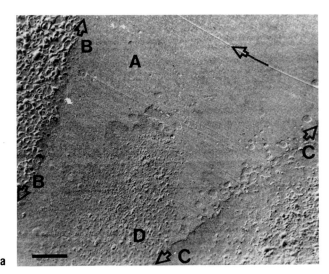

a

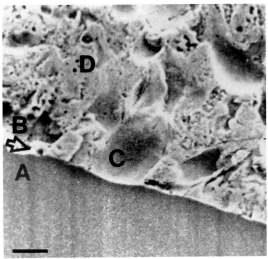

b

15 BULK CRACKING, FRACTURE, PERMANENT DEFORMATION

15.1. BULK CRACKING OR FRACTURE. FAILURE CODE: 00.22

15.1.1. Definition

In a contact component, *bulk cracking* designates cracks extending beyond the stress field of the Hertz contact. *Bulk fracture* is fracture leading to separation of a volume of material by a bulk crack.

Examples of bulk cracks and fractures of Hertz contact components:

1. Rolling bearings and cams.

   - Cracks starting in the contact zone but extending in depth into the component, beyond the Hertzian stressed volume.
   - Cracks of integral flanges; fracture of flanges.
   - Cracks of an entire cross-section; breakage of component into separate pieces.

   NOTE: Cracking of bearing separators is covered under FC 01.1.

2. Gears.

   - Tooth cracking (bulk); tooth fracture.
   - Cracking or fracture of gear body (web or hub).
   - Cracking of spline (tooth or body).

   NOTE: Cracking or fracture of integral shafts, away from the gear itself, is covered under FC 22.

15.1.2. Diagnostic Objective

Bulk cracking and fracture are, by far, the most common *ultimate* failure modes in mechanical components as a broad class. The causes and types of cracking are a wide field of study [10]. In this Atlas, the description of bulk cracking and fracture of contact components is limited to cases encountered as service failures of these tribological components.

Engineering diagnosis is aimed at the identification of engineering causes for failure. When diagnosing cracking, three questions must be answered in order to identify causes:

1. *Basic cracking mechanism:* Is the cracking initiated by overload, fatigue or chemical attack? (This is diagnosed from the crack surface topography.)
2. *Crack propagation direction:* Where did the stress field initiating the crack operate and in what direction did it drive the crack? (This is diagnosed by identifying the crack origination point and observing marks of crack growth.)
3. *Crack age:* How much of the crack is recent and at what rate did it propagate? (This is diagnosed from the oxidation and wear condition of the crack surfaces.)

15.1.3. Nomenclature

There are no designations other than "cracking" and "fracture" for this failure mode. However, there is a large number of differentiating adjectives for failure mechanisms, fracture appearances, etc. To avoid repetition, these are identified in the description of the failure process which follows.

15.1.4. Failure Process

Cracking may be categorized, according to its cause, as mechanical stress cracking, thermal stress cracking, and chemically promoted cracking.

Mechanical Stress Cracking

This category includes both overstress (ductile and brittle) and fatigue cracking, which are often intermingled.

Rolling Bearings

1. *Cracking under (tensile) hoop stress* occurs in rings interference-fitted on shafts and in the rotating inner-rings of high speed bearings, due to centrifugal forces.

   If excessive, hoop stress alone may cause fatigue or even overload cracking, starting at a nick or edge in the bore or the rolling track. A lesser tensile hoop stress may divert a fatigue crack starting from Hertzian stressing into progressing radially inward, so that a bulk crack rather than a spall forms.

2. *Cracking under bending stress.*

   Rings may be under bending stress if their mounting part (shaft or housing) is thin, soft, distorted or interrupted (for example, by a hole or keyway). *Balls or rollers* may be under bending stress if the balls are hollow, or if the rollers are drilled or axially mislocated, so that they overrun the track edge.

3. *Impact or overload cracking* may occur in hardened, especially through-hardened steel (and even more, ceramic) material, which is inherently of low toughness. Impacts or overloads in manufacture, mounting or service can propagate cracks. Local defects can create overloads and be potent crack initiators.

   Impact or overload cracking may occur on bearing rings and rolling elements (especially balls). Particularly vulnerable to impact or overload cracking are integral flanges of rings. These flanges can come under high load or impact from improper mounting practices, from axial service loads (cylindrical roller bearings) or excessive roller skewing. Cracks that chip or break flanges are common.

4. *Cracking after spalling.* Spalls are stress raisers, and rolling over spalls creates impacts. When the spalls are large, the condition may become sufficiently severe to propagate a mechanical stress crack in a ball, roller or ring, under the action of otherwise well-supported bulk stresses in the component (hoop stress, bending stress, etc.) Through hardened components are more vulnerable than case hardened components.

NOTE: Cam followers may undergo cracking due to the same causes from which bearings crack.

Gears

1. *Tooth bending* fatigue fracture is a primary failure mode in gears.
   • *Tooth root fracture* is the result of stress concentration at the tooth root.
   • *Tooth chipping* removes portions of the tooth tip, as a result of concentrated stress in that area, such as from a local defect.
2. *Web or hub* cracking or both may occur as a sequel to tooth cracking.
3. *Splines* may crack when transmitting excessive torque or impacts.
4. *Impact or overload* cracking of gears may occur as it does in rolling bearings.
5. *Cracking from spalling* is not uncommon. Spalls are stress raisers, and rolling over spalls creates impacts. When the spalls are large, the condition may become sufficiently severe to drive a fatigue crack through a tooth, under the action of tooth bending stresses.

NOTE: Cams may undergo cracking for many of the same causes as do gears, except for tooth fracture modes which do not apply.

Thermal Stress Cracking

Rubbing cracks. Cracks may form on (hardened steel) surfaces in *sliding* contact under heavy load, as a result of cyclic local overheating. This failure mode is in competition with galling and may dominate, if the lubrication, the surface coating or finish succeed in preventing the welding necessary for galling. The cyclic heating and cooling can result in thermal stress fatigue cracking.

For forging cracks and heat treat cracks, see FC 00.07. For grinding cracks see FC 00.08.

Chemically Promoted Cracking

Stress corrosion cracking and *hydrogen embrittlement* cracking both result from otherwise well-tolerated stresses applied to weakened intergranular bonds caused by chemical reactions. For a description of the hydrogen embrittlement process see FC 00.08, for that of stress corrosion, see FC 00.20.

15.1.5. Distinctive Appearance

Three appearance features of cracks are important in diagnosing cracking processes and causes: (1) crack progression features, which provide indications of the nature of the stress driving the crack; (2) crack initiation features and location, which can identify weak points and the direction from which the stress attacked; and (3) changes in crack surface appearance from events after cracking, which are indications of crack age and progression rate. They are preferably examined in the order listed, since interpretation of each is needed to shed light on the following.

Crack Progression Features

The following comments apply to the recognition of crack progression features. Extensive fractography literature [21] covers crack progression features in general. However, the body of data published on fractography of hardened steels is quite limited. In this Atlas, only appearance features relevant to Hertz contact machine element diagnosis are covered.

Great differences in crack surface appearance arise from the structure, toughness and residual stress of the component material and also from differences in the applied stress condition. In hard steels, the features are very fine and may require (scanning electron) microscopy for identification. The features may be less well developed in ceramics.

The classic distinguishing features of crack propagation follow.

Transgranular Cracking

Transgranular cracking is the normal cracking mode in the absence of grain boundary weakness:

Fatigue cracks resulting from repeated application of stress below the 'ultimate strength', show 'beach marks' which are ridges in roughly concentric arcs centered on the initiation point. Fatigue cracks may, if allowed to continue in service, convert to overstress cracks when the cross section has been weakened by the fatigue crack to the point where stresses exceed the ultimate strength.

Ductile cracks are comparatively slow-moving cracks resulting from stress slightly in excess of the 'fracture stress'. They occur in materials with sufficient ductility under the prevailing stress conditions and show microscopic 'dimples' that is, conical depressions where plastic flow has taken place during cracking. Ductile cracks may occur in tension or in shear. In tension, the dimples are non-directional; in shear they are oriented in the slip direction. Ductile cracking is clearly identifiable in tough, lower-hardness materials, but in hard steels, the distinguishing features are very subtle and may be unidentifiable.

Brittle cracks are fast moving cracks with little plastic flow which occur in material with low ductility under the existing stress conditions. They are driven by the applied stresses plus the elastic energy released by the crack from the stressed material (including residual stress). These cracks are flat-faceted (undimpled). The facets are cleavage planes across each grain.

Intergranular Cracking

Intergranular cracking occurs when grain boundaries are weakened, often by chemical effects (see FC 00.08 and FC 00.20). These cracks follow the grain boundaries. There may or may not be signs of corrosion on the surface.

Crack Initiation Features

Crack initiation points may be surface defects (nicks, dents, furrows, galling or rehardened areas); material defects (inclusions, voids, large carbides, or cold worked volumes); edges; previous macro- or micro-cracks or spalls. Often, the initiating feature is lost in cracking or is indiscernible.

Crack initiation location may be identified by the following criteria, depending on the nature of crack propagation.

In *fatigue cracks:* if the bulk fatigue crack initiates from a point (surface or subsurface defect), then the initiation point is the center of the beach marks (striations) of the crack surface. If the bulk fatigue crack initiates from a spall (or a Hertzian fatigue crack), then the visible remnants of the spall are the initiation zone.

NOTE: A bulk fatigue crack may initiate outside the Hertzian stressed volume, traverse the cross section to arrive at the rolling track and there serve as the initiation point of a spall. This can be verified by observing the beach marks.

In *ductile cracks:* Initiation area may be a fatigue crack, a local defect or other identifiable feature. If the ductility of the material is high, the crack may end in a *lip*, that is, a rim at an angle to the main cracking direction, at the surface it reaches *last*. The initiation point is then to be sought on the opposite side of the cracked section.

In *brittle cracks:* Macroscopic "chevron marks" may be found on the crack surface, which point with their tip in the direction of crack propagation. This means that the initiation point is located toward the open end of these marks. Microscopic 'river marks' may be observable by SEM on the crack face, consisting of depressions with the appearance of a river bed with tributaries. The crack progresses *upriver*—the initiation point is at the downriver end of the river mark.

The location of the initiation point on the component can indicate the *initiating stress condition,* as detailed below.

In *bearing parts*:
Cracks due to *Hertzian stressing* originate in the vicinity of the rolling track, most often at depths comparable to the maximum Hertz shear stress. Cracks initiating from *subcase failure* initiate at the case/core interface.

Cracks due to *mounting damage* originate from nicks, scuffmarks or in the undercut adjacent to an overloaded flange.

Cracks due to *tensile hoop stresses* in rings tend to initiate at the bore where these stresses are highest.

Cracks due to *bending* (in rings or hollow rolling elements) originate at the side of the component where the bending stresses are tensile.

Cracks in flanges due to *overload* of *flange contacts* are bending or shear cracks, originating on the contact side of the flange (tensile bending stresses), often in the undercut or at the outside edge.

Rubbing cracks are initiated on a surface undergoing overheating in sliding contact.

For heat treat crack initiation see FC 00.07. For grinding crack initiation see FC 00.08.

In *gears*:
Cracks due to *Hertzian stressing* originate in the vicinity of the tooth profile surface, most often at depths comparable to the maximum Hertz shear stress. Cracks initiating subcase failure initiate at the case/core interface.

Tooth root cracks initiate from high bending stress at the root blend radius, on the (tensile stressed) contact side of the tooth. The crack typically begins at the tooth radius, travels down below the tooth root, then veers and ascends to the tooth radius on the unloaded side of the same tooth.

NOTE: Tooth root crack initiation near an axial edge indicates a misaligned contact. Off-center initiation not near an edge may indicate contact geometry error.

Tooth shear cracks may occur along with, or in place of, tooth bending cracks if a high impact force is applied to the tooth contacts. The crack initiates at the root radius but instead of traveling downward into the web, cuts across the tooth dedendum.

Web and hub cracks may originate from tooth cracks (usually as a result of overstress generated by the tooth cracking), or from the bore of the hub. Crack propagation direction must be established.

Cracks due to *mounting damage* originate from nicks or scuffmarks.

In splines, *torsional cracking* due to moment overload or impact initiates cracks just outside the loaded area, running at about 45° across the spline tops and with connecting axial cracks at the spline sides.

Changes in Pre-existing Crack Face

Freshly formed crack faces are metallic. When exposed to air or to lubricant, especially at elevated temperature, they oxidize and become discolored. Discoloration of a *part* of a crack face indicates initiation of a crack which was subsequently arrested and recently restarted.

An extreme case of oxidation is a *heat treat crack* (FC 00.07), which develops a scaled face if it occurs in the first half of a two-stage heat treat cycle (example: carburizing with rehardening). A crack face which develops after (last stage) quenching but before tempering, may show temper color (see FC 00.19).

Cracks which undergo cyclic stressing after formation

may experience rubbing of the crack faces. If so, fine fracture features may be worn away and fretting or polishing may appear.

The fracture surface of a spall bottom may experience direct contact with a rolling element or with spall debris and acquire a hammered appearance.

15.1.6. Causes

A list of common causes of bulk cracking follows.

1. Casting or forming defects (FC 00.04 and FC 00.05).
2. Heat treatment defects (FC 00.07).
3. Residual stresses, such as:

   - *Forming stresses* (especially in cold formed parts).
   - *Heat treating stresses.* These may be deliberate (the compressive stresses in carburized cases) or unintended (residual stresses from uneven quenching).
   - *Grinding stresses* from the cutting forces and heat applied in grinding. Extreme case: grinding burns.
   - *Service induced stresses.* Rolling (or sliding) contact at high pressures builds up residual stresses in the Hertz stress field (from plastic flow and the decomposition of austenite).

4. Applied tensile or shear stress (steady-state, cyclic or impact), such as:

   - *Hoop stress* in tight fitted bearing rings, gears or cams or in centrifugally stressed rotating high speed bearing innerrings.
   - *Bending* or *shear stress* in bearing flanges or gear teeth under working load; in bearing rings fitted to out-of-round or interrupted housings or shafts.
   - *Torsion* overload in splines.

5. Secondary failure to spalling or galling.
6. Chemical intergranular attack.

15.1.7. Effects of Bulk Cracking or Fracture

Destruction of component is the most common consequence of a bulk crack wherein the crack grows at an accelerating rate and the component becomes grossly unserviceable through fracture. This may occur almost immediately in high hardness steel components or be more delayed in medium-hard or case hardened components.

Spalling may occur in bearing components. Small bulk cracks may be open to the rolling surface and be the originating defect for spalls.

Destruction of other components. Pieces broken off one component may wedge other components and cause them to fracture or deform. A split (but not disintegrated) bearing ring will turn on the shaft and damage it by galling.

15.2. PERMANENT BULK DEFORMATION. FAILURE CODE: 00.23

15.2.1. Definition

A contact component suffers permanent bulk deformation if any of its macroscopic dimensions is permanently altered from the as-installed condition.

Elastic deflection, or thermal expansion are not *permanent* bulk deformation.

Nicks, dents, and rolled-in marks are permanent deformation, but not *bulk* deformation.

15.2.2. Nomenclature

Permanent bulk deformation is also designated permanent set, permanent distortion, permanent bending or twisting (depending on shape assumed).

The following terms designate various types of permanent bulk deformation:

- bulk plastic deformation;
- rollout;
- material volume instability (structural transformation);
- distortion by residual stress.

15.2.3. Failure Process

The three failure processes commonly producing permanent bulk deformation are listed as follows.

Plastic Flow

A portion of the component is subjected to plastic deformation. Other portions deflect elastically to maintain coherence. If the plastically flowed volume is sufficiently large, macrogeometric changes of shape or size occur in the component. Examples are:

- *Bulk bending* of a gear tooth, ring gear, rolling bearing ring or cam follower ring, under service overload.
- *Rolldown* of the track in a rolling bearing ring or cam follower ring under very heavy load, resulting in circumferential plastic expansion. The parts of the cross-section not affected by rolldown stretch elastically, and this results in overall diameter increase.
- *Hot deformation* of rolling elements or gear teeth in heat imbalance failure (FC 00.19).

Distortion by Residual Stress

Part of a component contains residual stresses (from heat treatment, cold working, high-load operation). These and the counterbalancing stresses in the rest of the component together cause shape distortion. Examples:

- A carburized component with asymmetrical cross section is often distorted in heat treatment.
- A component with symmetrical cross-section undergoes dimensional change in heat treatment.

Deformation by Phase Change of Material

Changes in the structure of the material may cause a change in specific volume, leading to permanent deformation. The most important case is: the retained austenite phase in hardened martensitic steels can decompose with time, elevated temperature or cyclic mechanical stress. The resulting martensite phase is of greater specific volume causing dimensional growth, or, if the phase transformation occurs locally, distortion.

15.2.4. Distinctive Appearance

Permanent bulk deformation is identified by dimensional

measurement of size and shape of the component. Severe permanent deformation may be visible to the unaided eye. Differentiation from other failure modes is needed in two cases:

1. When the as-installed dimensions are unknown and a dimensional error may be due either to permanent bulk deformation or to manufacturing error. Diagnosis is generally possible by examining a second surface. For example: the fit of a rolling bearing innerring on the shaft is too loose. There is no interface wear. The loose fit may be (a) a manufacturing error, (b) due to rollout from running under heavy load; or (c) due to volume growth from retained austenite transformation.

   Differentiation: (1) If the roller path and ring width are both in tolerance, and the roller path is undamaged, manufacturing error is likely. (2) If the roller path shows local plastic flow (for example, a lip formed at the roller corners), then rollout is likely. (3) If the width of the ring also exceeds tolerance, then volume growth due to austenite transformation is likely.

2. When permanent bulk deformation is accompanied by wear which has added to, or counteracted some dimensional growth. In these cases diagnosis is possible if depth of wear can be measured and subtracted from, or added to the permanent deformation. For example: A rolling bearing innerring is loose on the shaft and the width is above tolerance, but internal radial looseness is correct. The roller track is worn. It is likely that track wear has offset some of the volume growth effect on internal radial looseness.

15.2.5. Causes

Each of the three major processes producing permanent bulk deformation has its own set of possible causes.

Bulk Plastic Flow.

• *Overload* exceeding the bulk strength of a component can lead to bulk plastic flow.

• *Overheating* to a temperature where the material looses hardness, with continued application of load, leads to bulk plastic flow. The overheating may be caused by excessive ambient temperature, but more often by heat imbalance in the machine element, where more heat is generated tribologically than is removed by all means of heat dissipation combined.

Distortion by Residual Stress

Residual stresses due to *forming*, in components not undergoing hardening heat treatment, may remain and cause distortion of the finish machined part.

Heat treat residual stresses from carburizing, nitriding, case hardening or through hardening treatments may be intentional (as the compressive stresses in a carburized case) or unintended (stresses left from uneven quenching), but each may cause distortion or dimensional change.

High contact load produces residual overrolling stresses which may combine with plastic deformation of the rolling track to create bulk permanent deformation.

Deformation by Phase Change in the Material

Carburizing and hardening of steels inherently creates volume change as the unhardened (pearlitic) structure differs in specific volume from the hardened (martensitic) structure. Manufacturers allow for anticipated volume changes in dimensioning the parts. If heat treat errors occur, volume changes may differ from the anticipated, creating deformation or dimensional error.

Hardened and tempered martensitic steels generally contain a metastable structural element—*retained austenite,* which can transform prior to or during service into martensite, with volume growth. The transformation is promoted by:

• *Elapsed time.* At normal operating temperatures, retained austenite tends to transform spontaneously. The percentage of volume growth is proportional to the percentage of *transforming* retained austenite. Manufacturers select heat treatments aimed at holding austenite transformation within permissible limits for the application. However, total dimensional stability of hardened steel is seldom achieved. Heat treat errors may cause more austenite to be retained than was allowed for, resulting in dimensional error as time elapses.

• *Component temperature.* The temperature at which the component dwells is a rate-controlling factor in austenite transformation. Operation at temperatures in excess of design values may create unacceptable volume growth rates.

• *Cyclic stress.* Cyclic stressing induces austenite transformation. Hertzian contact operation generally results in reduced retained austenite in the stressed material volume. With modest levels of retained austenite, normal component dimensions and loading, the volume of Hertz stressed material generally does not suffice to cause significant permanent bulk deformation. In heavily loaded thin walled rings it may nonetheless happen.

15.2.6. Effects of Permanent Bulk Deformation

The functional effect of permanent bulk deformation is generally that of any deviation from design dimensions or shape. The severity of the effect depends in obvious ways on its magnitude.

• *Massive permanent deformation* renders the component unfit for use through seizure, loss of positioning accuracy, loss of assembly integrity or interference with other components.

• *Permanent change (growth) in size,* especially in diameter, even when moderate, may result in loss of interference fit on a shaft, unwanted interference fit with loss of axial alignment in a housing, loss of internal clearance in a rolling bearing or loss of play in a gear or cam set.

• *Permanent distortion* in contact components may lead to alignment errors, roller skew and if severe, edge contact.

FAILURE CODE: 00.22–23

Cross-index of Secondary Failure Codes

Failure Code	PlateNo
00.22.01.1	5.10
	15.37
00.22.01.2	15.3
00.22.01.3	6.14
	10.15
	10.45
	10.46
	10.47
	13.10
	13.11
00.22.01.4	5.5
	6.8
	7.37
	10.24
	11.9
	12.5
00.22.01.42	7.35
00.22.01.43	15.17
00.22.01.44	7.36
	15.17
00.22.1	9.2
	10.15
	10.36
	13.2
	15.18
	15.20

Failure code	PlateNo
00.22.2	5.23
	6.8
	6.20
	9.2
	10.2
	15.4
	15.5
	15.6
	15.9
	15.10
	15.11
	15.12
	15.13
	15.14
	15.15
	15.20
	15.23
00.22.3	15.15
00.22.4	10.59
00.23.1	15.7
	15.26
00.23.1.1	10.16
00.23.2	10.36
	13.9
	13.11

Plates

DATA

Plate No: 15.1
Archive No: 018-602&601
Image type: a: light macro, b: light macro, magnetic particle test
Scalebar = a, b: 10 mm (micros: ±20%, others: +100%, -50%)
Component: SRB; IR, run
Speed: 150 KdN
Load: 1.2 GPa
Lubrication: mineral oil, 68 °C
Failure code1: 00.22.01.1 Axial cross section crack in ring
Failure code2: 00.16.1.1.2 Spall from subsurface defect
Failure code3: 22.5 Shaft deformed
Failure code4: 00.15.1.2.0.3 Excessive fretting, loose or inaccurate radial fit

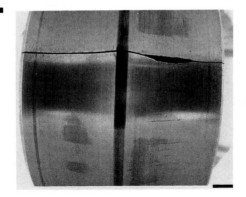 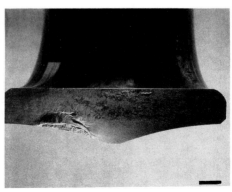

a   b

DESCRIPTIONS

FAILURE DESCRIPTION: (a): Several axial-radial crack indications are shown, from magnetic particle test. One cross-section crack shows a small spall. (b): Crack face of cross-section crack is shown propagating from the contact through the section into the bore. The shaft underwent large bending deflections, which caused hoop stresses in the IR. These, combined with the contact stress, initiated axial-radial cracks, and eventually a cross-section crack failure. Heavy fretting occurred in the IR bore.

IMAGE DESCRIPTION: (a): The IR is viewed on roller paths.

Heavy black axial line 1/4 from N image edge is a cross-section crack. Oblong widening in E roller path is a spall. Fine axial black lines on E roller path are incipient cracks highlighted by magnetic particles. (b): Cracked section at image center. Crack initiation is from the track at image W. There is dark fretting on the crack face, from extended running; also, heavy fretting in IR bore.

SUSPECTED CAUSES: Shaft is known to have undergone heavy deflection in bearing seat. Hoop stresses were generated in the IR. A contact path under tensile stress is known to form axial-radial cracks on overrolling (even at the light stress of this service). One crack has split the cross-section, fretted and spalled out. Bore fretting is secondary.

DATA

Plate No: 15.2
Archive No: 074-73&74
Image type: a: light macro, b: metallogram (unetched)
Scalebar = a: 10 mm, b: 100 μm (micros: ±20%, others: +100%, -50%)
Component: DGBB (mast support roller); OR, run
Speed:
Load:
Lubrication:
Failure code1: 00.22.01.1 Axial cross section crack in ring
Failure code2: 00.20.2 Corrosion pitting
Failure code3: -
Failure code4: -

a

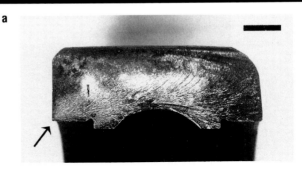

b

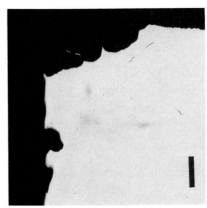

DESCRIPTIONS

FAILURE DESCRIPTION: Axial/radial bulk fatigue fracture of OR in DGBB used as mast support roller with rolling contact on OR OD. The crack initiated at the ID corner, at corrosion pitting, from cyclic tensile stresses caused by bending under OD contact load. This is a gross failure.

IMAGE DESCRIPTION: (a): Axial/radial fatigue fracture surface with striations centered on ID corner (arrow). (b): Unetched polished section at crack-initiating corner shows a scalloped edge around the corner, due to corrosion pitting.

SUSPECTED CAUSES: OR used as a support roller is subjected to cyclic bending under contact stresses at the OD, which are

reacted against the ball complement. Tensile stresses arise at the ID which have, at the sharp corroded corner, initiated bulk fatigue fracture of the ring.

DATA

Plate No: 15.3
Archive No: 087-023
Image type: view
Scalebar = 30 mm (micros: ±20%, others: +100%, -50%)
Component: CRBB; assembly, run
Speed:
Load:
Lubrication:
Failure code1: 00.22.01.1 Axial cross section crack in ring
Failure code2: 00.22.01.2 Circumferential crack
Failure code3: -
Failure code4: -

DESCRIPTIONS

FAILURE DESCRIPTION: Flange fracture and axial cross section crack in the OR of a CRB, is due to thrust impact load or greatly excessive axial load. This is a gross failure.

IMAGE DESCRIPTION: IR at image W, OR/R/G assembly at image E. 180° of thrust flange on OR (N–facing half) is fractured (chipped) off. An axial cross-section crack is visible at N. There is no evidence of roller damage, or separator fracture in this image. No clear evidence of IR damage is found in this image, although the flange thrust surface may be worn down past the undercut under the axial load.

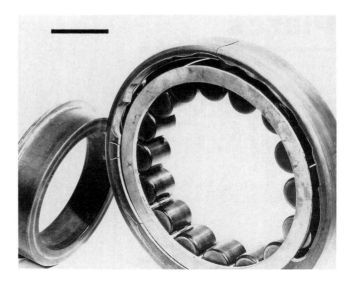

SUSPECTED CAUSES: In a thrust loaded CRB, integral ring flanges (with undercuts) are subject to overload cracking, especially if radial load is too low to prevent roller tilt. Axial cracking of ring occurs secondarily. Ring cracking may occur also if the axial load causes heavy flange galling with roller skewing. However, separator and roller damage should then be visible.

DATA

Plate No: 15.4
Archive No: 002-013c
Image type: light macro
Scalebar = 3 mm (micros: ±20%, others: +100%, -50%)
Component: CRB; IR, tool steel, run
Speed: 3.0 MdN
Load: 1.2 GPa
Lubrication: synthetic polyester oil, 204 °C
Failure code1: 00.22.01.1 Axial cross section crack in ring
Failure code2: 00.22.2 Bulk fatigue crack
Failure code3: -
Failure code4: -

DESCRIPTIONS

FAILURE DESCRIPTION: Bending fatigue crack was initiated at the surface of the oil slot located in the IR bore. Further cracking was initiated at the oil hole/slot corner. Eventually, the IR disintegrated.

IMAGE DESCRIPTION: Image is the fractured cross section of an IR. Flanges are at image NE and NW; the ring body at image center; the oil slot (labeled) at image S. The roller path and thrust surfaces are at N center. An oil hole (labeled) connects the roller path undercut and oil slot. Fatigue crack was initiated at (unlettered) arrow. Further cracking extends from oil hole/slot corner (arrow A).

SUSPECTED CAUSES: High speed CRB are subject to high centrifugal hoop stresses. Oil slots and oil holes may have sharp edges or machining marks. Bending fatigue can initiate at the oil slot where the cross section of the ring is weakened. Further cracking at oil hole/slot intersection is promoted by sharp edges. Tool steel bearing rings are especially crack sensitive.

DATA

Plate No: 15.5
Archive No: 074-61
Image type: light macro
Scalebar = 1 mm (micros: ±20%, others: +100%, -50%)
Component: DGBB; IR, run
Speed:
Load:
Lubrication:
Failure code1: 00.22.01.1 Axial cross section crack in ring
Failure code2: 00.22.2 Bulk fatigue crack
Failure code3: -
Failure code4: -

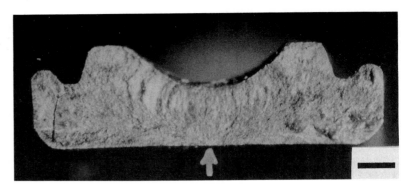

DESCRIPTIONS

FAILURE DESCRIPTION: Fatigue fractured cross-section of IR with crack originating at bore, from excessive hoop stress acting on a minor surface imperfection. This is a gross failure.

IMAGE DESCRIPTION: Axial/radial fatigue crack propagating through ring from an initiation point (arrow) at the bore and extending to an arc connecting the seal grooves. Striations, first parallel to the bore and then arcing, indicate fatigue. The fracture surface of the remaining part of the cross-section is coarse, indicating rapid overstress cracking.

SUSPECTED CAUSES: Excessive hoop stress, as from too great an interference fit between IR and shaft, combined with cyclic contact stressing, may initiate bulk cracking. Hoop stresses are greatest at the bore. A surface imperfection may initiate cracking at that surface.

DATA

Plate No: 15.6
Archive No: 074-64&65
Image type: a: view, b: light macro
Scalebar = a: 10, b: 1 mm (micros: ±20%, others: +100%, -50%)
Component: DGBB; OR, run
Speed:
Load:
Lubrication:
Failure code1: 00.22.01.2 Circumferential crack
Failure code2: 00.22.2 Bulk fatigue crack
Failure code3: 00.01.2 Scratch, toolmark, scuffmark
Failure code4: -

a
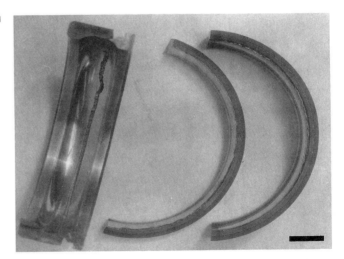

b

DESCRIPTIONS

FAILURE DESCRIPTION: Circumferential bulk fatigue fracture of a ring, connecting the snap-ring groove with the ball groove. A sharp corner or tool mark in the snap-ring groove may have initiated the crack. This is a gross failure.

IMAGE DESCRIPTION: (a): OR was cut in half by axial/radial cut for examination. Circumferential fracture has separated the ring, connecting a corner of the snap-ring groove with the ball path. (b): Fracture surface shows arced striations of crack propagation around the initiation point at the snap ring groove corner.

SUSPECTED CAUSES: Snap ring grooves, provided to receive rings locating the bearing axially, cause reduced cross section. If they have sharp corners, damaged surfaces or grinding burns, circumferential bulk fatigue cracks can initiate across these reduced sections.

DATA
Plate No: 15.7
Archive No: 074-62&63
Image type: a: view, b: light macro
Scalebar = a: 10, b: 1 mm (micros: ±20%, others: +100%, -50%)
Component: DGBB; IR, run
Speed:
Load:
Lubrication:
Failure code1: 00.22.01.2 Circumferential crack
Failure code2: 00.23.1 Plastic rolldown of contact path
Failure code3: 00.16.02.3 Incipient spalling, single spall
Failure code4: -

DESCRIPTIONS
FAILURE DESCRIPTION: Plastic rolldown occurred in the groove, due to excessive load. An incipient spall is followed by circumferential cracking. This is a gross failure.

IMAGE DESCRIPTION: (a): Plastically worked (battered) groove surface. A circumferential fracture separates the two ring halves. (Black penmarks in bore register the halves.) There is a deep gouge from a fragment, on the groove surface (at SW). The initiating spall is not shown. (b): Fracture surface near initiating spall. (Shallow craters are out of focus, about 1/4 image width to either side of image center).

SUSPECTED CAUSES: Long-term high-load over-rolling may produce plastic rollout resulting in compressive stresses in the contact surface. Balancing tensile stresses arise elsewhere in the cross section. A spall relieves the compressive stress at a

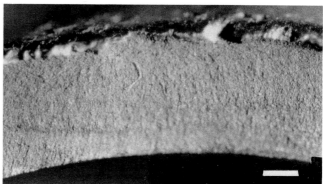

point; tensile stress, acting from the spall bottom and aided by continued overrolling, may drive a circumferential crack. (Cross-section cracks are more common.)

DATA
Plate No: 15.8
Archive No: 074-78
Image type: light microgram of section. Nital etch
Scalebar = 2 mm (micros: ±20%, others: +100%, -50%)
Component: CRB; R, induction hardened, run
Speed:
Load:
Lubrication:
Failure code1: 00.22.01.3 Rolling element (ball, roller) crack
Failure code2: 00.07.5.02 Heat treat crack
Failure code3: -
Failure code4: -

DESCRIPTIONS
FAILURE DESCRIPTION: Twisted cracks in core of an induction hardened small roller. Cracks do not emerge to the surface. The unhardened core of the roller is in high tensile residual stress due to heat treatment. Cracks may form before running and/or propagate under high cyclic contact loading. The roller is likely to fracture upon continued running.

IMAGE DESCRIPTION: Etched cross section of a roller shows induction hardened case as light grey and unhardened core as

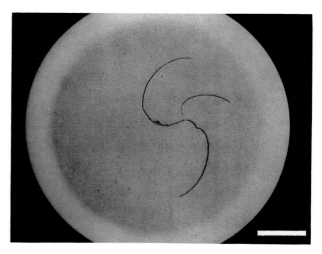

darker grey. The S-shaped black line with a side-branch is the crack in the core.

SUSPECTED CAUSES: Small rolling element with deep induction hardened case contains high compressive case stress and high tensile core stress due to volume growth in the martensitic case. Spontaneous heat treat cracks may exist in the core. Cracks may initiate or grow in the high tensile stress environment of the core due to the rotating stress field imposed by contact loading.

DATA
Plate No: 15.9
Archive No: 074-80&81
Image type: a: view, b: light micrograph
Scalebar = a: 10, b: 1 mm (micros: ±20%, others: +100%, -50%)
Component: DGBB; B, run
Speed:
Load:
Lubrication:
Failure code1: 00.22.01.3 Rolling element (ball, roller) crack
Failure code2: 00.22.2 Bulk fatigue crack
Failure code3: -
Failure code4: -

DESCRIPTIONS
FAILURE DESCRIPTION: Spiral fracture of a ball in fatigue under contact loading, from material defect below the surface. High heat treat stresses may contribute to this gross failure.

IMAGE DESCRIPTION: (a): Mating fracture surfaces on two halves of a fractured ball. Radial steps on the two halves match. The failure origin is the small circular area with an irregular fracture surface, close below the ball surface (arrow). Cracks have propagated in both directions around the periphery and met in a step. (b): Failure origin on W ball-half. Ball surface is at N, and is chipped. A dark patch is visible at the crack origin, followed by dark/light striations of fatigue propagation.

SUSPECTED CAUSES: Water quenched balls may contain substantial heat treat stresses. If a material imperfection is present and contact loads are heavy, bulk fatigue cracking may result.

a

b
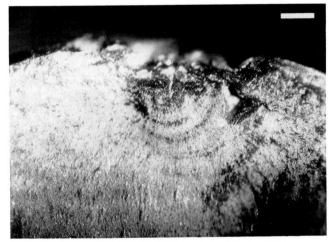

DATA

Plate No: 15.10
Archive No: 002-019b&d&e
Image type: a: light microgram, b, c: SEM
Scalebar = a: 2 mm, b: 50, c: 20 μm (micros: ±20%, others: +100%, -50%)
Component: ACBB; B, tool steel, run
Speed: 0.8 MdN
Load: 2.2 GPa
Lubrication: synthetic polyester oil, 149 °C
Failure code1: 00.22.01.3 Rolling element (ball, roller) crack
Failure code2: 00.22.2 Bulk fatigue crack
Failure code3: -
Failure code4: -

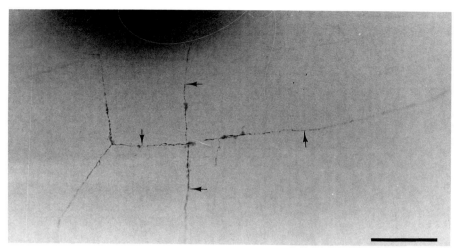

a

DESCRIPTIONS

FAILURE DESCRIPTION: Bulk fatigue cracking of a ball, forming crossing straight crack openings at the surface (minimal spalling) and extending radially inward. Tool steel balls of aerospace bearings occasionally exhibit such bulk fatigue rather than conventional spalling, for reasons not ascertained. Occasionally, coarse martensite is suspected. The ball has failed.

IMAGE DESCRIPTION: (a): Crossing, dark, straight-line cracks on the ball surface (arrows), with minimal spalling (broadened patches). (b): Fatigue crack propagated from spall (labeled "chipped out section") at (labeled) ball surface, to artificial fracture at image S (curved boundary). (c): Fatigue striations visible near a crack tip (arrows).

SUSPECTED CAUSES: Tool steel used in aerospace rolling bearing occasionally exhibits crack sensitivity, especially under tensile hoop stressing. Tool steel balls, (not hoop stressed) may fail in bulk fatigue. Forming and heat treating of heavy-section tool steel balls appear to be difficult and critical operations, occasionally causing brittleness. The crossing crack pattern at the surface is not explained.

b

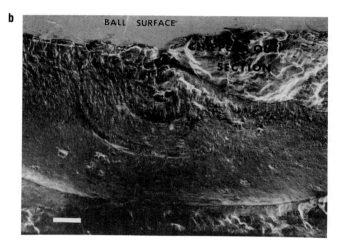

c

DATA
Plate No: 15.11
Archive No: 074-75
Image type: view
Scalebar = 10 mm (micros: ±20%, others: +100%, -50%)
Component: CRB; R, run
Speed:
Load:
Lubrication:
Failure code1: 00.22.01.3 Rolling element (ball, roller) crack
Failure code2: 00.22.2 Bulk fatigue crack
Failure code3: 00.09.2 Galling from forcible assembly or mounting
Failure code4: -

DESCRIPTIONS
FAILURE DESCRIPTION: Axial bulk fatigue crack in a roller OD following an axial galling streak inflicted in assembly or mounting. The roller is likely to fracture or spall in continued running.

IMAGE DESCRIPTION: Cylindrical roller surface of varying hue

of grey due to magnetic particle inspection. At roller centerline is a light grey axial galling mark in the center of the W roller half. A black, slightly curved line following the galling mark to the S, is the magnetic particle indication of a bulk crack.

SUSPECTED CAUSES: Galling due to mounting damage creates high local residual stresses and surface damage. Most commonly, such a defect will spall in running. However, if a roller contains high tensile residual stresses (possibly from the quench), then bulk fatigue cracking may occur.

DATA
Plate No: 15.12
Archive No: 026-12&19
Image type: a, b: light macro
Scalebar = a: 60, b: 30 mm (micros: ±20%, others: +100%, -50%)
Component: CRB (multirow); R & G, run
Speed:
Load:
Lubrication: mineral oil mist, ? °C
Failure code1: 00.22.01.3 Rolling element (ball, roller) crack
Failure code2: 00.22.2 Bulk fatigue crack
Failure code3: 00.16.1.1.2 Spall from subsurface defect
Failure code4: 00.18.02.2 Severe or advanced denting

DESCRIPTIONS
FAILURE DESCRIPTION: Rollers with bore accommodating pin-type separator. Cross-section cracking in fatigue is probably initiated from machining defect or decarburization at the bore which is subjected to cyclic tensile stress in bending. The crack penetrates to the rolling surface; it spalls, creates extensive debris which are rolled over and eventually the roller splits. This is a gross failure.

IMAGE DESCRIPTION: (a): In N image half, a row of rollers is held between two rings of the separator, by pins through the bore along each roller axis. Three rollers to W are intact; the next roller is fractured, then one is cracked and spalled. Parts of the broken roller are at S. (b): Four cracked, spalled and chipped rollers are held in the separator.

SUSPECTED CAUSES: Rollers with bore for a separator pin are crack-prone. The bore is usually in the as-machined condition. Unfavorable residual stresses may exist. Bending under cyclic stressing tends to initiate cross-section cracking, with subse-

quent spalling. These rollers are carburized, with bores usually masked from carburizing atmosphere. Incomplete masking may cause patchy carburizing, resulting in high local residual stresses.

DATA

Plate No: 15.13
Archive No: 002-009c&d&e&g
Image type: a, b, c: light macro,
d: metallogram, etched
Scalebar = a, b: 3, c: 2 mm,
d: 20 μm (micros: ±20%, others:
+100%, -50%)
Component: SLG, run
Speed: 106 m/sec
Load: 0.5 GPa
Lubrication: synthetic polyester oil,
149 °C
Failure code1: 00.22.01.4 Gear tooth
crack or fracture
Failure code2: 00.07.5.01 Forging
crack
Failure code3: 00.22.2 Bulk fatigue
crack
Failure code4: -

DESCRIPTIONS

FAILURE DESCRIPTION: Forging crack extending
along 7 mm of spline tooth, to full tooth height.
Crack face details in (d) show minimal fatigue
crack propagation. Oxide layer is in main crack
which occurred prior to final heat treatment; fatigue cracks are not oxidized. The spline may
eventually fracture from these cracks.

IMAGE DESCRIPTION: (a): Spline viewed from end
face. Three arrows show a radial crack from spline
tooth tip past tooth roots. (b): In the sectioned
spline, the same crack is the white, axial jagged
line (magnetic particle indication) (arrows). White
spots are loose magnetic particles. (c): The tooth
is fractured along the crack (dark area with arrows). (d): Section across the crack. The heavy
branching line is a forging crack. Fine branches
may be bulk fatigue cracks.

SUSPECTED CAUSES: Forging of the gear introduced cracks in the blank. When the spline was
machined, cracks remained in the tooth. The gear
has been run extensively, but only minimal fatigue
crack propagation has occurred.

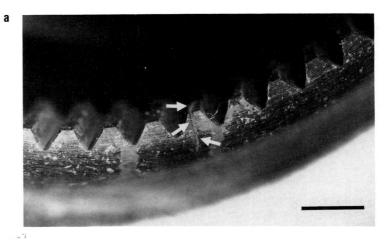

DATA
Plate No: 15.14
Archive No: 080-107
Image type: light macro
Scalebar = 30 mm (micros: ±20%, others: +100%, -50%)
Component: SG; W, high hardness, run
Speed:
Load:
Lubrication:
Failure code1: 00.22.01.4 Gear tooth crack or fracture
Failure code2: 00.22.2 Bulk fatigue crack
Failure code3: -
Failure code4: -
See also PLATEs: 15.17 & 15.18

DESCRIPTIONS
FAILURE DESCRIPTION: Fractured segment of a tooth, from bulk fatigue crack which has propagated across the section. Fatigue striations are visible. This is a gross failure. See PLATE 15.18 for an overstress crack and PLATE 15.17, for a fatigue crack with no striations.

IMAGE DESCRIPTION: Segment of a tooth, with artificially cut surface averted. The contact surface is at image S, followed by the bulged fracture surface toward image N. The arrow *A* indicates crack initiation. Elliptic fatigue striations extend over W, N and E border areas of the fracture. They are most clearly seen near arrow *B*. The fracture surface is smooth, not fibrous. This is typical of *fatigue* cracking, especially in hard materials.

SUSPECTED CAUSES: Tooth fatigue cracking under contact loading may initiate from a surface or subsurface defect and gradually extend to sever the tooth.

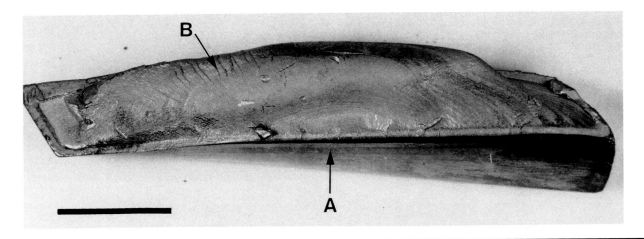

DATA
Plate No: 15.15
Archive No: 002-010c&d&e
Image type: a, b: macro, c: light
metallogram, Nital etch
Scalebar = a: 2, b: 3 mm, c: 20 μm
(micros: ±20%, others: +100%,
-50%)
Component: BG; W, high hardness, run
Speed:
Load: 0.5 GPa
Lubrication: synthetic polyester oil,
176 °C
Failure code1: 00.22.01.4 Gear tooth
crack or fracture
Failure code2: 00.22.3 Rubbing crack
Failure code3: 00.22.2 Bulk fatigue
crack
Failure code4: 00.12.6 Wear at
unintended surface contact

DESCRIPTIONS
FAILURE DESCRIPTION: A crack propagated through the bevel
gear tooth root from initiation at the back of the gear disk
which unintentionally rubbed against a stationary part. Rubbing
created plastic working, overheating and crack initiation, and
propagated through the tooth by fatigue, disintegrating the
gear. This is a gross failure.

IMAGE DESCRIPTION: (a): Fractured gear disk; tooth face is in
NE quadrant, followed by crack surfaces. A rubbing crack initiated at the arrow (see view (b)), propagated in fatigue through
much of the disk and finally fractured the disk in overload.
(b): Gear disk bottom surface, (at arrow of (a)); rubbed the
area at the bracket; crack initiated at the arrow. (c): Etched
section through rubbed area (bracket); the worked material appears light, the tempered zone dark. The crack starts at the arrow.

SUSPECTED CAUSES: The back face of the gear disk unintentionally rubbed against a stationary component, creating high
heat, plastic working and eventually a 'rubbing crack,' from
which fatigue drove a crack in depth toward the teeth. Eventually the weakened gear disk fractured at a tooth root radius.

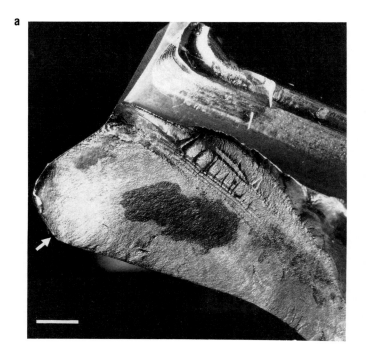
a

b

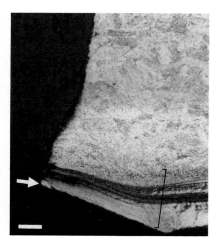
c

DATA

Plate No: 15.16
Archive No: 099-140
Image type: light macro
Scalebar = 30 mm (micros: ±20%, others: +100%, -50%)
Component: WG; W, bronze, run
Speed:
Load:
Lubrication:
Failure code1: 00.22.01.41 Tooth root fracture
Failure code2: 00.12.5.1 Tooth polishing
Failure code3: -
Failure code4: -

DESCRIPTIONS

FAILURE DESCRIPTION: Fatigue cracking from the tooth root corners into the wheel rim. There is light polishing of contact surfaces. The rim is likely to fracture in further running.

IMAGE DESCRIPTION: Worm gear wheel viewed obliquely. On second tooth from image E, fine dark crack lines extend from both root corners two-thirds into the machined rim. Light polishing marks (arced lines and bands of different luster) are on the tooth flank surfaces.

SUSPECTED CAUSES: Bulk overload of the tooth rim in bending, combined with stress concentration at sharp tooth root corners, has initiated fatigue cracking. The mild contact wear indicates no abusive operation.

DATA

Plate No: 15.17
Archive No: 080-108
Image type: view
Scalebar = 40 mm (micros: ±20%, others: +100%, -50%)
Component: SG; P, high hardness, run
Speed:
Load:
Lubrication:
Failure code1: 00.22.01.41 Tooth root fracture
Failure code2: 00.22.01.43 Mid-tooth fracture
Failure code3: 00.22.01.44 Tooth tip chipping
Failure code4: 00.16.01.3 Tooth spalling
See also PLATEs: 15.14 & 15.18

DESCRIPTIONS

FAILURE DESCRIPTION: Extensively chipped, fractured and spalled teeth. One tooth is fractured at the root in fatigue, but without striations. This is a gross failure. See also PLATE 15.14 for tooth fatigue fracture and PLATE 15.18 for overstress tooth fracture.

IMAGE DESCRIPTION: Counting from image S, teeth No. 1, 4, 5, and 7 are chipped. Tooth 7 has spall cratering in the deden-dum. Tooth 6 is broken off at the root, showing a smooth, fine fracture surface (not fibrous), typical of fatigue in hard material, but no fatigue striations.

SUSPECTED CAUSES: Heavily loaded gear suffered spalling and, (probably from impacts and/or debris passage), tooth chipping and breakage. The missing tooth was broken in fatigue.

DATA
Plate No: 15.18
Archive No: 080-106
Image type: light macro
Scalebar = 40 mm (micros: ±20%, others: +100%, -50%)
Component: SG; W, high hardness, run
Speed:
Load:
Lubrication:
Failure code1: 00.22.01.41 Tooth root fracture
Failure code2: 00.22.1 Overstress crack
Failure code3: -
Failure code4: -
See also PLATEs: 15.14 & 15.17

DESCRIPTIONS
FAILURE DESCRIPTION: Overload fracture of a gear tooth, with signs of bulk plastic flow during fracture. This is a gross failure. See PLATEs 15.14 and 15.17 for fatigue fracture of teeth.

IMAGE DESCRIPTION: The center tooth of the gear segment

shown is broken at the root. Fracture began at W flank of the tooth with fibrous, uniform texture. About midway through the fracture, a "hump" begins, as material plastically bent and was sheared. This hump and the absence of fatigue striations distinguishes overstress fracture.

SUSPECTED CAUSES: Overstress fracture from accidental overload or following a severe material defect occurs in one or a few load cycles.

DATA
Plate No: 15.19
Archive No: 002-004a&c
Image type: a: view, b: light macro
Scalebar = a: 40, b: 2 mm (micros: ±20%, others: +100%, -50%)
Component: BG; W, high hardness, run
Speed: 106 m/sec
Load: 0.5 GPa
Lubrication: synthetic polyester oil, 176 °C
Failure code1: 00.22.01.42 Tooth corner fracture
Failure code2: 00.06.2 Inclusion stringer
Failure code3: -
Failure code4: -

a

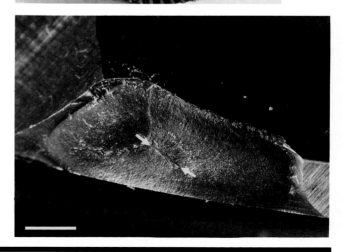

b

DESCRIPTIONS
FAILURE DESCRIPTION: Two consecutive gear teeth are fractured in fatigue across the small-diameter edge. Both teeth were found to contain large (2 mm long) alumina inclusion stringers in the core material, from which the fracture is seen to initiate. The gear has failed.

IMAGE DESCRIPTION: (a): Entire gear, with two teeth marked by arrows having fractures at small-diameter edges under arrows. (b): Fracture surface of one tooth, showing crack spreading from long non-metallic stringer indicated by opposing arrows.

SUSPECTED CAUSES: Large inclusion stringers are severe stress concentrators which may initiate fatigue failure. The inclusion in this gear was so deep beneath the surface that it initiated bending fatigue, and not contact fatigue.

DATA
Plate No: 15.20
Archive No: 080-109
Image type: light macro
Scalebar = 20 mm (micros: ±20%, others: +100%, -50%)
Component: BG; P, high hardness, & CRB, run
Speed:
Load:
Lubrication:
Failure code1: 00.22.01.42 Tooth corner fracture
Failure code2: 00.22.2 Bulk fatigue crack
Failure code3: 00.09 Geometry, assembly or mounting defect
Failure code4: 00.22.1 Overstress crack

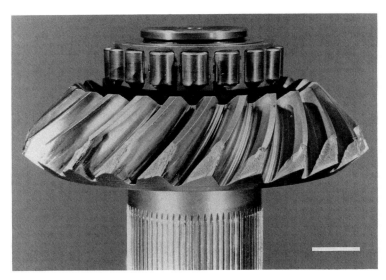

DESCRIPTIONS
FAILURE DESCRIPTION: Fatigue fracture of the corner of several teeth in a spiral bevel gear, due to a misaligned mesh causing overloading of that corner. The misalignment results from improper mounting geometry. Other teeth are then broken in impact. This is a gross failure.

IMAGE DESCRIPTION: Spiral bevel pinion is in image center; supporting CRB at N. Corners on the large-diameter end of all visible gear teeth are broken off in a diagonal line from (or near) root level (at the gear face) to the tooth tip (further inboard). In this case-hardened gear, the case shows fatigue striations; the core is a woody fracture.

SUSPECTED CAUSES: Improper relative position of the wheel and pinion, due, for example, to excess looseness in the support bearings or wrong position adjustment leads to misaligned mesh which may place most of the tooth load at one corner of the mesh. Fatigue cracking of several teeth may result, with the others then broken by impact.

DATA
Plate No: 15.21
Archive No: 099-141
Image type: view
Scalebar = 60 mm (micros: ±20%, others: +100%, -50%)
Component: HG; P, medium hard, run
Speed:
Load:
Lubrication:
Failure code1: 00.22.01.42 Tooth corner fracture
Failure code2: 26 Support bearing damage (of gear, cam)
Failure code3: -
Failure code4: -

DESCRIPTIONS
FAILURE DESCRIPTION: Tooth corners broken away in three consecutive incidents due to mislocation of pinion resulting from support bearing failure (not shown). The load was shifted in each case to a tooth sector which failed to support it. This is a gross failure.

IMAGE DESCRIPTION: A pinion is viewed on OD. Tooth corners facing image W were broken away. The pinion then shifted to image W and another length of tooth tip broke away, extending from the first fracture to roughly the gear center plane. After a second shift, a third row of fractures occurred, now extending to the E half of the face width.

SUSPECTED CAUSES: Gross support-bearing failure was observed to have dislocated the gear mesh, causing local overload in repeated passes.

DATA
Plate No: 15.22
Archive No: 064-204&902
Image type: a, b: color view [SEE IMAGE IN APPENDIX]
Scalebar = a: 30, b: 20 mm (micros: ±20%, others: +100%, -50%)
Component: HG; P, high hardness, & TRB; IR&R&G, run
Speed:
Load:
Lubrication:
Failure code1: 00.22.01.43 Mid-tooth fracture
Failure code2: 00.16.01.3 Tooth spalling
Failure code3: 00.12.5.3.2 Adhesive (destructive, non-galling) tooth wear
Failure code4: 00.20.01.1 Generalized corrosion

[See Image in Appendix]

DESCRIPTIONS
FAILURE DESCRIPTION: (a): Mid-tooth fractures cover entire contact length of all pinion teeth, starting from multiple initiation points. Corrosion is visible. The shell-shaped chipping in the fractures suggests case/core interface failure. (b): Wear step and axial line of spalls near one tooth edge. General corrosion has occurred after failure. (a, b): Gears are no longer serviceable.

IMAGE DESCRIPTION: (a): In image center is a HG on integral shaft, with a TRB at S. The teeth show many mid-tooth fractures, with concentric striations, initiated by spalls. Shell-like shapes suggest case/core failure. A brown rust color is apparent. Purple dye is used for examination. (b): HG from same application. Wear step and heavier spalling near W tooth edge indicate misaligned loading. There are brown rust deposits.

SUSPECTED CAUSES: (a): Massive failure of gear results from long running after spalling and chipping was initiated. Rust stains in fractures negate instant catastrophic failure. A possible heat treat defect contributing to deep spalling at case/core interface requires metallurgical examination. (b): Similar, earlier stage failure. Misalignment of mesh caused edge loading; failure initiated there and propagated across the tooth width. Rust is incidental.

DATA
Plate No: 15.23
Archive No: 099-238
Image type: light macro
Scalebar = 5 in = 127 mm (micros: ±20%, others: +100%, -50%)
Component: HG; P, medium hard, run
Speed:
Load:
Lubrication:
Failure code1: 00.22.01.43 Mid-tooth fracture
Failure code2: 00.22.2 Bulk fatigue crack
Failure code3: 00.16.01.3.1 Tooth pitchline or dedendum spalling
Failure code4: 00.18.4.2 Gear tooth rippling (transverse wavy plastic flow)

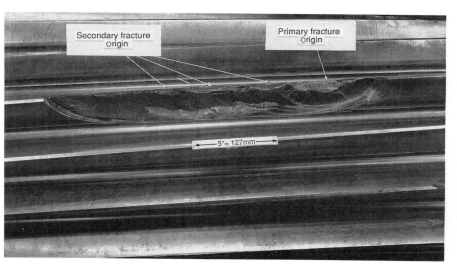

DESCRIPTIONS
FAILURE DESCRIPTION: Multiple midtooth fracture on one tooth of a wide, medium-hard pinion. The primary fracture initiated from a pitchline spall. Slow crack progression is indicated by fretting of the early fracture surfaces. Radial plastic surface flow (rippling) occurred on several contact surfaces indicating high load. Metallurgical examination showed impaired structure with less fatigue resistance than specified. This is a gross failure.

IMAGE DESCRIPTION: The third tooth from N shows a large midtooth fracture, with primary and secondary fracture origins labeled. A spall and tooth tip chipping are visible at E end of second tooth from S. Rippling is (faintly) visible on E quarter of the first tooth from S. A dark half-moon on the crack face below the primary fracture origin appears fretted.

SUSPECTED CAUSES: The gear was found, in metallurgical examination, to have a marginal structure. Combined with loading sufficient to cause plastic surface flow, spalling and eventual mid-tooth fracture were produced.

DATA

Plate No: 15.24
Archive No: 099-138&139
Image type: a, b: light macro
Scalebar = a: 25, b: 10 mm (micros: ±20%, others: +100%, -50%)
Component: a: HG, medium hard, b: BG, high hardness, run
Speed:
Load:
Lubrication:
Failure code1: 00.22.01.44 Tooth tip chipping
Failure code2: -
Failure code3: -
Failure code4: -

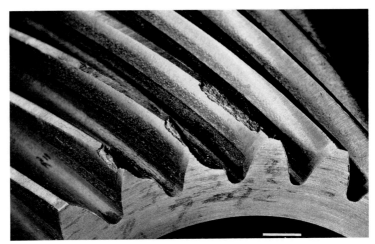

DESCRIPTIONS

FAILURE DESCRIPTION: Appearance comparison of tooth tip chipping between medium-hard and high hardness (case hardened) gear. (a): Medium-hard gear with tooth tip chipped, probably from edge contact. (b): Case hardened gear with cracks in tooth tips at mid-contact, possibly due to geometry error, failing at case/core interface. In both gears, progressive failure is likely.

IMAGE DESCRIPTION: (a): Gear is viewed obliquely, with the three tooth corners (in center) chipped off at the tip. Fracture surfaces are coarse in medium-hard material. (b): Gear is viewed on OD. Of the three tooth tips fully shown, the two toward image N show cracks and some spalling on the contact surface, extending onto the tooth OD. Proximity to the tooth tip suggests that the failure is at the case/core interface.

SUSPECTED CAUSES: Tooth tip overload from geometry error, or passage of hard contaminants may combine with material weakness (as in the case hardened gear where case/core interface appears weak), to cause tooth tip chipping.

DATA

Plate No: 15.25
Archive No: 080-110
Image type: light macro
Scalebar = 40 mm (micros: ±20%, others: +100%, -50%)
Component: SG; W, high hardness, run
Speed:
Load:
Lubrication:
Failure code1: 00.22.01.44 Tooth tip chipping
Failure code2: 00.16.01.3 Tooth spalling
Failure code3: 00.16.1.1.3 Subcase-fatigue spall
Failure code4: -

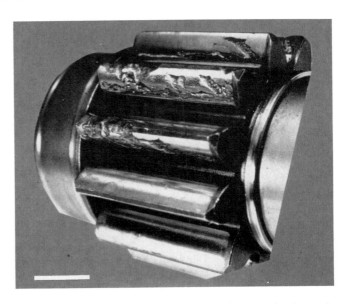

DESCRIPTIONS

FAILURE DESCRIPTION: Portions of tooth tips are chipped off following extensive spalling, penetrating to the case/core interface. In this high-hardness gear, the spalling has lead to bulk fatigue fracture. This is a gross failure.

IMAGE DESCRIPTION: Three teeth at image N have lost much of the contact surface. At N-most tooth, spalls have reached the case/core interface. The next two teeth to S are heavily spalled, and chips have fractured out of the tooth tips.

SUSPECTED CAUSES: Severe spalling, as from overload, possibly combined with insufficient case depth, have caused subcase spalling (also referred to as 'case crushing') in this carburized gear. Subsequent bulk fatigue cracking has produced chipping of tooth tips.

DATA

Plate No: 15.26
Archive No: 014-59
Image type: view
Scalebar = 15 mm (micros: ±20%, others: +100%, -50%)
Component: TRB; OR, carburized, run
Speed:
Load:
Lubrication: grease, ? °C
Failure code1: 00.22.1 Overstress crack
Failure code2: 21.4 Housing worn
Failure code3: 00.23.1 Plastic rolldown of contact path
Failure code4: -

DESCRIPTIONS

FAILURE DESCRIPTION: Radial/axial overstress crack across OR ('cup') section has resulted from plastic rolldown of the cup roller track in a housing worn oversize by the cup turning in a loose seat. This is a gross failure.

IMAGE DESCRIPTION: OR (cup) viewed from OD shows axial/radial fracture, with surfaces widely separated. Cup OD finishing lines are worn off. Housing bore (not shown) was severely worn.

SUSPECTED CAUSES: The bearing was used in a wheel hub and the housing to OR OD fit was loose. The OR turned and wore the housing bore. Subsequent rolldown of the roller path stretched the contact path circumferentially, causing increased residual compressive stress in the contact path case, and increased core tension. Eventually, the core ruptured, causing cross-section fracture. Case stress relief opened the fracture.

DATA

Plate No: 15.27
Archive No: 002-008a&b
Image type: a: view, b: light macro
Scalebar = a: 40, b: 5 mm (micros: ±20%, others: +100%, -50%)
Component: BG; W, high hardness, run
Speed: 91 m/sec
Load: 0.6 GPa
Lubrication: synthetic polyester oil, 176 °C
Failure code1: 00.22.2 Bulk fatigue crack
Failure code2: -
Failure code3: -
Failure code4: -
See also PLATE: 5.10

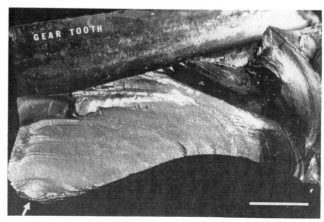

DESCRIPTIONS

FAILURE DESCRIPTION: Radial and circumferential disk fracture of a bevel gear is from fatigue originating at a sharp machining discontinuity. See PLATE 5.10 for originating defect. This is a gross failure.

IMAGE DESCRIPTION: (a): Shaft with two integral gears, of which the larger, to image S, is a bevel gear. This has fractured at three points radially across the teeth and around 360° of arc in the disk. Arrows point to the fracture origin, shown in detail in (b): An edge, left in machining acted as a stress raiser. (See defect in PLATE 5.10.) From this origin, a striated fatigue crack extended NE across the disk, to the tooth root, ending in overload fracture.

SUSPECTED CAUSES: The highly loaded bevel gear ring undergoes high alternating bending stresses. The (off-specification) machining marks acting as stress raisers precipitated bending fatigue.

DATA

Plate No: 15.28
Archive No: 002-024b
Image type: light macro
Scalebar = 2 mm (micros: ±20%, others: +100%, -50%)
Component: ACBB; B, tool steel, run
Speed: 1.7 MdN
Load: 1.4 GPa
Lubrication: synthetic polyester oil, 176 °C
Failure code1: 00.22.2 Bulk fatigue crack
Failure code2: 00.04.2 Forming seam
Failure code3: 00.16.1.1.2 Spall from subsurface defect
Failure code4: 00.17.2 Localized surface distress (halo at defect)
See also PLATEs: 5.23 & 5.24

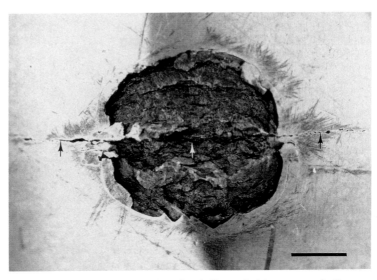

DESCRIPTIONS

FAILURE DESCRIPTION: Bulk fatigue crack in ball, resulting in a spall and surrounding halo of surface distress, during continued running. Metallography has found a forming seam which originated the crack. See also PLATEs 5.23 and 5.24, for material defects in this ball. The ball has failed.

IMAGE DESCRIPTION: At image center is a circular spall crater, exfoliated from a straight-line bulk crack (along arrows). Burnishing marks around crater edge are from over-rolling of the edge.

SUSPECTED CAUSES: Forming seam and other material structure defects in ball have originated a radial fatigue crack which subsequently spalled out.

DATA

Plate No: 15.29
Archive No: 005-11
Image type: light metallogram. Nital etch
Scalebar = 250 μm (micros: ±20%, others: +100%, -50%)
Component: C; CM, case hardened, run
Speed:
Load: 2.1 GPa
Lubrication: Diesel fuel, ? °C
Failure code1: 00.22.2 Bulk fatigue crack
Failure code2: 00.07.5.02 Heat treat crack
Failure code3: 00.07.2 Off-specification martensite platelet size
Failure code4: -

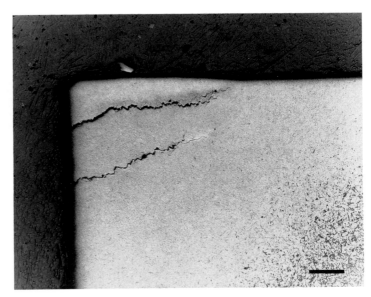

DESCRIPTIONS

FAILURE DESCRIPTION: At the edge of the cam lobe, two large cracks in the case are attributed to defects of the heat treated structure, and possible inter-granular heat treat cracks, which have propagated in fatigue. The cam has failed.

IMAGE DESCRIPTION: The image is an etched metallographic cross-section of a cam lobe, including side face at W image edge and contact surface near N image edge. The core transition zone (dark mottled area) is in the SE corner. The dark area at N and W edges is mounting material. Two twisting (dark) bulk cracks extend from the side face in E–NE direction into case but do not reach contact surface. The highly tortuous crack path indicates inter-granular crack.

SUSPECTED CAUSES: A heat treatment error led to a coarse structure after heat treatment, with weakened intergranular bonds. Intergranular heat treat cracks may have been initiated, and were extended by inter-granular fatigue cracks (rare in contact devices). The origin of the cracks at the sidewall suggests edge-loading and weakened (perhaps decarburized) sidewall surface.

DATA
Plate No: 15.30
Archive No: 002-007g
Image type: light metallogram, Zephiran etch
Scalebar = 200 μm (micros: ±20%, others: +100%, -50%)
Component: ACBB; B, tool steel, run
Speed: 1.7 MdN
Load: 1.4 GPa
Lubrication: synthetic polyester oil, 176 °C
Failure code1: 00.22.2 Bulk fatigue crack
Failure code2: 00.07.5.02 Heat treat crack
Failure code3: 00.07.5.1 Crack with oxidized surface
Failure code4: -
See also PLATE: 6.17

DESCRIPTIONS
FAILURE DESCRIPTION: An open crack, probably formed during heat treatment, runs from the ball surface towards center. Closed bulk fatigue cracks have extended the crack front during running. Heat treat cracking creates a severe defect which precipitates both spalling and bulk fatigue cracking. See PLATE 6.17 for surface view and crack surface appearance.

IMAGE DESCRIPTION: The etched, mottled metallographic section is fine-structured steel. N image edge is mounting material. Wide N–S crack between opposing arrows is a heat treat crack. Branching cracks at arrows *A* are bulk fatigue cracks which have propagated during running.

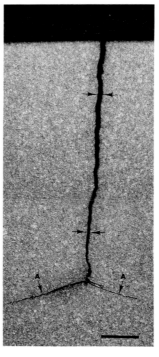

SUSPECTED CAUSES: The oxidized surface of the primary crack suggests causation by forging or heat treatment. The tortuous course of the crack (see PLATE 6.17) suggests a heat treat crack. The severe defect represented by the heat treat crack initiated the bulk fatigue cracks shown here.

DATA
Plate No: 15.31
Archive No: 003-001
Image type: light macro
Scalebar = 10 mm (micros: ±20%, others: +100%, -50%)
Component: ACBB; IR, run
Speed: 1.1 MdN
Load: 1.9 GPa
Lubrication: synthetic polyester oil, 110 °C
Failure code1: 00.22.2 Bulk fatigue crack
Failure code2: 00.08.2 Rehardened grinding burn
Failure code3: 00.16.1.1.2 Spall from subsurface defect
Failure code4: 00.16.02.5 Advanced spalling

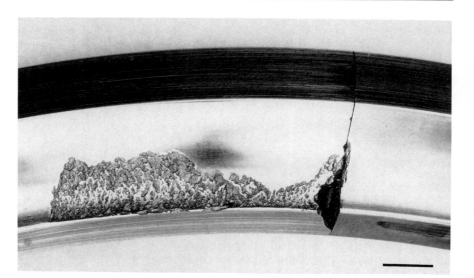

DESCRIPTIONS
FAILURE DESCRIPTION: Cross-sectional fatigue crack in an ACBB (split) IR, found to have originated from a grinding burn (FC 00.08.2) in the bore, through the action of high centrifugal hoop stresses in the ring. The spall has propagated in the rolling direction from the crack. The bearing has failed.

IMAGE DESCRIPTION: One of two parts of a split innerring from an ACBB, with land (dark band) bordering ball groove on image N and split-face at S. A black axial crack crosses the entire ring, ¼ of the image width from E edge. Extensive spall cratering extends from crack toward W (in rolling direction). In width, the spall reaches a split-face edge. Reported grinding burn is not shown.

SUSPECTED CAUSES: Grinding with excessive pressure overheats material and causes rehardened grinding burn at the surface. High residual stresses and brittleness of untempered martensite may serve as an initiating defect for bulk fatigue cracking, which then initiates spalling.

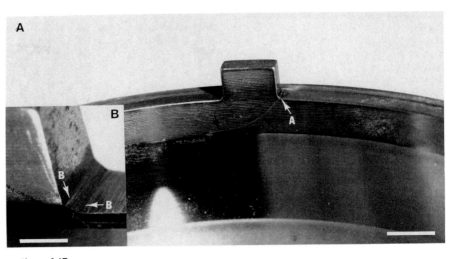

DATA
Plate No: 15.32
Archive No: 002-016b1&016b2
Image type: a, b: light macro
Scalebar = a: 9, b: 2 mm (micros: ±20%, others: +100%, -50%)
Component: CRB; OR, run
Speed: 0.9 MdN
Load: 0.8 GPa
Lubrication: synthetic polyester oil, 149 °C
Failure code1: 00.22.2 Bulk fatigue crack
Failure code2: 00.09.0 Geometry defect
Failure code3: -
Failure code4: -

DESCRIPTIONS
FAILURE DESCRIPTION: Fatigue crack across section of IR, from an inadequately blended corner of the anti-rotation lug exposed to bending forces during service. The lug may break off with a chip out of the ring.

IMAGE DESCRIPTION: (a): OR with one of four anti-rotation lugs facing image N, followed, going S, by a free ID band, then the roller track (lustrous) and another free band. At A, inadequate corner blend (not full radius), as shown in (b), as the detail between arrows B. A light-colored fine crack line extends on the ring ID, running from A in SW direction and then curv-

ing W (black arrows). Crack also extends N from A across ring face.

SUSPECTED CAUSES: Some aerospace bearings have anti-rotation lugs engaging notches to prevent creep of thin OR under moving load direction. Forces driving ring creep may cause sizeable stresses in the lug. At the lug root, the corner is a stress concentrator which requires corner blending. The chamfered blend achieved in this bearing left small radii at B and was insufficient to prevent cracking.

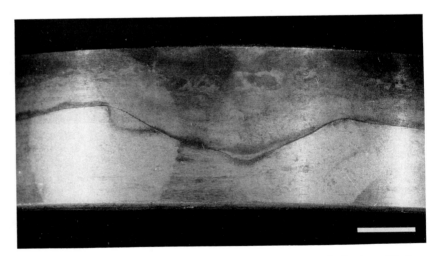

DATA
Plate No: 15.33
Archive No: 116-001
Image type: light macro
Scalebar = 7 mm (micros: ±20%, others: +100%, -50%)
Component: DGBB; OR, run
Speed:
Load:
Lubrication:
Failure code1: 00.22.2 Bulk fatigue crack
Failure code2: 00.15.1.2.0.6 One-sided radial fit fretting from taper
Failure code3: 00.15.1.2.0.7 Irregular fretting in distorted radial fit
Failure code4: -

DESCRIPTIONS
FAILURE DESCRIPTION: OR with OD fretting in irregular circumferential band covering roughly one ring half, indicating taper and circumferential irregularity in the housing seat. A ring-splitting circumferential crack follows the edge of the fretting. The ring has failed.

IMAGE DESCRIPTION: The OR is viewed on the OD. A dark, blotchy band of fretting covers half of the ring width to image N, with a wavy line of heavier fretting delineating this half from the unfretted S half. A circumferential crack in or near the fretting boundary is a sharp dark line.

SUSPECTED CAUSES: A housing with taper in the bore fitted the OR more tightly where not fretted. The irregularity of the fretting boundary indicates that the housing was not round. Poorly supported (fretted) half underwent cyclic bending against the supported half as balls rolled over the track, creating tensile stresses in the axial direction in the OD and, with surface damage caused by fretting, eventually lead to cracking.

DATA
Plate No: 15.34
Archive No: 074-34
Image type: view
Scalebar = 40 mm (micros: ±20%, others: +100%, -50%)
Component: CRB; OR, (Sendzimir-mill bearing), run
Speed:
Load:
Lubrication: mineral oil mist, ? °C
Failure code1: 00.22.2 Bulk fatigue crack
Failure code2: 00.16 Spalling (Hertzian contact fatigue)
Failure code3: 00.13.2.1 Rolling surface galling
Failure code4: -

DESCRIPTIONS
FAILURE DESCRIPTION: Gross material removal to about 7 mm depth, from contacting OD of a Sendzimir mill bearing, apparently initiated as contact spalling. The lobed crack propagation and uniform-width flat band at spall bottom are not explained, in the absence of failure history from the mill. This is a gross failure.

IMAGE DESCRIPTION: The short cylindrical part shown is the thick-walled OR of a CRB, with the OD used as a roller supporting a cluster roll in a sheet mill. The center and E-facing end of the ring are missing a deep layer of material removed by surface-parallel cracks running about 7 mm below the original surface. The center shows a smooth, flat band. The sides of the spall are lobed. Deep axial galling marks are on the unspalled OD.

SUSPECTED CAUSES: Sendzimir mills are cluster mills with two

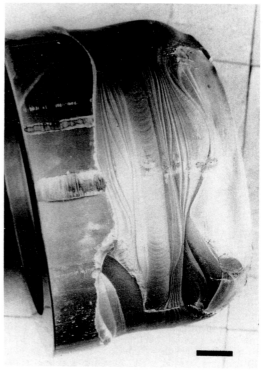

small-diameter work rolls supported by layers of backup rolls, of which the outermost consist of CRBs stacked on long shafts. Rolling forces are great, contamination is possible and temperatures may be high. A specific analysis of the peculiar failure appearance requires detailed machine failure history, which is lacking.

DATA
Plate No: 15.35
Archive No: 018-114
Image type: view
Scalebar = 40 mm (micros: ±20%, others: +100%, -50%)
Component: SRB; IR, run
Speed:
Load:
Lubrication:
Failure code1: 00.22.2 Bulk fatigue crack
Failure code2: 00.19.2.1 Hot plastic flow without welding (rollout)
Failure code3: 00.19.3 Scale formation
Failure code4: 22.9 Geometry or assembly defect in shaft

DESCRIPTIONS
FAILURE DESCRIPTION: An improper taper angle on the bearing seat of the shaft has supported only one ring half. The other half failed by circumferential cracking in bending fatigue, causing massive overheating, plastic rollout and scaling. This is a gross failure.

IMAGE DESCRIPTION: A fracture surface from circumferential cracking bounds the ring at image N. The adjacent roller path is severely rolled out, and the fracture surface is battered. The N ring half is scaled. Shaft contact (circumferential wearmarks) is visible in the S half of the bore. The N half of the bore is

scaled but unworn; it probably had no or little shaft contact. This suggests an angle error in the shaft seat.

SUSPECTED CAUSES: Severe angle error in a tapered shaft seat creates support only under one ring half (the large-bore end in this case). The other ring half is cantilevered and undergoes severe bending fatigue stressing. Circumferential fatigue cracking may result. As this crack progresses, normal bearing geometry is destroyed, parts (such as a separator) break, overheating and plastic flow occur.

DATA
Plate No: 15.36
Archive No: 018-117
Image type: light macro of cut ring
Scalebar = 10 mm (micros: ±20%, others: +100%, -50%)
Component: SRB; IR, run
Speed:
Load:
Lubrication:
Failure code1: 00.22.3 Rubbing crack
Failure code2: 00.12.1.2 Advanced mild wear of fit surface
Failure code3: 22.9 Geometry or assembly defect in shaft
Failure code4: -

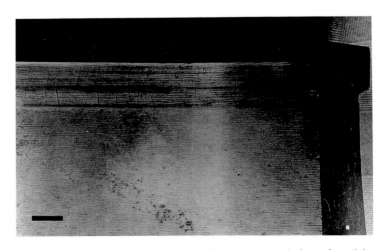

DESCRIPTIONS
FAILURE DESCRIPTION: Multiple, generally axially running fine rubbing cracks are visible in the IR bore, near the side-face. Circumferential wear marks are crossing the cracks. The ring has rotated on the shaft, creating severe local heating in the band where the cracks arose. The ring is likely to crack through, if it is mounted with an interference fit.

IMAGE DESCRIPTION: IR, cut to expose the bore is viewed on the bore. The corner radius is near the N image edge, a section plane is near the E edge. A band S of the corner radius shows (dark) circumferential wear marks and multiple, dark ax-

ial crack lines. Wear markings (dark interrupted circumferential lines) elsewhere in the bore are less pronounced.

SUSPECTED CAUSES: Interference fit between IR and shaft was insufficient for the loading and severe sliding occurred. Wear marks resulted. In the band near the corner radius (presumably with tighter fit than elsewhere), heating was excessive and thermal and structure transformation stress caused cracking. Such cracks are typically axial in radial fit surfaces due to the interaction of rubbing-induced stresses with mechanical (hoop and/ or contact) stresses.

DATA
Plate No: 15.37
Archive No: 093-018a
Image type: light macro
Scalebar = 10 mm (micros: ±20%, others: +100%, -50%)
Component: DGBB; IR (segment), run
Speed:
Load:
Lubrication:
Failure code1: 00.22.3 Rubbing crack
Failure code2: 00.13.1 Fit surface galling
Failure code3: 21.7 Housing mismounted
Failure code4: 00.22.01.1 Axial cross section crack in ring

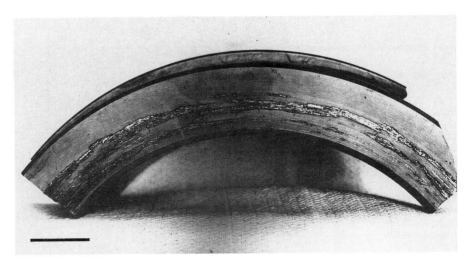

DESCRIPTIONS
FAILURE DESCRIPTION: Rubbing cracks and galling on the side face of an IR, from unintended rubbing against the stationary end cover attached to the housing, leading to material transfer in unlubricated sliding. Overheating of surface and cracks from thermal stresses or stresses induced by structural transformation. Heat imbalance failure may be in progress. The ring is fractured by axial/radial crack emanating from a rubbing crack. This is a gross failure.

IMAGE DESCRIPTION: The IR is viewed on the side face. There are circumferential galling marks (light and dark, irregularly

bounded streaks) and dark fine radial rubbing cracks. The E contour of the ring is an axial/radial fracture.

SUSPECTED CAUSES: Mislocation of the shaft assembly in the housing, or of the bearing on the shaft, or of the end cover in the housing, has produced unintended rubbing between the stationary end cover and the rotating bearing IR end face. Galling and severe local overheating caused sufficient thermal stress or structural transformation stress to initiate cracks. One has penetrated across the ring and broken it.

DATA
Plate No: 15.38
Archive No: 001-40
Image type: color macro [SEE IMAGE IN APPENDIX]
Scalebar = 6 mm (micros: ±20%, others: +100%, -50%)
Component: CRB; IR, run
Speed: 700 KdN
Load: 1.2 GPa
Lubrication: mineral oil, 70 °C
Failure code1: 00.22.3 Rubbing crack
Failure code2: 00.13.2.1.1.2 Contact galling from high acceleration
Failure code3: 00.12.3.2.1.4 Wear track at contact edge
Failure code4: 11.1 Friction polymer, oil lubrication

[See Image in Appendix]

DESCRIPTIONS
FAILURE DESCRIPTION: On contact surface of IR, are several axial/radial cracks, initiated from an extensive galling streak near the contact center. Also, wear bands appear near both roller ends. In a high-speed CRB innerring, acceleration-caused galling may injure the centrifugally stressed OD to cause cracking. Wear streaks may indicate roller skew. Friction polymer indicates high temperature. Continued running is likely to cause ring fracture.

IMAGE DESCRIPTION: Center portion of the image is a CRB IR roller path. Two interrupted light brown bands near N edge of rolling track are wear bands with friction polymer. Two interrupted bands with dark brown edging, near the rolling track center, are wear bands with galled metal (white-and-brown patchy deposit) along their centerline. Dark and light, irregular axial lines across the galling bands and beyond are bulk cracks penetrating radially.

SUSPECTED CAUSES: Very high speed bearing IR, especially CRB IR, are subject to high centrifugal hoop stress. Roller sliding (from high acceleration, skewing, or both) may cause wear, and if severe, galling, which is a severe tractive stress in the surface. Thus, the damage done to surface integrity by galling, and the centrifugal hoop stress can combine to form radially going axial cracks, and eventually cross-section fracture.

DATA
Plate No: 15.39
Archive No: 001-4
Image type: light macro, section
Scalebar = 1 mm (micros: ±20%, others: +100%, -50%)
Component: ACBB; IR, run
Speed: 1.1 MdN
Load: 1.4 GPa
Lubrication: synthetic polyester oil, 120 °C
Failure code1: 00.23.1.1 Contact path rolldown in bearing
Failure code2: -
Failure code3: -
Failure code4: -
See also PLATE: 10.5

DESCRIPTIONS
FAILURE DESCRIPTION: Overrolling of the contact path at extreme pressures causes plastic flow in Hertzian dimensions. If the contact is well centered, the result is profile distortion and residual stresses in the subsurface material. If the contact extends to the track edge (as shown), a lip or ridge forms at the edge. Operation under a load sufficient to cause plastic rolldown destroys geometry and leads to early spalling.

IMAGE DESCRIPTION: The image shows a cross section of an ACBB innerring against a black background. At image E is the edge of the ball path; the straight line from center to W is a land. The edge between track and land, which should be rounded, shows a protrusion above the land caused by plastic flow of material from under the ball path.

SUSPECTED CAUSES: In a ball bearing, contact overriding the track edge results from (1) severe overload; (2) insufficient land height for the load condition; (3) excessively tight conformity as built or due to plastic rolldown. In any of these cases, plastic rolldown occurs as a result of very high Hertzian pressures. PLATE 10.5 shows rolled-in lines on one of the mating balls.

DATA
Plate No: 15.40
Archive No: 099-131
Image type: light macro
Scalebar = 30 mm (micros: ±20%, others: +100%, -50%)
Component: SG; W, medium hard, run
Speed:
Load:
Lubrication:
Failure code1: 00.23.1.2 Gear tooth contact rolldown
Failure code2: -
Failure code3: -
Failure code4: -

DESCRIPTIONS
FAILURE DESCRIPTION: Excessive contact pressure in medium-hard gear causes plastic flow in the contact surface. Pressure was evenly distributed to the contact edge, and lips formed protruding past the tooth face and the tooth tip. Geometry was lost. Gear is noisy and if flow progresses, may suffer tooth fracture.

IMAGE DESCRIPTION: Side view of gear. Tooth contact surfaces facing image W form lips protruding past the side face. (Black streak on side face is paint mark.)

SUSPECTED CAUSES: Excessive contact pressure produces continued plastic flow of surface material. In a medium-hard material, sufficient plasticity is available to produce substantial gross deformation before fracture.

DATA
Plate No: 15.41
Archive No: 080-126
Image type: light macro
Scalebar = 10 mm (micros: ±20%, others: +100%, -50%)
Component: SG; G, high hardness, run
Speed:
Load:
Lubrication:
Failure code1: 00.23.1.2 Gear tooth contact rolldown
Failure code2: 00.07.1.1 Insufficient bulk hardness
Failure code3: -
Failure code4: -

DESCRIPTIONS
FAILURE DESCRIPTION: Overloaded teeth of insufficiently hardened gear have plastically deformed by rolling down the contact surface and extruding material at the tooth tips and ends. The insufficiently hardened gear is unable to carry the design load. Plastic deformation destroys the geometry and may be followed by galling, spalling or tooth fracture as possible further failures.

IMAGE DESCRIPTION: Gear segment (three teeth) is viewed from gear face. The E-facing tooth flanks are more-or-less unchanged. The W-facing (loaded) tooth flanks are hollowed out and material is extruded, forming extensions ('lips') at the tooth tips and also at the tooth-end edges facing the viewer.

SUSPECTED CAUSES: On unhardened or insufficiently hardened gears, heavy continuous or impact loading may roll or hammer out the tooth surfaces. (In properly hardened high-hardness gears, tooth fracture is more likely.)

tions on the contacting surfaces by friction welding of contacting asperities, and their subsequent separation along a plane other than the weld interface.

A separator galls against contact components, which are of different material (different composition and/or hardness), and thus transfers foreign material (mild steel, yellow metal, etc) onto the (hard steel) contact component.

Separator contacts are highly vulnerable to galling, because: (a) motion in them is *simple sliding,* so that an asperity contact is not interrupted by surface lift-off as in a rolling contact; (b) separators have complex shapes including sharp edges; (c) if metallic, separators are made of relatively soft metals and (d) separators are manufactured by methods including stamping, milling and turning, none of which produce as fine a surface finish as that on contact components of rolling bearings.

The forces acting on separators are widely variable and their control is more problematic than that of the Hertz contact forces; galling is often the result of unanticipated force excursions.

Miscellaneous Notes on the Failure Process

• While it is more common for the (softer) separator material to transfer onto the contact components, *reverse* transfer of hard steel onto separators has also been observed.

• Separators made of plastics do not usually suffer galling failure. However, some thermoplastic materials are capable of transfer to the mating contact surface and this transfer may be considered galling. Unintended transfer of plastic separator material to a contact part may cause noise, inaccuracies and overheating, in addition to placing large forces on the separator.

• Bearings operating in cryogenic fluids may be equipped with separators made of reinforced teflon. Controlled transfer of teflon to the rolling surfaces is a design requirement aimed at supplying dry lubrication and thereby improving the functioning of such bearings. This intentional transfer is not considered to be a failure.

16.1.4.4. Distinctive Appearance

The appearance of galling in a separator is similar to that described for contact components under FC 00.13, with the following special features:

• *Galled material wears* at once in the sliding separator contact, therefore wear marks will appear on it.

• *Dissimilar material* may appear on the galled surface, if separator and Hertz contact component materials are visually different (example: a brass separator against steel rolling elements).

16.1.4.5. Causes

The *common* causes of galling listed under FC 00.13. also apply to separator contacts.

Causes specific to separator galling include the load-increasing conditions listed under FC 01.13 and additionally the following:

• *Overheating* of the separator contact, precipitating the loss of lubrication and facilitation of welding postulated in Blok's flash temperature theory [13].

• *Loss of clearance* in the separator contact due to deformation, contamination, entrapment of the separator under rolling elements, etc.

16.1.4.6. Effects of Separator Galling

Separator galling may be arrested (*healed*) if the precipitating condition is alleviated before material transfer has destroyed significant areas of contact interface.

Unless there is relief in the severity of operating conditions, to permit healing, separator galling typically leads to the following failure modes:

• *Bearing noise and vibration* may be caused by the metal transferred through galling.
• *Heat imbalance failure* (FC 00.19).
• *Separator fracture* (FC 01.11).
• *Seizure* of the bearing (FC 00.13), possibly with bulk cracking or fracture (FC 00.22).

16.1.5. Separator Corrosion. Failure Code: 01.15

16.1.5.1. Definition

Chemical attack causing failure in a separator is designated in this Atlas as *separator corrosion.* This is analogous to the definition of corrosion for Hertz contact components under FC 00.20. The damage categories distinguished from corrosion under FC 00.20 (fretting (FC 00.15), pitting as a casting defect (FC 00.05), temper coloring and friction polymer deposition (FC 00.19)) must also be distinguished from corrosion when they occur in a separator, although fretting is not a likely separator failure.

16.1.5.2. Nomenclature

The nomenclature for subclasses of corrosion (corrosion staining, corrosion pitting, intergranular corrosion), cited under FC 00.20, equally applies to *metallic* separators. In non-ferrous separators, the staining is often designated 'discoloration'.

Chemical attack on plastic separators includes *dimensional change* (swelling) due to humidity and *embrittlement.*

16.1.5.3. Failure Process

See FC 00.20 for a general description of failures by chemical attack.

Metal Separators

Separators made of *steel* corrode under conditions and by mechanisms similar to steel contact components.

Because of the rougher surfaces and lower hardness of steel separators, they are likely to be more sensitive to corrosion than the surfaces of contact components.

Separators made of *yellow metal* (bronze, brass) corrode by electrochemically enhanced corrosion in the presence of steel components and an electrolyte. *Ester base* synthetic lubricants of some formulations are aggressive to yellow metal. Yellow metal must be excluded from systems using such ester lubricants.

Aluminum alloy separators, if used, are protected by an anodizing surface treatment. This layer may wear away and the exposed metal forms an electrolytic couple with steel that can precipitate corrosion of the aluminum alloy leading to cracking.

Plastic Separators

Chemical attack on plastic separators can assume many forms, depending on material and attacking chemical. The most common are:

• *Dimensional change in nylon* due to change in absorbed water content (not strictly a chemical reaction, but included here as being the effect of an environmental chemical).

• *Embrittlement of plastic* due to incompatible lubricants or aggressive atmosphere. When embrittlement occurs, micro- or macro-cracks are likely to result under deflections otherwise readily tolerated by the material.

16.1.5.4. Distinctive Appearance

• Separators made of *steel* show corrosion similar to steel contact components, except for the appearance differences due to dissimilar original surface finishes.

• Separators made of *yellow metal* (brass, bronze) usually show brown or blackish stains under chemical attack.

• Separators of *aluminum alloy* show a disruption of the anodized coating, possibly with cracking.

• *Plastic* separators, when embrittled, tend to show discoloration, possibly cracking.

16.1.5.5. Causes

The causes of separator corrosion are similar to those listed under FC 00.20 for contact components.

16.1.5.6. Effects of Separator Corrosion

Metal Separators

The corrosion product on *steel* separator surfaces is abrasive. When worn off by contact with the rolling elements, it contaminates the lubricant and causes wear of contact components, of the separator and of guidering or seals (if present).

Separator corrosion may change separator clearance. Separator corrosion may weaken the separator (especially a thin stamped sheet metal separator) and cracking may result.

Corrosion of any part in the chamber containing the separator tends to enhance corrosion of other components in the chamber. Corrosion of contact components may result.

Plastic Separators

Embrittlement of plastic separators produces substantial weakening and typically leads to cracking, especially since plastic separators are often designed utilizing their great tolerance for deflection, much of which may be lost due to embrittlement.

16.1.6. Separator Heat Imbalance Failure. Failure Code: 01.16

Heat imbalance failure of contact components generally involves separator interaction, that is, these components cooperate to generate the excess of heat. For a description of heat imbalance failure, see FC 00.19.

16.1.7. Separator Spalling. Failure Code: 01.17

On rare occasions, spalling is seen in the contact between a (machined metal) separator pocket and a rolling element. This contact fatigue failure arises from repeated application of normal contact pressure as the rolling element (usually a ball) is pressed against the separator pocket bore, upon changes in rolling element orbital speed, (for example, when the load zone is entered and left), or upon misalignment of the bearing. See FC 00.16 for a description of spalling.

16.2. GUIDERING FAILURE. FAILURE CODE: 01.2

This Section covers failures of *guiderings* in rolling bearings. Guiderings are *separate* rings, loosely fitted to one of the Hertz contact rings of the bearing. They serve to guide the other components. Guiderings serve two distinct functions, as described below. In some designs, the guidering performs only one of the functions, in others, it performs both.

Separator guiderings participate in the positioning (centering) of separators. Such guiderings have conforming (non-Hertzian) sliding contact with separators.

Roller guiderings are used to provide a face for axial guidance of rollers in designs where integral flanges are not provided at all required roller-end contact points.

Examples:

1. Combined separator- and roller-guiderings are used in some designs of spherical roller bearings. They are usually loosely fitted over a center land of the inner-ring, and help center the separator(s) with their OD, while axially guiding the rollers with their sidefaces. They feature sliding contact with the separator bore and sliding/rolling contact with the roller endfaces. They are commonly made of cast iron, powder metal or plastic.

2. In some single-row cylindrical roller bearings, integral flanges are supplemented by loose end-rings with an L-shaped cross-section which guide the roller ends. This arrangement permits axial mounting, with both bearing rings mounted on shaft or in housing before insertion of the rotor.

3. In some designs of multi-row cylindrical roller bearings, spacing rings between rows guide rollers axially with their sidefaces and also center the separators with their OD. Such rings are made of materials similar to Hertz contact rings—most often hardened steel.

Table 16.1. Correspondence of guidering failure codes.

Guidering failure mode	Guidering failure mode description.	Correlated failure code
01.2.1	Guidering manufacturing defect.	00.01-08
01.2.2	Guidering bulk discontinuity failure.	00.22
		01.11
01.2.3	Guidering bulk permanent deformation.	01.12
01.2.4	Guidering wear.	00.12
		01.13
01.2.5	Guidering heat imbalance failure.	00.19
		01.16
01.2.6	Guidering galling.	00.13
		01.14
01.2.7	Guidering denting.	00.18
01.2.8	Guidering corrosion.	00.20
		01.15

Guiderings have similar failure modes as the flanges of Hertz contact rings. If the guidering is of plastic, the failure modes of plastic separators may also occur.

16.2.1. Definition
The failure modes listed in Table 16.1 are defined by reference to failure codes for contact components or separators.

16.2.2. Nomenclature
Nomenclature of failure modes is the same as for the corresponding failure codes covering Hertz contact components or separators.

16.2.3. Failure Process
Failure processes are the same as for the corresponding failure codes covering Hertz-contact components or separators. Since some guiderings are of thin section, cracking or fracture of guiderings is not uncommon.

16.2.4. Distinctive Appearance
Guiderings of *spherical roller bearings* are typically rings of trapezoidal cross section (cylindrical bore and OD and angled side faces) which slide on the innerring land along their ID, slide on the separators along their OD and undergo compound rolling/sliding against roller ends on their sidefaces. *Wear* or *galling* may appear on any of these surfaces. Bore and OD marks will be circumferential, as in a separator. Sidefaces will show epicyclic marks, as in the contact between a roller end and the flange of a bearing ring.

Guiderings of *cylindrical roller bearings* may have rectangular or L-shaped cross sections. L-shaped guiderings of single-row cylindricals have a side surface intended for contact with roller ends. In spacing rings of some multirow cylindricals, the OD or the bore surface serves to guide a separator, and side surfaces guide roller ends. Failures of the type appearing on bearing ring flanges are seen on

the roller-contact surfaces. Separator support surfaces show circumferential marking.

16.2.5. Causes

Separator Guide Surface Failures

• *Manufacturing defects*: casting errors, geometry errors (especially those of sideface angle), incorrect clearance between guidering ID and innerring land OD or between guidering OD and separator, or incorrect surface finish.
• *Excessive sliding speed over the innerring* (excessive clearance between guidering and innerring land; geometry errors leading to high roller end loads from roller rows contacting *both* sidefaces).
• *Contaminant* ingress into the guidering/land or guidering/separator interface gap.
• *High roller contact load.*
• *High separator radial loads* from large differences in epicyclic roller speeds.
• *Inadequate lubrication.*
• *Chemical attack.*

Roller Guide Surface Failures
Failures may arise from any of the causes of roller end/flange contact failure. When the guidering also carries a separator guiding surface, the two sets of failure causes may interact.

Since guiderings are separate parts, misalignment between the roller-end guide surface on the guidering and the ring carrying the rolling track may arise in mounting or in service. This source of misalignment may cause failures in the roller end contacts, for example, roller skew and edge contact with resulting wear and galling.

16.2.6. Effects of Guidering Failure

• The effects of *separator* guide surface failure are similar to those of separator failure.
• The effects of *roller* guide surface failure are similar to those of the failure of integral flanges on Hertz-contact rings.

FAILURE CODE: 01

Cross-index of Secondary Failure Codes

Failure code	PlateNo	Failure code	PlateNo
01.10	16.4		16.15
	16.23		16.16
01.11.2	7.20		16.30
	12.20	01.13.1.2	16.10
	13.10	01.13.1.3	7.21
	13.15	01.13.1.4	7.20
	16.26		16.26
	16.29	01.13.2.2	16.11
	18.4	01.13.3	13.5
01.11.4	16.5		16.12
01.11.5	16.6		16.13
01.11.6	16.24		16.25
01.12	16.6		16.28
	16.10	01.14	16.13
	16.12	01.14.1	13.5
	16.33		16.25
01.13	7.14		16.34
01.13.1	16.7	01.16	16.11
	16.8	01.17	16.27
	16.9		

DATA
Plate No: 16.7
Archive No: 018-629
Image type: light macro
Scalebar = 3 mm (micros: ±20%, others: +100%, -50%)
Component: ACBBB & G (S-monel separator), run
Speed:
Load:
Lubrication: synthetic polyester oil,? °C
Failure code1: 01.11.2 Separator fracture, cracking
Failure code2: 01.13.1 Separator pocket worn
Failure code3: -
Failure code4: -

DESCRIPTIONS
FAILURE DESCRIPTION: Total fracture of separator side-rails at their minimum thickness in the ball pocket, preceded by heavy ball/pocket contact wear. Failure is attributed to excessive ball/separator forces, probably from a misaligned bearing. This is a gross failure.

IMAGE DESCRIPTION: Oblique view of a segment of machined S-monel ACBB separator, on side face. Total fracture of both siderails occurred across the ball pocket at image center. The tensile fracture appears "woody." There is a lustrous, dark-edged white wear patch N of the fracture, covering one-half the pocket width near ID.

SUSPECTED CAUSES: Strongly variable ball contact angles arose in operation under heavy, excentric axial load. They caused the large orbiting velocity differences among the balls, placing excessive tensile stresses on the separator, which fractured at its weakest cross-section. High ball/separator contact pressures are indicated by heavy pocket wear.

DATA
Plate No: 16.8
Archive No: 004-1
Image type: color view [SEE IMAGE IN APPENDIX.]
Scalebar = 4 mm (micros: ±20%, others: +100%, -50%)
Component: DGBB; G (polyimid separator) run
Speed: 1.2 MdN
Load:
Lubrication: Ga-In-WSe solid, graphite weave, 300 °C
Failure code1: 01.11.2 Separator fracture, cracking
Failure code2: 01.13.1 Separator pocket worn
Failure code3: -
Failure code4: -
See also PLATE: 16.9

[See Image in Appendix]

DESCRIPTIONS
FAILURE DESCRIPTION: Wear of separator pocket with eventual breakout of a cross-bar. Siderails have worn, with deformation near the fracture. OD has worn against the guide surface. The self-lubricating, graphite fiber reinforced polyimid polymer separator was tested at high temperature and speed, resulting in this failure mode. See PLATE 16.9 for another failure image of the same bearing type.

IMAGE DESCRIPTION: View on separator OD. Dark and shiny striations on OD show OD wear on the shiny bands. Two ball-pockets at image center are connected through wear and fracture of cross-bar. The siderails adjacent to the missing cross-bar are distorted.

SUSPECTED CAUSES: This is an experimental separator for a dry lubricated high-speed, high-temperature application, using graphite fiber 3-D weave reinforcing for the polyimid polymer separator carrying a solid lubricant. The separator failed during exploration of limiting failure modes. In this case, these modes are: excessive ball/pocket forces resulting in wear, and fracture. The separator is land-guided and shows wear on the contacting OD.

DATA
Plate No: 16.9
Archive No: 004-12
Image type: light macro
Scalebar = 4 mm (micros: ±20%, others: +100%, -50%)
Component: BB (assembly); Si-N B, polymer G, run
Speed: 1.2 MdN
Load:
Lubrication: Ga-In-WSe solid, graphite weave, MoS$_2$, 300 °C
Failure code1: 01.11.2 Separator fracture, cracking
Failure code2: 01.13.1 Separator pocket worn
Failure code3: 13 Solid or gas lubricant failure
Failure code4: -
See also PLATE: 16.8

DESCRIPTIONS
FAILURE DESCRIPTION: Two ball pockets in separator are connected by fracture of cross-bar. Pocket wear occurred. Wear marks are on the separator ID. Ball surfaces are partly coated with solid lubricant and separator debris. The bearing has silicon nitride balls and a reinforced polymer separator. MoS$_2$ is sputtered on rings and balls and is a powder filler in the separator. The bearing was tested at high load and speed, without external lubrication, resulting in this failure mode.

IMAGE DESCRIPTION: Bearing assembly with one IR half removed is viewed on bore. Housing with cutout N of separator obscures the OR. Two separator pockets are connected by fracture of the cross-bar, and worn open. Separator ID shows axial wear stripes (possibly related to separator whirl). Balls show a peppered surface, found to result from deposits of separator and lubricant material.

SUSPECTED CAUSES: This is an experimental bearing with graphite fiber reinforced polymer separator carrying solid lubricant, for a dry lubricated high-speed, high-temperature application. The separator failed in a test for the exploration of limiting failure modes. In this test excessive ball/pocket forces resulted in wear, and fracture. See also PLATE 16.8.

DATA
Plate No: 16.10
Archive No: 014-31
Image type: view
Scalebar = 20 mm (micros: ±20%, others: +100%, -50%)
Component: TRB; G (stamped steel separator), run
Speed:
Load:
Lubrication:
Failure code1: 01.11.2 Separator fracture, cracking
Failure code2: 01.13.1.2 Separator cross-bar worn, both pocket sides
Failure code3: 01.12 Separator plastic deformation
Failure code4: 00.19 Heat imbalance failure

DESCRIPTIONS
FAILURE DESCRIPTION: Fractured stamped steel roller separator, following heavy wear of cross-bars on both sides of pockets. Lubrication was inadequate; rollers exerted great friction forces on the separator. These wore the contacts, plastically extruded the metal past the edges in the pocket corners and eventually fractured the side-rails in bending fatigue. Heat imbalance of the bearing is conjectured. This is a gross failure.

IMAGE DESCRIPTION: A stack of broken separator segments is shown. Light grey wear areas appear along the ID edge of all cross-bars. Separator material is plastically flown at the corners of two pockets at image E. Fracture surfaces of the siderails are plastically battered.

SUSPECTED CAUSES: The bearing was observed to have inadequate lubrication, producing excessive separator/roller forces and wear. The separator becomes looser and drops down in the bearing, further increasing roller forces. The separator bending stress may be so large that bending fatigue of the rails results. The separator may become trapped between a roller and the OR. (There is no direct evidence in this image).

DATA
Plate No: 16.11
Archive No: 027-257
Image type: color view [SEE IMAGE IN APPENDIX.]
Scalebar = 10 mm (micros: ±20%, others: +100%, -50%)
Component: ACBB; G (phenolic one-piece separator), run
Speed:
Load:
Lubrication: grease, ? °C
Failure code1: 01.11.2 Separator fracture, cracking
Failure code2: 01.13.2.2 Land guided separator, guide surface worn, local
Failure code3: 01.16 Separator heat imbalance failure
Failure code4: -

[See Image in Appendix]

DESCRIPTIONS
FAILURE DESCRIPTION: Fragmented phenolic plastic one-piece land-riding separator, with OD wear over one area and ID wear over another area of the circumference. The separator, likely to have been unbalanced, ran progressively more excentrically and eventually fractured due to competing guiding forces from balls and land. Darkening in one pocket indicates high temperature due to large friction force.

IMAGE DESCRIPTION: Three fragments of the broken separator are at image NW, NE and S. Extreme NW and NE pockets show a dark spot, probably from overheating. The surfaces on the OD of the NE fragment and on the ID of the S fragment are ablated by wear.

SUSPECTED CAUSES: Land-guided plastic separators are used in high speed angular contact ball bearings, especially in low noise applications. If separator forces are not symmetrical (dynamic unbalance, inaccurate pocket geometry, heavy combined bearing load), then the separator forces at the guidelands rise, resulting in wear and distortion. The separator may make unintended contact on the opposite ring land, accelerating wear. Hoop stresses may cause fracture.

DATA
Plate No: 16.12
Archive No: 087-017
Image type: view
Scalebar = 15 mm (micros: ±20%, others: +100%, -50%)
Component: DGBB (assembly) (2), run
Speed:
Load:
Lubrication:
Failure code1: 01.11.2 Separator fracture, cracking
Failure code2: 01.13.3 Separator wear from unintended contact
Failure code3: 01.12 Separator plastic deformation
Failure code4: -

DESCRIPTIONS
FAILURE DESCRIPTION: Disintegrated 'ribbon-type' riveted stamped steel ball bearing separators. The separator OD was stretched and touched the OR land unintentionally. Separator wear occurred at the OR contact. The failure is attributed to misaligned operation creating excessive ball/separator forces stretching the separator, causing unintended contact and bending fatigue fracture. This is a gross failure.

IMAGE DESCRIPTION: Two DGBB viewed on side face. The separators are deformed and fractured in both. The separator edge touches the OR land ID at E in both bearings and is worn irregularly. The separator is fractured at SE (in the bearing at

image W). The separator is fractured at W and S (in the bearing at image E).

SUSPECTED CAUSES: Heavily misaligned operation of DGBB results in "cross-corner loading" of the balls by a high overturning moment. Contact angles and ball orbital speeds vary drastically around the circumference, placing excessive hoop stresses on the separator. The separator stretches, touches the OR or IR land, creating additional forces. Eventually, fatigue fracture occurs.

DATA
Plate No: 16.13
Archive No: 014-49
Image type: view
Scalebar = 20 mm (micros: ±20%, others: +100%, -50%)
Component: TRB; IR&R&G (stamped steel separator), run
Speed:
Load:
Lubrication:
Failure code1: 01.11.2 Separator fracture, cracking
Failure code2: 01.13.3 Separator wear from unintended contact
Failure code3: 01.14 Separator galling
Failure code4: 21.9 Geometry or assembly defect in housing

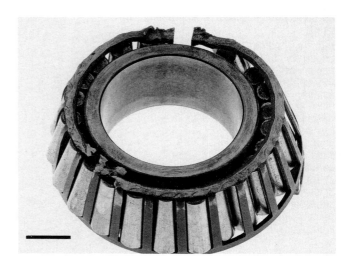

DESCRIPTIONS
FAILURE DESCRIPTION: Gross wear, galling and eventual fracture on (small-end) sideface of separator, resulting from unintended contact with housing end-cap. High friction generation and high temperatures prevailed during running. This is a gross defect resulting in gross failure.

IMAGE DESCRIPTION: The TRB IR/roller/separator assembly is viewed obliquely on its small endface. The separator siderail is severely worn, battered and galled on its entire circumference.

At image N, total separator fracture occurred. At image SW, partial fracture of small-end siderail is visible. Rollers have fallen into the separator at image E.

SUSPECTED CAUSES: A design error of the housing end-cap failed to allow clearance for a separator normally protruding above the IR ('cone') sideface. Rubbing contact between separator and end-cap produced gross wear, overheating and fracture.

DATA
Plate No: 16.14
Archive No: 093-201
Image type: light macro
Scalebar = 10 mm (micros: ±20%, others: +100%, -50%)
Component: CRB; G (cast bronze separator), unrun
Speed: -
Load: -
Lubrication: -
Failure code1: 01.11.4 Separator casting or molding defect
Failure code2: -
Failure code3: -
Failure code4: -

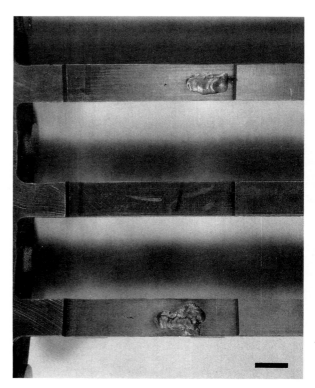

DESCRIPTIONS
FAILURE DESCRIPTION: "Repaired" macro-porosity in the separator cross-bars was due to casting defect. An attempt was made to repair the porosity by filling the pores with weld material. Porosity weakens the cross-section and, if exposed on working surfaces, may lead to galling. Weld repair is generally unsatisfactory, due to poor bonding and high residual stresses. This is an unacceptable separator blank.

IMAGE DESCRIPTION: CRB separator with one integrally cast siderail and cross-bars is viewed on its ID. Milled recesses are on each cross-bar. Of the three cross-bars shown, those at image N and S show large, irregularly shaped pits, from macro-porosity filled with arc-weld material (hence the rippled surface).

SUSPECTED CAUSES: Sand casting of large bronze components of complex shape such as this separator is a difficult process.

Clearing of gas during mold filling may fail, leaving bubbles entrapped which create macro-porosity. As a salvage operation, tungsten-inert-gas (TIG) arc welding is at times attempted to fill the pores.

DATA
Plate No: 16.23
Archive No: 087-006
Image type: light macro
Scalebar = 10 mm (micros: ±20%, others: +100%, -50%)
Component: ACBB; G (machined bronze separator), run
Speed:
Load:
Lubrication:
Failure code1: 01.13.1 Separator pocket worn
Failure code2: 01.10 Separator manufacturing geometry defect
Failure code3: 11.1 Friction polymer, oil lubrication
Failure code4: -

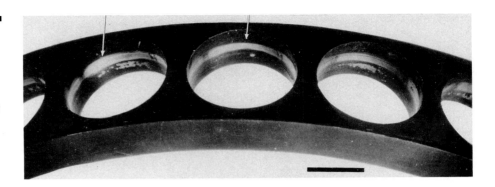

DESCRIPTIONS
FAILURE DESCRIPTION: 360° circumferential wear band in all ball pockets of a machined bronze separator, indicating insufficient pocket clearance due to dimensional error in manufacture. Bearing is likely to run at excessive temperature leading to heat imbalance failure. Decomposed oil coating ('friction polymer') on non-contacting retainer surfaces indicates high-temperature operation.

IMAGE DESCRIPTION: A segment of a machined bronze separator that has ball pockets cylindrical at OD and spherical at ID to retain balls. Dark coating (possibly friction polymer) is on the surfaces, except in a 360° circumferential shiny wear band (arrows) in the cylindrical part of the pockets, and a few wear patches in the spherical part of the pockets.

SUSPECTED CAUSES: Normally dimensioned ball pockets show wear marks near front and rear center, where ball forces produce contact under load. A pocket with insufficient clearance rubs over entire circumference. Contact in spherical retaining part of pockets does not appear excessive.

DATA
Plate No: 16.24
Archive No: 002-012c&d
Image type: a: light microgram, b: SEM
Scalebar = a: 1 mm, b: 20 μm (micros: ±20%, others: +100%, − 50%)
Component: ACBB; G (silver plated steel separator), run
Speed: 0.5 MdN
Load: 2.2 GPa
Lubrication: synthetic polyester oil, 137 °C
Failure code1: 01.13.1 Separator pocket worn
Failure code2: 01.11.6 Separator plating defect
Failure code3: 11.3 Solid contaminant in oil
Failure code4: -

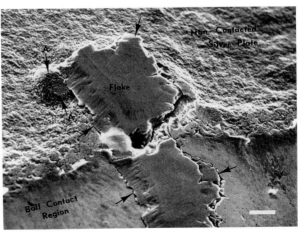

DESCRIPTIONS
FAILURE DESCRIPTION: Separator ball pockets damaged by (1) embedded solid contaminant; (2) wear; (3) irregular plating ('nodules'). The contaminated pockets were found to damage balls and hence races. The irregular plating wears prematurely. Ball surface damage is expected to result, and bearing failure may follow.

IMAGE DESCRIPTION: (a) Sectioned separator pocket is shown, exposing ball contact surface. The dark E–W band near the pocket centerline is the ball contact path. Inside and to N of this band, the many small grainy protrusions are plating 'nodules.' Arrows show embedded metal contaminant. (b): Edge of the ball contact path (labeled) runs E–W just S of image center, with the smooth surface of the band to the S. Extraneous metal flakes are rolled in at the arrows. *A* is a plating nodule.

SUSPECTED CAUSES: The plating nodularity is due to a processing deficiency. The embedded metal flakes come from extraneous contamination. The contaminant has been observed to damage balls.

DATA
Plate No: 16.25
Archive No: 027-256
Image type: color view [SEE IMAGE IN APPENDIX.]
Scalebar = 20 mm (micros: ±20%, others: +100%, -50%)
Component: DGBB (cartridge); IR&G (stamped steel), run
Speed:
Load:
Lubrication: grease, ? °C
Failure code1: 01.13.1 Separator pocket worn
Failure code2: 01.13.3 Separator wear from unintended contact
Failure code3: 00.12.4 Wear of guiding-component support surface
Failure code4: 01.14.1 Separator pocket galled

[See Image in Appendix]

DESCRIPTIONS
FAILURE DESCRIPTION: The ball pockets are worn and galled. Wear and chipping (FC 01.11.2) occurred on separator ID in unintended contact with IR land, which is also worn. The circular shape of the separator is distorted (FC 01.12). High separator/ball forces caused pocket wear, increased separator looseness and unintended contact with the IR land. The separator was temporarily caught between ball and groove edge causing greater forces, pocket galling, chipping, and distorted shape.

IMAGE DESCRIPTION: At image W is the IR, with dashed dark wear marks on lands and a dark contact band in the groove.

The separator half at image E has lost its circular shape. The W-most pocket is chipped at the ID. All pockets are worn. Galled patches in: the S-most pocket; in two pockets to its E and in one to its W.

SUSPECTED CAUSES: The separator may have been distorted in assembly or lubrication may have failed causing high separator/ball forces, resulting in complex wear, galling and distortion. Erratic orbital separator motions may occur, causing the dashed marks on the IR. Cartridge-type (wide) DGBB are grease lubricated. Bearing may have been run past functional grease life, precipitating lubricant failure.

DATA
Plate No: 16.26
Archive No: 003-007
Image type: light macro
Scalebar = 4 mm (micros: ±20%, others: +100%, -50%)
Component: CRB; G (machined bronze separator), run
Speed: 2.2 MdN
Load:
Lubrication: synthetic polyester oil, ? °C
Failure code1: 01.13.1.1 Separator cross-bar worn, one pocket side
Failure code2: 01.13.1.4 Roller separator, pocket bottom worn
Failure code3: 01.11.2 Separator fracture, cracking
Failure code4: -

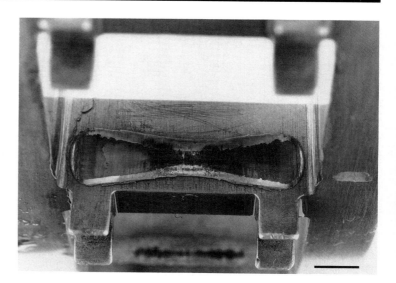

DESCRIPTIONS
FAILURE DESCRIPTION: Wear of separator cross-bar and side-rails. Plating on the cross-bar is worn through. The plating peeled and the cross-bar probably cracked through. Roller forces from a skewed roller produced "dog-bone" wear pattern. The bearing is likely to fail soon due to separator fracture.

IMAGE DESCRIPTION: Oblique view of separator pocket from OD. The siderails are at E and W. The roller contact face of the cross-bar is at S center, with retaining tangs at S. A second cross-bar is out-of-focus at N image edge. Sharp wear marks (gouges) are at both corner radii of the cross-bar. A "dog-

bone" shaped dark wear scar is in the cross-bar side face, with plating worn through (dark). A jagged dark crack line appears near the W corner. The edge of the plating is lifted at the crack.

SUSPECTED CAUSES: High-speed CRB at times suffer severe roller/separator loading when rollers skew (example: from unbalance). Loads between roller end and siderail cause roller end and separator wear (see the sharp cut into corner radius). Load on the cross-bar from roller edge contact (skewed roller) causes "dog-bone" wear pattern and secondarily, cracking.

DATA
Plate No: 16.27
Archive No: 003-003
Image type: light macro
Scalebar = 4 mm (micros: ±20%, others: +100%, -50%)
Component: ACBB; B&G (silver plated steel separator), run
Speed: 2 MdN
Load:
Lubrication: synthetic polyester oil, 120 °C
Failure code1: 01.13.1.1 Separator cross-bar worn, one pocket side
Failure code2: 01.17 Separator contact spalling
Failure code3: -
Failure code4: -

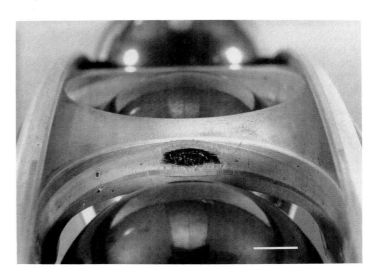

DESCRIPTIONS
FAILURE DESCRIPTION: Wear through the silver plate of a separator pocket. Spalling in the underlying steel separator material. This unusual failure mode is attributed to high ball-contact loads from bearing misalignment, under very good lubrication of the separator ball contact, which limited wear and prevented galling, allowing the contact load to produce a spall. Bearing failed by separator fracture initiated at another spall (not shown).

IMAGE DESCRIPTION: View is on separator OD, with balls dropped below normal position by removal of the IR. The pocket toward image S shows light crescent-shaped ball contact with silver plate over 180° angle. At the pocket center, a dark,

feathered ellipse has worn through to steel. The central area of the ellipse shows the fracture surface of a spall crater. An additional small spot of silver plate removal is 1/4 from W image edge, in the same pocket.

SUSPECTED CAUSES: Misalignment of bearing was observed, leading to severe angular velocity and phase differences among balls and very high ball contact forces on the separator. Wear, galling, possibly heat imbalance would be expected. Spalling of the medium-hard steel separator is unusual and indicates excellent cooling and lubrication of the contacts.

DATA
Plate No: 16.28
Archive No: 018-127
Image type: light macro
Scalebar = 10 mm (micros: ±20%, others: +100%, -50%)
Component: SRB; G (machined bronze separator), run
Speed:
Load:
Lubrication:
Failure code1: 01.13.2.1 Land guided separator, guide surface worn, general
Failure code2: 01.13.3 Separator wear from unintended contact
Failure code3: -
Failure code4: -

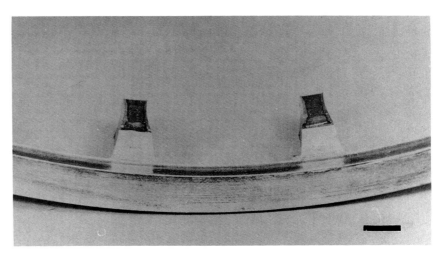

DESCRIPTIONS
FAILURE DESCRIPTION: Machined bronze land-guided SRB separator with center ring and cantilevered prongs is worn heavily on center ring guide surface contacting IR center flange OD. The resulting radial displacement has caused IR contact at the ID of the prongs, and wear. Separator fracture or bearing seizure is likely.

IMAGE DESCRIPTION: One-half of a two-part machined bronze SRB separator is shown, with center ring facing to image S and prongs to N. The sideface at the S made contact with the other separator half and shows slight polishing near the ID.

The adjacent cylindrical ID was originally at the prong ID level; now it is heavily worn down. The prong ID shows dark wear pattern. Corresponding wear of the prong sides contacting the rollers is not visible in this image.

SUSPECTED CAUSES: Inadequate lubrication, probably with contaminated lubricant, possibly combined with rough IR center flange OD surface, can cause heavy wear. The separator will drop down on the rollers as the roller contact surfaces wear, eventually contacting the ID roller path at the prong ID, causing wear.

DATA
Plate No: 16.29
Archive No: 087-010
Image type: view
Scalebar = 15 mm (micros: ±20%, others: +100%, -50%)
Component: BB (maximum complement); G (2-piece separator), run
Speed:
Load:
Lubrication:
Failure code1: 01.13.3 Separator wear from unintended contact
Failure code2: 01.11.2 Separator fracture, cracking
Failure code3: 20.01.2.1 Fouling of mounting part by other moving part
Failure code4: -

DESCRIPTIONS
FAILURE DESCRIPTION: Separator sideface and rivet head wear from unintended contact with stationary mounting part. Three cracks run across the thin cross-sections over the ball pockets. This is a gross failure.

IMAGE DESCRIPTION: Maximum complement ball bearing with machined, riveted two-piece separator is viewed on sideface. The dark grey separator sideface (including rivet heads) shows deep wear, with plastically flown edges. The worn areas are of lighter color. Black, jagged cross-section cracks are at the arrows.

SUSPECTED CAUSES: Incorrect dimensioning of housing or

end-cap allowed contact of the separator sideface with a stationary part. (In most ball bearings, the separator is wholly contained in the OR outline, but not in this design.) Heavy wear and large ball/separator forces resulted, which have ultimately led to cross-section cracking under the hoop stresses.

DATA
Plate No: 16.30
Archive No: 093-13.1.12
Image type: light macro
Scalebar = 40 mm (micros: ±20%, others: +100%, -50%)
Component: CRB; G (2-piece machined bronze separator), run
Speed:
Load:
Lubrication: oil, ? °C
Failure code1: 01.14.1 Separator pocket galled
Failure code2: 01.13.1 Separator pocket worn
Failure code3: -
Failure code4: -

DESCRIPTIONS
FAILURE DESCRIPTION: Extensive galling (and wear) of separator prong/roller contact surface, probably initiated by solid contaminant. Galling of this severity causes a large volume of debris, adding to the contamination. This may precipitate continued wear, galling, heat imbalance failure and seizure.

IMAGE DESCRIPTION: The machined bronze separator consists of a siderail with integral prongs and a separate closing ring (not shown), attached by rivets passing through the prongs. The image views the separator from the OD. The entire prong surface marked *A* is covered with circumferential streaks of

light-appearing galled metal on a dark background of the original material. The transferred metal is higher than the original surface and is polished by wear against the rollers.

SUSPECTED CAUSES: This very large multirow CRB worked in a steel rolling mill in severely contaminated environment (both water and solids). Galling at high-speed sliding contacts between the separator and rollers can result and is progressive, since contamination continues and water degrades the oil mist lubrication.